Rivers and Wildlife Handbook –
a guide to practices which further the conservation of wildlife on rivers

Gill Lewis and Gwyn Williams

Contents

INTRODUCTION 1: WHY A HANDBOOK?

The tone of this Handbook is optimistic, for it describes work on rivers – mainly carried out by drainage authorities in England and Wales – which has successfully integrated the conservation of wildlife habitat with land drainage and flood alleviation schemes. It shows that it is possible to take account of wildlife conservation in all river engineering. Its intention is also to suggest ways in which further techniques can be developed in the future.

This is a time of increasing public interest in the countryside. There is a sincere and growing concern that the trend of present change diminishes the richness of wildlife and landscapes. As a result, any public body which is an agent of change in the countryside is in a sensitive position. This is certainly true of drainage authorities, having as they do a public responsibility to undertake works which, at least on occasion, become the object of public criticism. The desirability that such bodies take account of conservation was first recognised over two decades ago – first by Section 101 of the Water Resources Act 1963, and later, in expanded and restated form, by Section 22 of the Water Act 1973. However, the provision 'to have regard' to the needs of conservation was of limited value and it was a significant advance when, in 1981, this was amended by Section 48 of the Wildlife and Countryside Act to give water authorities (and also internal drainage boards) the duty to 'further' conservation (see also DoE, MAFF and WOAD, 1982). Now they have a clear ability and responsibility to commit funds to the conservation of wildlife and landscape, so far as is consistent with their primary functions.

At the same time, it has become apparent that the interests of conservation can usually be reconciled with the other functions of rivers, and that the techniques involved are generally low in cost – though high in skill. The first step in promoting knowledge of them was taken with the publication of the 'Conservation and Land Drainage Guidelines' by a working party of the Water Space Amenity Commission in July 1980. Since then, the Nature Conservancy Council's publication 'Nature Conservation and River Engineering' has outlined the general principles for river conservation in practical terms, placing particular stress on the need to safeguard the interests of riverine Sites of Special Scientific Interest.

The Handbook is intended to take the process a stage further, by gathering together and describing in detail examples of river engineering works which have taken wildlife conservation into account – and, in many cases, amenity, angling and financial concerns as well. Although primarily designed as a reference work for water authority design and project engineers, it should also provide a source of information and ideas for anyone involved in river engineering – whether drainage engineers or biologists, professional conservationists or interested members of the public. We hope it will provide a starting point from which design and project engineers can develop solutions to their own particular problems, in association with landowners, conservationists and other interested parties.

Skill, imagination and tolerance are the basic requisites of good river management. The technical know-how can easily be taught, but the way it is applied is a product of experience and creativity. We hope that this manual will communicate some of the experience now available in the British water industry in retaining and recreating river habitats. But it is the personal qualities of decision-makers and operators – in river management as in any other field – which will largely determine the success or failure of their conservation efforts when judged by the wider world outside their own profession.

Some of the techniques which this Handbook describes are simply continuations of traditional practices, some the new application of traditional practices, and yet others are new practices: underlying all, however, is the concept of working with the physical and biological processes of river systems, rather than in spite of them. Their adoption represents a new challenge and a new opportunity for river engineers.

The Handbook could not have been compiled without substantial practical help from the ten water authorities in England and Wales. With the generous co-operation of many engineers, designers, biologists and others, we have attempted to describe their work in integrating the needs of wildlife with those of river management. We must also thank the staff of other conservation organisations – especially the Nature Conservancy Council, Vincent Wildlife Trust and World Wildlife Fund – for their substantial contributions in bringing this project to fruition.

THE USE AND ARRANGEMENT OF THE HANDBOOK

The Handbook is presented in three parts:

- Part I: Introduction
- Part II: Biological
- Part III: Technical

The Introduction contains background information on the physical, hydrological and ecological processes of river systems. The Biological section provides a series of short essays centering on the habitat requirements of different groups of plants and animals; as far as possible, tables summarise the detailed data about typical and key species, and select bibliographies help to introduce the reader to the most important sources of further information. The third and main part of the Handbook is the Technical section, which describes the series of options available to integrate habitat retention and

reinstatement with river engineering works. The arrangement of the Technical part is detailed in its introduction on pages **67** to **69**.

Ideally, the user should read the introductory sections before going on to the material in the Biological and Technical parts, for the Introduction provides the conceptual basis on which the remainder of the Handbook is based.

If information about a particular species is required (eg otter), the reader should first look at the relevant Biological section (in this case 'Biological 5: Mammals', on page 55) for general data about habitat requirements, food and distribution, and then turn to the relevant Technical section where general habitat conservation techniques of potential value to the species and any special structural conservation methods are detailed (in this example 'Technical: Otters', on page **277**).

For the reasons given in 'Introduction 3: River Ecology and Wildlife Conservation' habitat retention is always preferable to reinstatement. In assessing the options available for integrating wildlife conservation with the engineering needs of a given scheme, therefore, the first questions to be answered are whether the river channel or riverbanks could, or should, be left entirely untouched. The possible answers – 'yes', 'partially' and 'no' – lead on to a variety of options that can then be considered in relation to the scheme. These are set out in the tables on page **68** and the inside back cover. The numbers used in the tables key into the page numbers of the Technical part.

If the reader requires information on a particular river engineering technique and its advantages or disadvantages for nature conservation, then he should turn directly to the relevant section. These are listed in the 'Contents'.

AUTHORSHIP

The Handbook was conceived by John Andrews and Gwyn Williams, RSPB. Unless otherwise acknowledged, it was written by Gill Lewis and edited by Gwyn Williams, RSPB, with the help of Tim Sands and Andrew Heaton, RSNC, and John Andrews, RSPB. Design was by Patsy Hinchliffe, RSPB, and the work was produced by the RSPB Publications Department.

References

Department of the Environment, Ministry of Agriculture, Fisheries and Food and Welsh Office Agriculture Department, 1982. Land Drainage and Conservation: Guidance Notes on Procedures for Water Authorities, Internal Drainage Boards, Nature Conservancy Council and Countryside Commission. Section 22 of the Water Act 1973 as amended by Section 48 of the Wildlife and Countryside Act 1981.

Newbold, C, Purseglove, J and Holmes, N, 1983. Nature Conservation and River Engineering. Nature Conservancy Council.

Water Space Amenity Commission, 1983. Conservation and Land Drainage Guidelines (2nd Edition). WSAC.

INTRODUCTION 2: RIVER PROCESSES AND FORM

Malcolm Newson, Fluvial Geomorphology Unit, Institute of Hydrology.

THE CLASSIFICATION OF RIVERS BY SEDIMENTATION PROCESSES

Everybody knows how rivers work. Nobody one meets on a river bank will ever decline to give his or her view on the state of the channel, the velocity of the water or the relationship between the two. In such a humid island as Britain, with its high density of water courses, few are deprived of the sight of rivers in all their moods and our poets and novelists have supplied us with folk images of mountain torrents, placid winding brooks and majestic lowland rivers.

Possibly this explains why scientists have fallen into the trap of giving rivers human characteristics, in attempting to classify their courses. The most famous classification, by the American geologist, W M Davies, is into 'youth', 'maturity' and 'old age' (figure 1) Davies 1899; King and Schumm, 1980). This classification has pervaded geographical education throughout this century, but other equally simplistic sub-divisions of a river's course have been made by fish biologists (eg: trout, grayling, barbel, bream zones). However, classification is necessary as a framework for understanding river processes, and it is perhaps more serious that river engineers have seen fit to do without one than that earth scientists have been misled by theirs.

The most misleading feature of the Davis classification is its plausible suggestion that the upland 'youth' stage is accompanied by high velocity, a property gradually lost as the river progresses into the lowland 'old age'. Generations of scholars have noted the apparent speed of the mountain torrent as it 'rushes' over large boulders in its course, and inevitably concurred with Davis when seeing the Thames or Great Ouse 'casually' meandering between smooth, grassy banks. Impressions, however, are wrong. The energy for stream flow is provided by gravity and mainly used up in overcoming the resistance of bed and banks. There is, in fact, a nice balance in the entire river system between gradient and the frictional resistance of the river channel. Modern measurements in rivers show a similar velocity throughout the river system, especially in floods. At low flows a mountain stream's average velocity may actually be slower than that of lowland sections in the same system, because of friction with all the obstacles in its path. The greatest increase in velocity occurs between drought and flood conditions in the same reach, not between different reaches of a river under the same conditions.

During a rising flood, as the depth of water increases, the effect of frictional resistance on velocity is progressively reduced, so freeing energy for erosion. The energy of motion is used to detach and to transport any available particle on the bed or banks whose mass is sufficiently low to be rolled, bounced or suspended in the flow. Thus, the river in flood, in effect, seeks to change its bed and banks by erosion and deposition until adjusted to the increased discharge and sediment load it is carrying.

Since velocity is more or less steady throughout the system, it is by the type and availability of sediment particles on channel bed and banks that the real zones in rivers can be most easily distinguished. Consider, for example, the mountain stream. It is only 12,000 years (not long, geologically) since its valley was filled by a glacier. The sediments on its bed and banks are likely to be mainly those moved by glacial transport and their coarseness means that it is only in rare floods that

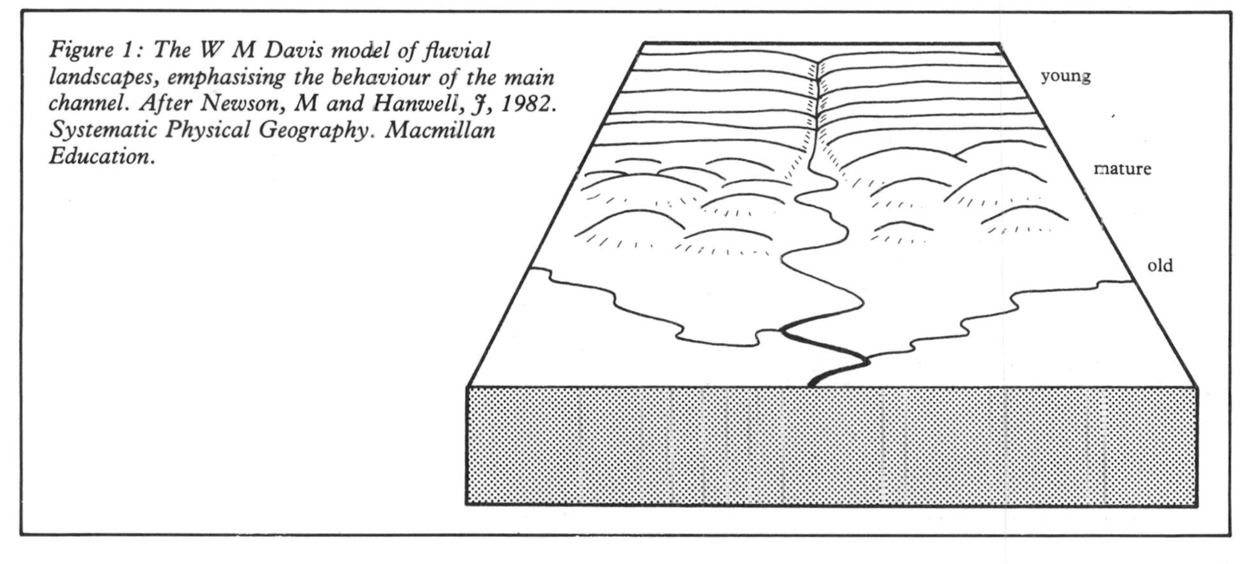

Figure 1: The W M Davis model of fluvial landscapes, emphasising the behaviour of the main channel. After Newson, M and Hanwell, J, 1982. Systematic Physical Geography. Macmillan Education.

the modern river, responding to a modern climate, can transport them. Far from the aggressive erosion Davis associated with the 'young' streams, there is little sediment in motion during most conditions. The modern development of valley slopes bordering a mountain stream is important, however, for these are the major producers of river sediment by weathering, not the mechanical action of the river itself. Both slow soil creep and more rapid slips and falls provide a periodically large sediment input to the river system. Lower down, a flood plain intervenes between the slopes' supply of material and its transport away in flood. The upper parts of a river's course may be distinguished as the *sediment production zone*.

Outside the mountains and uplands, wide flood plains border the channel, and since the flood plains' sediment largely represents the products of river erosion over the millennia since de-glaciation, the river is now dealing with fluvial, not glacial material. Sediment is available to be transported from the bed and banks of the channel, although there is a zonation from just outside the upland margin, where the predominant size of bed material is gravel (which means that floods are still important), to lower down where silt or clay alluvium forms the bed and banks and all but the lowest flows carry some material away in suspension. Most of the lowland zone may, therefore, be called the *transfer zone*, since the river's erosive activities are not so much lowering the landscape as re-distributing sediment brought in from upstream and derived from bank erosion within the zone (figure 2). Finally, in the estuary, the river reaches its main *depositional zone*, largely outside the scope of this Handbook.

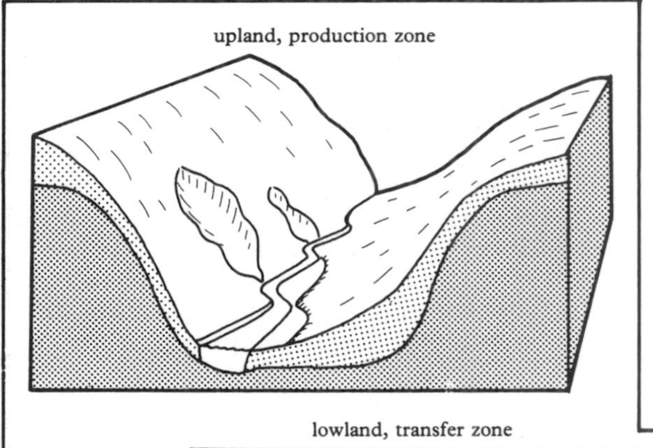

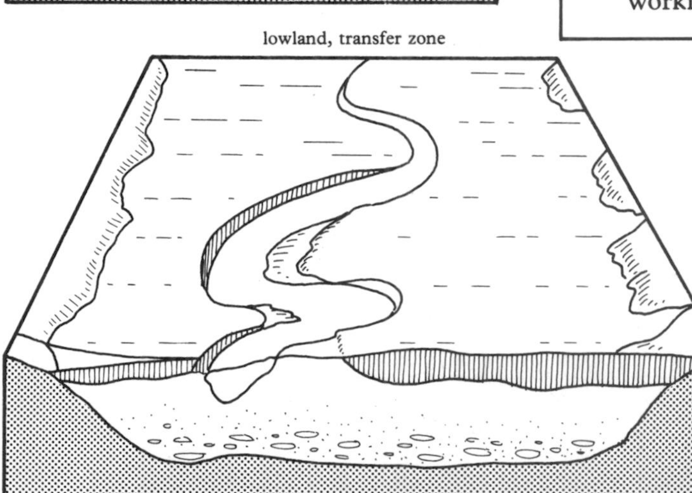

Figure 2: An alternative to Davis: the division of rivers into upland and lowland based on the transport of material from slope channel and the nature of that material. After Newson and Hanwell, 1982.

RIVER CHANNEL STABILITY: TIMESCALES IN NATURE AND THEIR RELATIONSHIP TO RIVER ENGINEERING.

It is the river engineer's job to treat problems of river instability at a specific site, yet it is important to have a synoptic view of the river from source to mouth, as a continuous transport system sub-divisible, as shown above, only by sediment size and availability which, in turn, control morphology. Nevertheless, it has been traditionally thought in Britain that 'upstream' controls on river form had little influence on what happened in a given reach: average flows of both water and sediment have been considered unvarying in the long-term. Consequently the engineer has used empirical data, often from such non-dynamic environments as canals, to guide him on the selection of the basic channel dimensions of width and depth and the stream's velocity. The anticipated success of such channel designs can be judged from the terms 'regime' and 'grade' which are used to describe a 'trained' river in perfect equilibrium with its dominant flow, usually taken to be the annual flood. However, rivers respond over different timescales to different influences and any one person is given only 'three score and ten' years to observe and predict river behaviour. Engineering schemes must be designed to last much longer in most cases.

Over geological timescales rivers can clearly cut down to sea level. Davis deserves credit for working out this long timescale, but it coloured

much of his argument and eventual classification. At the timescale over which riparian owners these days expect the river to be stabilised, it is the lateral migration of the channel and not downcutting which is of most concern. Research has proved that on this timescale – say 100 years – channel developments are characterised by '*metastability*' rather than equilibrium; they are experiencing changes in sediment load or flow, which may produce relatively sudden changes between quiescent phases.

Flow changes can be expected following changes in land-use, land management (*eg* drainage) and the manipulation of river flows by the water industry (*eg* abstraction for water supply). The developments occurring in upland areas today – afforestation, timber harvesting, and farm improvements – mean that changes in sediment supply can also be expected. Such changes are already being monitored in a few catchments and give some guide to the scale of change to be expected in others (figure 3). However, the complexity of inter-related factors suggests that accurate predictive models for a particular system cannot yet be confidently extrapolated from data derived elsewhere. Erosion rates and stream loads need to be monitored as well as water flows so that in river management and project planning the system's degree of metastability can be taken into account.

Figure 3: River channel changes on the river Severn at Caersws, Powys. After Thorne, C R and Lewin, J. Bank processes, bed material movement and planform development in a meandering river. In Rhodes, D D and Williams, G P, (eds) 1979. Adjustments of the Fluvial System. George Allen and Unwin.

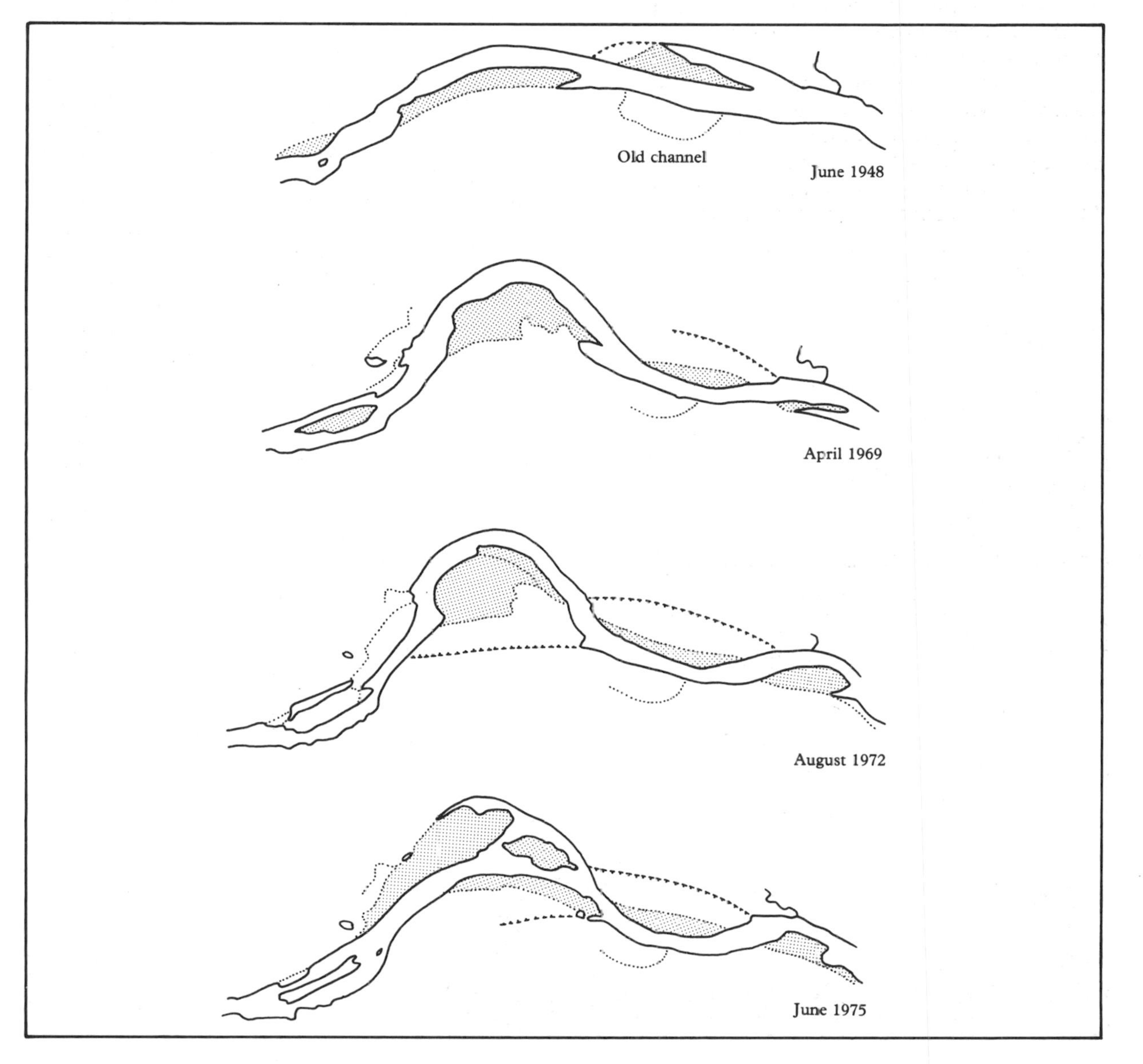

MEANDERS AS A PROPERTY OF RIVER FUNCTION AND PROCESSES

The tendency of rivers to follow curved rather than straight courses is another systematic problem of river engineering. The Davis classification, by linking meanders to the 'mature' or 'old age' river, has tended to give the impression that a river wanders aimlessly without energy for erosion. This is a fallacy, since meanders develop in floods, when the river has maximum available energy. Energy not used to overcome bed and bank friction is far from equally distributed across a river. Instead, turbulence breaks up into a number of cells, producing currents which act laterally with as much force as the main thread of downstream flow (figure 4a). These *secondary flows* are generated in any stream and with a regularity which relates to the stream's width, *ie* to the space available for the cells to develop.

In streams where banks are compact and unerodable, secondary flows create midstream shoals, or riffles, and pools at fairly regular intervals (figures 4b and 4c). Where the banks are erodable riffles and pools still occur, but the secondary cells produce a sinuous river planform by lateral erosion and deposition. Cut banks occur opposite shoals and together they create the familiar pattern of the meandering river. Given further development, rivers may also exhibit a form in which both banks are cut and the shoals are mainly in midstream; this is the braided river, typical of streams in recently glaciated areas.

This natural tendency to sinuosity, and the tendency for meanders and other less regular river bends to migrate by erosion and deposition, means that the equilibrium regime approach which is mostly indexed from data on straight reaches is seldom successful in coping with sinuosity. Much expense and environmental degradation is involved in forcing a river to flow where it is put, when the designed planform is inappropriate to the reach's position within the system. Clearly, however, river engineers would willingly use a new empirical method of predicting river planform pattern, if one existed. The most hopeful method is that based upon the secondary flow pattern itself, because it describes the pattern with which energy is expended within the channel. Current meters now exist which can measure cross currents such as these; even simple photography will identify the locus of maximum stress on the banks and reveal just where any necessary structural or vegetative bank protection can be positioned.

There are too many cells at any one site to provide detailed advice in the context of a general paper, and so a simple device to predict the total energy for erosion of planform is necessary – the slope/discharge diagram (figure 5). Numerous versions of this graph are now published, but each shows how, with increasing slope in a reach, or increasing flood discharge (both of which could be caused by changes upstream) river planform, or 'habit', changes between meandering, braided and straight. Such graphs can be used to predict whether a reach

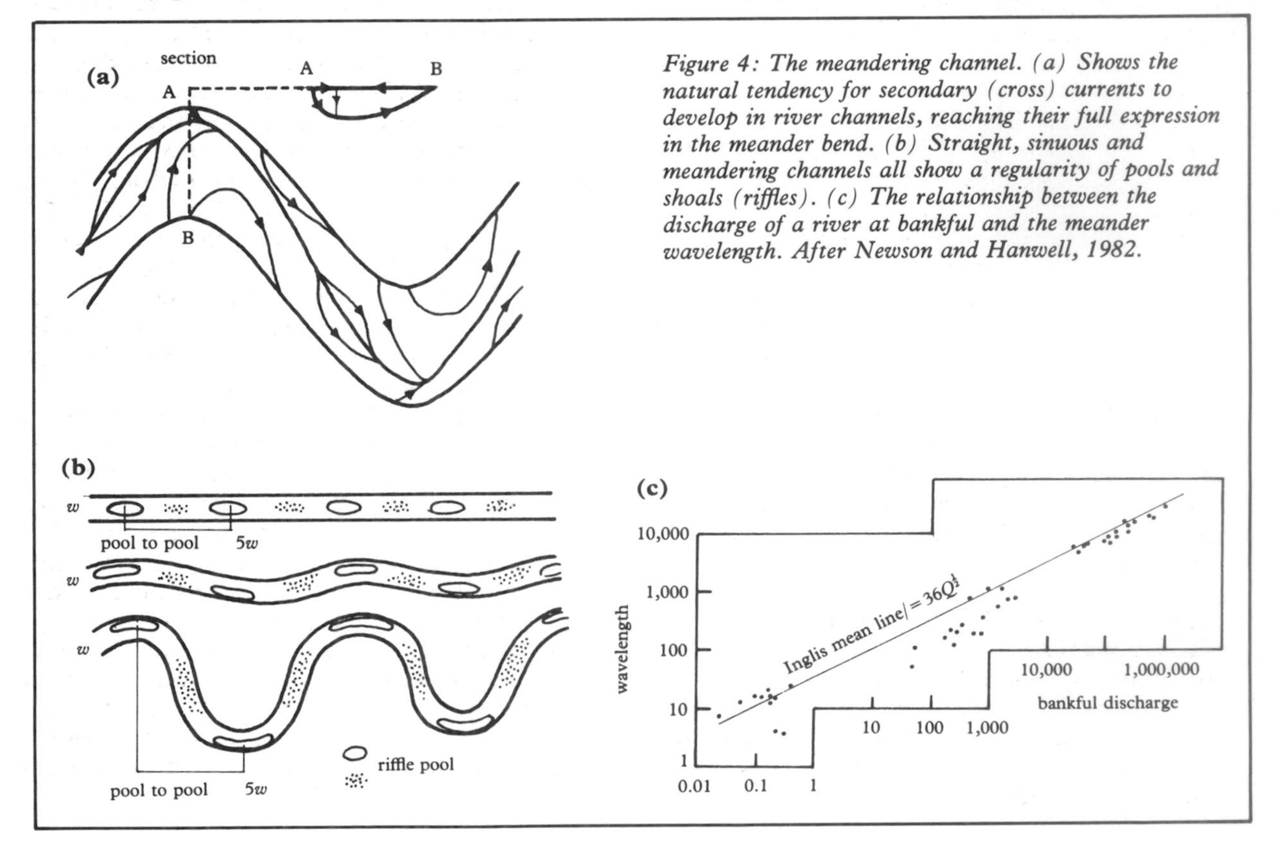

Figure 4: The meandering channel. (a) Shows the natural tendency for secondary (cross) currents to develop in river channels, reaching their full expression in the meander bend. (b) Straight, sinuous and meandering channels all show a regularity of pools and shoals (riffles). (c) The relationship between the discharge of a river at bankful and the meander wavelength. After Newson and Hanwell, 1982.

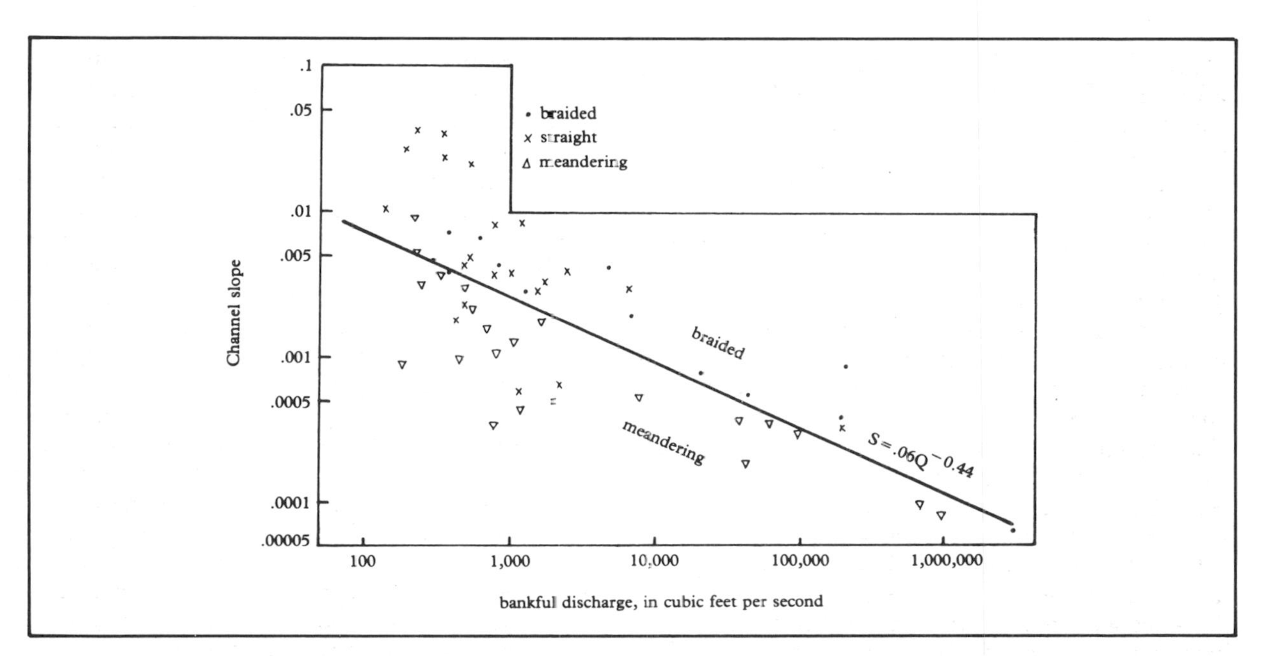

Figure 5: Slope and bankful discharge: critical distinction of meandering from braiding. After Leopold, L B and Gordon Wolman, M. River Channel Patterns. In Dury, G H (ed), 1970. Rivers and River Terraces. Macmillan.

which is being artificially straightened will tend to meander again after a few years, at great expense to the scheme, or whether an increased input of sediment from upstream (say from afforestation) will turn a sensitively poised, meandering reach into a braided one. One can even use slope/discharge graphs to index the risk of channel change and, therefore, make a better economic judgement of the costs and benefits of a river scheme.

Recognising this interdependence of form and process in fluvial systems, streams in North America have been experimentally designed to form and maintain riffles, pools and meanders where desired (principally by fisheries interests). No structures were used; control of bank slopes and variation in channel cross-sections resulted in the emergence of point bars and pools after the first above normal flow, in the required locations, even in straight reaches. It is too much to expect that there could be similar research before all new channelization projects in the UK. However, computer modelling has enabled more complex designs to be attempted and tested, with encouraging results in the field for 'natural' habitats and landscapes.

CHANNEL ROUGHNESS AND VEGETATION

Also at the site scale, one needs to analyse the factors responsible for erosion and scour, or lack of it. High on the list must come the cohesiveness and vertical arrangement of soils and alluvium in the banks, and the vegetation cover.

Whereas the stability and roughness of inert materials in the channel is taken as invariable, except by massive and costly works, that attributable to vegetation has traditionally been considered manageable, and a large part of river management work is to that end.

However, there is a dual attitude to the value of vegetation in rivers. On the one hand, its role in preventing scour and protecting bed and banks is recognised, both through the binding action of roots and through the streamlining of flexible leaves and stems which smooth the channel and reduce friction at high flows. The Hydraulics Research Station (Charlton, Brown and Benson, 1978) have established, for example, that unvegetated and short grass channels are, on average, 30 per cent wider than their tree-lined counterparts. On the other hand, there are, in lowland rivers, known flood risks resulting from additional roughness of profuse 'weed growth', the reduction of channel capacity by the bulk of plants, the possibility of increased turbulence around trees in floods, the risk of sudden bank failure if a tree falls, and the possibility of log-jams or weed-jams at bridge points damming the flow.

The balance would appear to favour removing everything except short perennial grasses – and, sadly, miles of watercourses in lowland areas have been reduced to that. But, fortunately, many river managers are glad to retain and even develop varied river vegetation, for its beauty, its landscape value and for the wildlife it harbours. Since conserving natural vegetation is often the key to furthering the conservation and enhancement of natural beauty and flora and fauna, it is as important for river managers to understand the growth of vegetation and its effects on channel capacity as it is to understand the physical mechanics of flow over inert materials. Unfortunately, only a small amount of work has been done in this country by drainage authorities and other organisations on the effects of vegetation on channel capacity, although at present there is rising interest. That published so far suggests very stongly that designers taking empirical data on roughness coefficients, such as given in Ven T Chow, 1959, may be underestimating the real, vegetation roughness by up to a factor of 10 (see table 1).

Studies show that the factors influencing roughness due to vegetation are very complex. They include distribution of plant patches on bed and banks, density of clumps, height, form and morphology (*eg* branching, stem diameter, leaf shape), and the stiffness or flexibility of different parts of the plant. As might be expected in living organisms, these attributes vary on a daily, seasonal and long-term basis.

Trees and bushes on natural banks or within a flood channel create perhaps more controversy than smaller, softer vegetation. Their presence in the river corridor is as vital to the biological community as is any other species – and in some ways more important, because of their structural contribution. Their roots bind the soil and protect banks as do other plants – the roots of alder probably protect against scour better than any other species. Yet their size, rigidity, and the problems caused to man if they fall into the channel has encouraged tree clearance programmes along many rivers, and discouraged replanting close to the summer (low) water level. However, of all riverine vegetation, the roughness caused by trees has been least studied, nor has the damage resulting from bad management been assessed. One study has shown that trailing tree branches and debris accounted for only 23 per cent of a channel's roughness coefficient of 0.0662; in contrast, wooden piling for bank protection increased roughness by 50 per cent in another channel, when compared to a non-piled stretch (Severn, 1982).

Traditional methods of river management frequently used the attributes of native plants to stabilise banks and deflect flows where needed. Routine, regular maintenance by hand labour ensured that plant cover did not degenerate. Thus, sallows and alders were planted on rivers, reed-beds along canal banks, and turf walls packed

Table 1: Summary of various channel roughness calculations, using Manning's 'n' roughness coefficients.

A. Lancashire (after Severn, 1982)
* – *weed clearance sites* + – *tree and debris clearance sites*

Site		reach 1-2	reach 2-3	Overall 1-3	% decrease
*Moss Sluice	before	0.3385	0.3209	2.2458	79%
	after	0.0627	0.0900	0.0613	
*Main Dyke	before	0.3725	0.4043	0.3886	62%
	after	0.1230	0.1699	0.1487	
*R. Yarrow	before	0.1278	0.1755	0.1484	58%
	after	0.0624	0.0649	0.0627	
+R. Lostock	before	0.0448	0.0924	0.0662	23%
	after	0.0250	0.0702	0.0512	

B. Netherlands (after Pitlo, 1982, quoted in Severn, 1982). Weed clearance site.

Shallow ditch	before	0.85	Large channel	before	no significant
	after	0.034		after	change

C. Dorset (after Dawson, 1978). Comparison between winter and summer.

Bere Stream	Max:	0.3-0.4 – plant growth in July
	Min:	0.5 – silt only in winter

down as toe protection along dykes. With first-hand experience of a river's responses to management, the resulting changes in water flows, sediment transport, bank and bed stability, could be noted and assessed during successive years' maintenance. However, traditional practices have, in many places, been forgotten or are seen as a 'luxury' under present financial and staffing arrangements. In the rush to capitalise (in more ways than one) on the products of the last 50 years' technology in machinery and materials, the water industry has abandoned its roots.

CONCLUSION

The major variables affecting the relationship between river processes and form have been stressed; the problems of a given reach must be seen and solved in the context of the whole river catchment and the changes, natural and artificial, that are going on in it over various timescales. Secondary flow cells are largely responsible for river sinuosity; much expense and environmental damage has resulted from past lack of knowledge of the character of energy flows within the river. Finally, the use of vegetation in river management has been commended; this too is an area inadequately understood. In fact, the traditional river bailiff knew empirically how the pattern of flow and the strength of the river banks should be reconciled. There are many other ways in which the former semi-natural rivers showed a better process-form adjustment, with river processes being aided and abetted by man's management techniques, rather than being 'taken on' in the heroic, but costly, and some would claim misguided, schemes of the modern era.

REFERENCES

Charlton, F G, Brown, P M and Benson, R W, 1978. The Hydraulic Geometry of Some Gravel Rivers in Britain. Report IT 180, Hydraulics Research Station, Wallingford.

Chow, V T, 1959. Open-channel Hydraulics. McGraw-Hill, New York.

Davis, W M, 1899. The Geographical Cycle. Geographical Journal **14**: 481-504.

Dawson, F, 1978. The Seasonal Effect of Aquatic Plant Growth on the Flow of Water in a Stream. Proc EWRS 5th Symposium on Aquatic Weeds, pages 71-78.

King, P B and Schumm, S A (eds), 1980. The Physical Geography of William Morris Davis. Geo Books, Norwich.

Severn, F, 1982. The Conflict Between Land Drainage and Habitat Conservation: the Effect of Watercourse Vegetation on Channel Capacity. Unpublished MSc thesis, Imperial College of Science and Technology, University of London.

SELECT BIBLIOGRAPHY

Blench, T, 1957. Regime Behaviour of Canals and Rivers. Butterworth, London.

Gregory, K J (ed), 1977. River Channel Changes. John Wiley, Chichester.

Hey, R D, Bathurst, J C and Thorne C R (eds), 1982. Gravel Bed Rivers: Fluvial Processes, Engineering and Management. John Wiley, Chichester.

Jansen, P Ph, van Bendegom, L, van den Berg, J, de Vries, M and Zanen, A, 1979. Principles of River Engineering. The non-tidal alluvial river. Pitman, London.

Lewin, J (ed), 1981. British Rivers. George Allen and Unwin, London.

Rhodes, D D and Williams, G P (eds), 1979. Adjustments of the Fluvial System. George Allen and Unwin, Boston.

Richards, K, 1982. Rivers: Form and Process in Alluvial Channels. Methuen, London.

Schumm, S A, 1977. The Fluvial System. John Wiley, New York.

INTRODUCTION 3: RIVER ECOLOGY AND WILDLIFE CONSERVATION

John Andrews, Head of Conservation Planning,
Royal Society for the Protection of Birds,
Sandy, and Gill Lewis.

INTRODUCTION

A major barrier to the inclusion of nature conservation requirements in river engineering is that often neither side is fully informed about the concepts, principles and techniques which govern the other's work. In an attempt to reduce one cause of this communication failure, this section aims to outline the ecological principles which underlie conservation practice.

A definition of ecology is 'the study of factors affecting the distribution and abundance of plants and animals'. Ecology is still a very young science when compared to civil engineering and, as there are millions of plant and animal species to consider, and almost infinite variation in environmental conditions, it is hardly surprising that ecologists often have to admit uncertainty as to the exact effect of a particular action on a particular living organism. However, much wide-ranging field observation, followed up with extensive experimental work both in the field and the laboratory, has revealed that there are broadly consistent patterns in the interaction of living things with each other and with their environment. This knowledge enables the ecologist to predict with fair certainty the broad consequences of human intervention in natural processes of which river engineering is a classic example.

As with engineering, it is often necessary to return to basic concepts when investigating complex ecological structures and an examination of energy flow through systems is a good starting point.

FOOD CHAINS

All systems, whether mechanical or natural, require energy to power them and materials for their structure, maintenance and growth. In almost all natural systems, sunlight is the initial energy source and inorganic matter is the material source. Essentially, green plants use sunlight to produce organic carbon compounds from inorganic carbon dioxide and water. Mineral salts in soil water are absorbed through the roots (although some submerged water plants also absorb through stems and leaves). The products of photosynthesis and

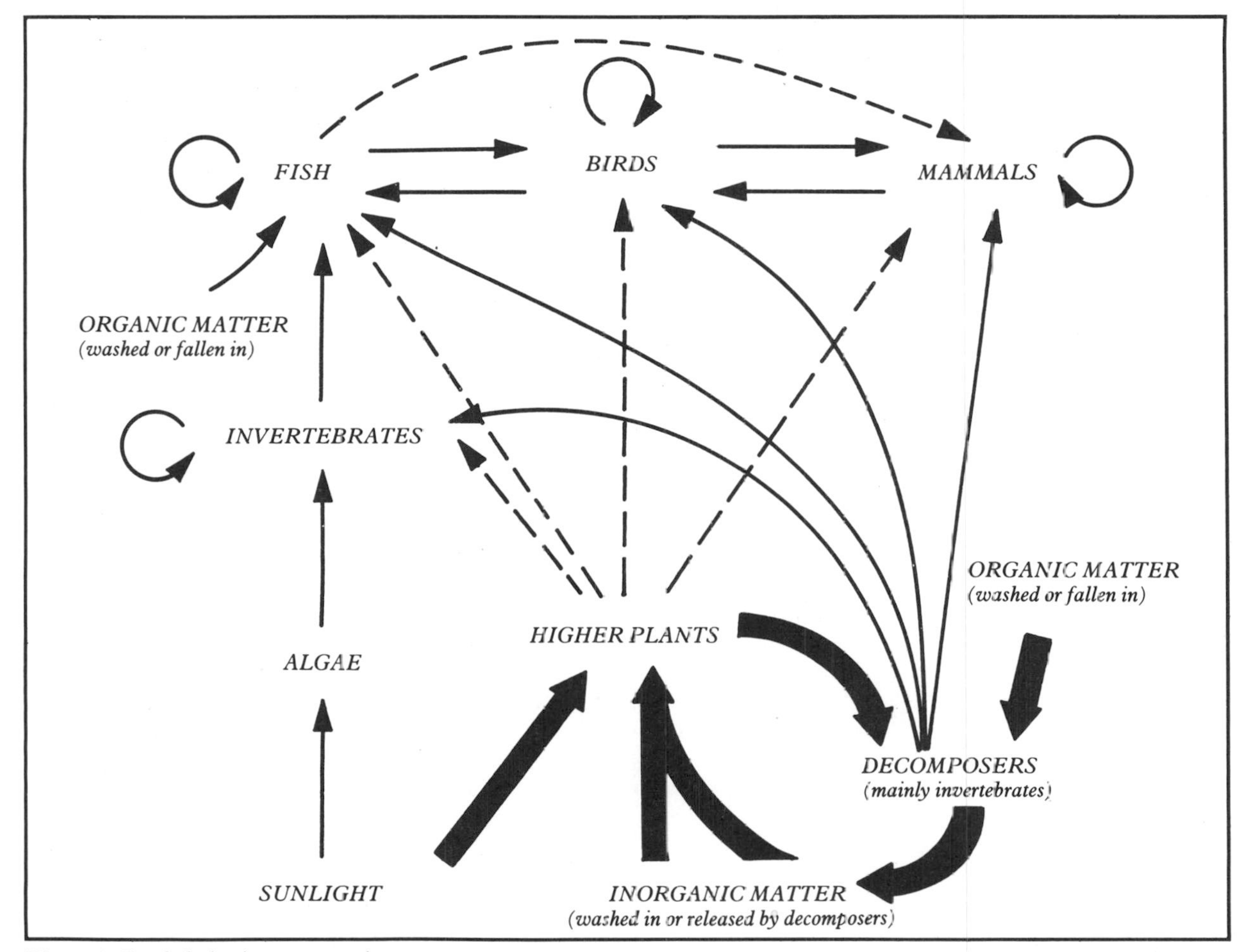

Figure 1: Food chains in a community.

mineral salts are used by plants to carry out biochemical work, notably growth and reproduction.

Green plants, thus, function as the *producers* within the *food chain*, while all animals (and a few plants) follow on as *consumers*. Within the consumers are a specialised group of *decomposers*, mainly free-living micro-organisms in soil or water (though others live in the stomachs and guts of larger animals, breaking down foodstuffs into a digestible form). All three links in the chain – producers, consumers and decomposers – are essential if the system is to function (figure 1).

The productivity of food chains varies from place to place, and this is most important because it largely determines what types and abundance of wildlife can exist at any given site. Gross availability of sunlight depends on latitude and climate, but net availability and ambient temperature vary considerably depending on precise location – the *microclimate*. Thus a north-facing slope may be less productive than one facing south, or a river running in deep shade between banks clad by mature trees may be less productive than one flowing in the open. Similarly, production potential and growth rate may be slower for an organism which lives in the shade beneath a stone than for one which lives on the sunny upper surface.

The availability of inorganic material depends primarily on the underlying rocks – thus rivers rising in limestone are normally more productive than those flowing from acid catchments. Locally, soil quality is of importance. In addition, nutrients and organic material may be transported from place to place, and rivers are powerful mechanisms in this respect. The availability of sunlight and nutrients also varies seasonally, influencing growth periods, breeding times and – in many birds and some fish, insects and mammals – necessitating migration. Depending on the productive capability of a site, so the numbers and variety of plants and animals present will vary around the year.

Looking at the food chain in the river channel, bankside trees and plants, and so on, although the seeds and some leaves of larger plants are consumed by birds, fish and some specialised invertebrates, the majority of their bulk merely dies back to be used by the decomposers. These are, therefore, an abundant and varied group of animals: nearly all are invertebrates – hog lice, shrimps, fly larvae, tree worms and thread worms, for example – and they directly receive the largest quota of energy and matter from river plants. These decomposers are also the major life forms in rivers flowing over nutrient-poor rocks with few rooted plants, because they can utilise the energy held in leaves and other organic matter which falls into these rivers. They are the main food for many other, larger invertebrates and for many fish, birds and some mammals. At the top of the food chain are the largest predators – such as pike, otter, heron and kingfisher – which are entirely dependent on the variety of smaller fish, birds and mammals below them in the system.

Because each animal uses energy in its respiration and general metabolism, the process of consumption is not totally efficient in transferring energy and only some is converted into body weight. This can be 30 to 60 per cent in the case of the water flea *Daphnia*, but as low as 7 to 10 per cent in adult fish. So, at each level of consumption (*trophic level*), the number of individuals which can be supported becomes less. In practice, this means that higher predators need abundant prey, in turn requiring still larger inputs of plant material (figure 2). Because all animal life depends, directly or indirectly, on plants, it follows that the more abundant and productive the plant life of a river, the more animals will be able to live there.

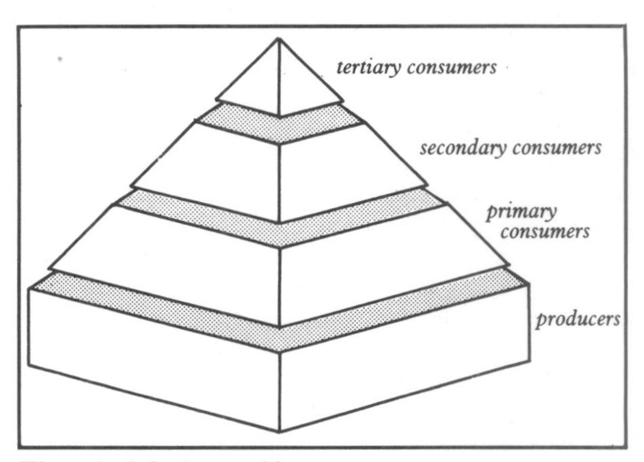

Figure 2: A food pyramid.

SPECIALISATION AND ADAPTABILITY

Given the differences in the physical environment which exist not only in different climatic zones or in different river systems but even on opposite sides of the same boulder, it follows that plants require different physical and behavioural characteristics to get the best out of the local circumstances. For example, a large leaf-size might be ideal for the capture of that all-important sunlight but, if it fails to withstand floods or other hazards, it will not be a successful design for a thriving river plant. A plant's form and habit have to be modified to suit a variety of habitats, yet at the same time respond to interactions with other plants which may compete with it for light or nutrients. Animals also exert their effect and thus the ideal light-gathering leaf may prove too attractive to grazing animals or too readily damaged by trampling. It is basically the pressures of these external forces which cause *speciation*, each species evolving to get the best from one particular type of environment. Similarly, the specialisation of animals derives from the pressures of their total environment.

The degree of specialisation varies. Some living things have very precise requirements – for example, many aquatic invertebrates are very sensitive to reduced oxygen content, or to pollution: others have precise requirements for temperature; thus several dragonfly species are confined to the southern counties of England. Plants too may have quite particular needs. Birds tend to be somewhat less fussy – in part this is because their mobility enables them to commute between sites which offer one or more but not all of their needs. Thus, mallards may spend the day roosting on a reservoir which offers no feeding habitat, moving over at night to feeding places which are not usable by day due to human activity; the bulk of the wintering population leaves Britain entirely in the breeding season, due to a shortage of suitable nesting habitat.

Plants and animals cannot readily alter their special adaptations. Conventional evolutionary theory suggests that change comes about only through genetic variability. Thus, the offspring of an animal or plant are nearly but not quite identical to their parents. These small differences will mean that some offspring may be slightly better equipped than their parents to exploit the environment. Of course, the environment itself may be changing slowly (climatic shifts are usually gradual but nonetheless potent influences), and provided the change is slow then genetic variability may be able to keep pace so that the species survives in modified form or habit. It is often said of common or widespread organisms – weeds or pests – that they are adaptable, implying an ability to change themselves rapidly with changing circumstances. This is rarely the case. Rather, human activity provides an abundance of a specialised situation to which an organism is pre-adapted. The predictable consequence is that it will expand in numbers to expoit this opportunity. On the other hand, if circumstances such as human manipulation of the environment cause the removal of one or more components of the habitat of a given species, then that species will suffer accordingly.

COMMUNITIES, HABITATS AND ECOSYSTEMS

As all organisms must be specialists, adapted to a particular set of conditions, it follows that a given physical environment will support a particular group of interdependent and interacting organisms, each having a consistent relationship with the others, and that in a different physical situation, a different group of organisms will be found. Such groups are known as *communities* and the physical environment in which they are found is their *habitat*. The particular role or place which a member of a community occupies within the habitat is its *niche*. For example, an upland stream is a habitat typified by turbulent flows, unstable bed, high dissolved oxygen content, generally low nutrient levels, tendency to spate and so on. Some of these factors, notably problems with rooting, inhibit aquatic plant growth. However, there are abundant invertebrates feeding on algae and organic matter transported on the current. These provide food for fish and for birds such as grey wagtail and dipper. The latter two species avoid direct competition by feeding in different niches, the wagtail taking insects in flight and from the surfaces of stones and vegetation above water, while the dipper feeds submerged.

Plants and animals also modify their physical environment in a variety of ways. Thus, abundant plant growth in a river channel may so slow the current as to increase sedimentation and thus create significant changes in the river's course and behaviour. The process of interaction may be more or less complex.

Though the main forces of interaction operate within the community and its habitat, there are also influences passing from one community or habitat type to another. For example, in rivers, nutrients tend to travel from upland habitats to lowland habitats, while bird species which winter in the lowlands may breed in the uplands. A group of interconnected habitats forms an *ecosystem*.

Taken to its logical extreme, the world is a single ecosystem – the *biosphere*, in which all organisms play a role and all events have far-reaching effects – but for convenience and understanding it is common practice to put artificial boundaries around closely associated groups of communities and habitats, treating them as separate ecosystems. Hence, for example, ocean basins, small islands, mountain areas, deserts and river catchments can conveniently be described as separate ecosystems without losing sight of the fact that they may have effects on each other or that living organisms may move between them.

The relevant ecosystem for studying the ecology of rivers is the catchment: it is physically separate from other catchments whilst, within it, habitats and communities interact so that they cannot be considered in isolation. Thus a river channel may contain many habitats between upland source and estuarine marsh, and most are affected by events upstream, some by events downstream and many by activities on adjacent land. The variety and abundance of different plants and animals in the channel and elsewhere in the river ecosystem reflects this. Nor is the river wholly isolated from external events crossing catchment boundaries, including weather systems, or human intervention such as inter-river water transfer.

When studying the interactions within the community or habitat and ecosystem, it is convenient to separate physical, chemical and biotic factors. Biotic factors arise from interactions of living organisms – both plants and animals – in a community. They include competition for light, nutrients or food and for space, territory, or mates; the effects of grazing or trampling; predation; and, of course, human interference. Chemical factors include mineral nutrient status, soil character, acidity or salinity of water, availability of oxygen and the presence of pollutants. Physical factors include substrate, water depth and sediment loads, light level and temperature, together with their daily and seasonal fluctuations. Theoretically, they all affect each other, but in practice, in river ecosystems, the physical factors of flow characteristics and substrate are critical to the system, determining the character of the whole wildlife community. In turn, these two factors are dependent on climate, geology, slope, discharge and channel morphology. Recent work on classifying rivers according to their vegetation indicates that the altitude of a river's source correlates with the type of plant communities it contains (Holmes 1980, 1983). This is presumed to be a result of, amongst other factors, fundamental differences in flow rate and substrate types in upland-rising and lowland-rising rivers.

Within the river, organisms have evolved to survive the rigours of high or irregular flows, turbulence, hard substrates or soft, temporary sites which are disrupted by the next spate, and so on. In occupying a site they inevitably modify it; this is particularly so for plants which have a direct effect on their physical surroundings – stabilising sediments and reducing flow rate to a greater or lesser extent according to their size and form. Other plants can grow in the shelter of larger plants, and invertebrates and fish shelter from the current amongst plant stems and leaves. The presence of aquatic plants is a major determinant of the physical structure of the habitat for many invertebrates, fish and water birds. In general, plants tend to reduce the extremes which would exist in a bare environment.

In taking account of the various interactions of flow rates, substrate types, slope, channel morphology and plant community, an ecological view of river function comes closest to a hydrological view. In addition, the ecologist takes account of the interactions between plants in the river modifying the extent and nature of available space, light and nutrients, for example, and of interaction between plants and animals. Nearly all the proposals for river engineering practices which incorporate wildlife conservation principles are intended to increase variety in the form of the physical environment, since this permits the development of a more varied living community, allowing a diverse and, ultimately, a stable community to develop.

SUCCESSION, DIVERSITY AND STABILITY

A community of plants and animals is not naturally unchanging or unchangeable. As the processes of production and decay go on, organic matter tends to accumulate and physical and chemical changes occur in the environment as a result. In turn, the community itself is changed – new species arrive and others die out. This all takes time, and so the age of a community (since its last disturbance) is vital to its structure and composition.

These changes over time are broadly similar in all terrestrial communities, are apparently self-regulating to a certain extent, and are more or less predictable. The series of changes is called *ecological succession*. They come to an end, and the community reaches its *climax*, when some external factor, such as climate, becomes limiting.

In its most uncomplicated form a succession starts in a bare habitat with no living creatures at all – for example, a newly excavated channel in infertile soil. Organic production is nil, so there are no consumers, or decomposers. The physical conditions are harsh and unsuitable for plant growth – for example, below water level there is no shelter from the current, and the substrate may be unstable and nutrient-poor, while above water level there is no shelter from extremes of temperature or humidity.

Very quickly, however, organisms arrive on the site, from a variety of sources. Only those which are hardy enough to survive the rigorous conditions will establish themselves and reproduce, but they have the advantage of no competition for light, space or resources. These first colonisers are usually small plants with a low output. However, just by growing on the site they begin to change it. As a result, more species, less hardy than the pioneers, can survive, perhaps in the shelter of the pioneers, or feeding on them or their decayed remains. Production increases and more space is taken up by plants. Organic matter begins to accumulate and creates physical and chemical changes in the soil.

As time goes on, the highly specialised pioneers are ousted and a series of other plants come to dominate the community. Because of increasing competition for light (a fixed commodity) in the increasingly rich environment, successive plants are taller and taller, until – if the succession can get that far – trees are dominant. The bulk of living organisms (the *biomass*) increases accordingly (figure 3).

Parallel to the increasing biomass, there is an increase in the numbers of species, both plant and animal. In early and mid-stages of succession, most of them are plants – the producers; in late and stable stages the numbers of animal species is greater, and the majority are (usually) decomposers (figure 4). Partly as a result of this, the rate of production (ie the rate of increase of biomass as gram/

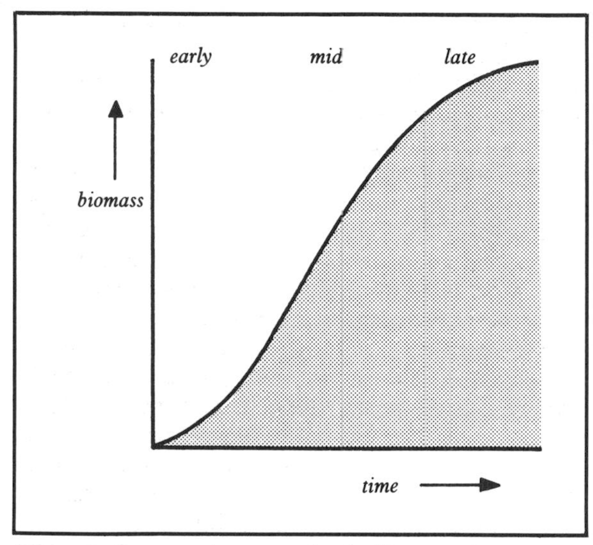

Figure 3: As succession proceeds, the biomass of a given community increases.

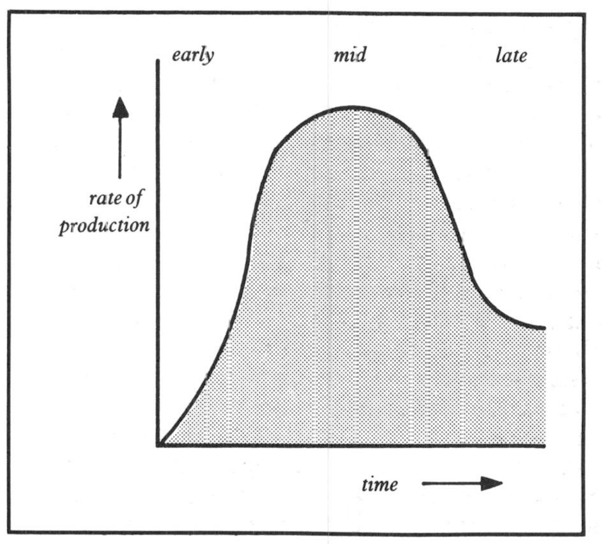

Figure 5: The rate of increase of biomass – or the rate of production – falls, however.

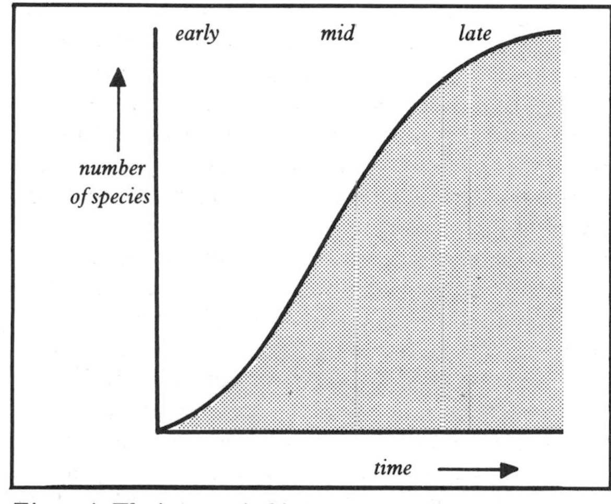

Figure 4: The increase in biomass is paralleled by an increase in species diversity.

gram unit time) peaks in the middle of a succession, and is lower in the stable state (figure 5).

The late stages of any unhindered succession are usually tree-dominated, but with patches of mid-succession communities wherever the habitat is naturally unstable, shifting or recently disturbed or damaged – for example, by gales, flood or fire, or simply by the decay and collapse of some forest giant permitting summer sunlight to reach the forest floor, perhaps for the first time in a century or more. For river systems, where the current and flow regime limit the progress of succession, trees are confined to the banks, and if the channel is narrow it will contain only shade-tolerant plants.

There is, therefore, a high biomass on the banks, and a low one in the channel. As tree-lined rivers tend to be narrower and swifter than others, there is an extra deterrent to flowering plants growing in them. Organic production (leaves, etc) by the trees, falling into the river, passes through decomposer and consumer food chains there (invertebrates, fish, some birds, and mammals). Amongst the tree roots, in bark, on leaves and flowers, are many *micro-habitats* for an enormous number of invertebrate species which in turn provide food for larger invertebrates, birds and mammals. The complexity of food-chain interactions and available habitats is much richer than in earlier stages of the succession.

It is rare to watch a natural succession from beginning to end! Time scales vary, but are usually measured in centuries rather than decades. It is fairly easy, though, to watch sections of the process, for example the recovery of a community after being 'set back' by some event, natural or otherwise. Any disturbance which removes species, or reduces biomass, or removes accumulated organic matter, disrupts the succession, deflecting it from its normal path or pushing it back to an earlier stage. Unless all organic matter and all species are removed, the recovery community goes back to only mid-successional stages, in which numbers of species and biomass increase very rapidly and rates of production are at a maximum. This is why weed-cutting is such an infuriating never-ending job! Cutting actually maintains the community in its most productive, mid-successional stage.

In some cases a community maybe held at an equilibrium, due to the action of biotic factors, and prevented from progressing towards its natural climax. An example of such a *plagioclimax* community is grassland under continuous pasture, where grazing prevents the development of scrub and ultimately woodland. The maintenance of the community and its wildlife interest depends on the maintenance of the management system or a system closely related to it.

There are other interactions within communities, however, for which figure 6 provides a helpful

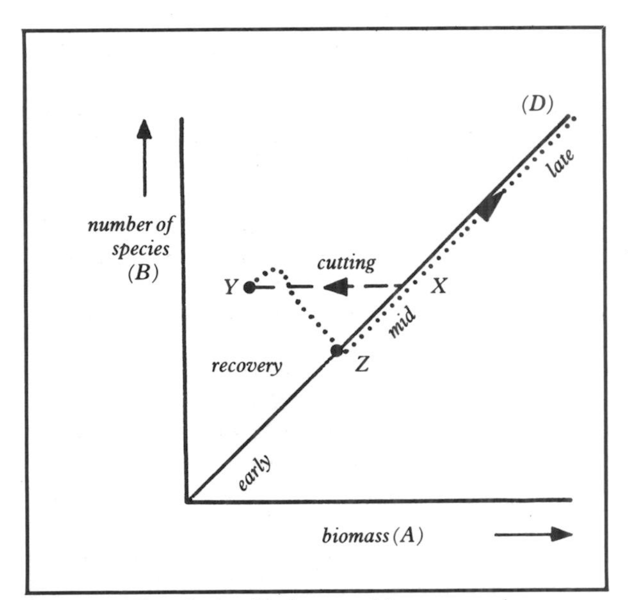

Figure 6: The relationship between biomass, species diversity and weed cutting.

model. Since the biomass (A) and the number of species (B) increase at approximately the same rate, plotting them against each other gives a straight line graph (D). Weed-cutting in a mid-succession of a weedy river community will suddenly reduce biomass dramatically, and probably reduce the numbers of species very slightly. Hence the plot of the community moves to the left to point Y (dashed line).

In recovery (dotted line), there may be a slight initial increase in species number – as new plants move into the vacant spaces – but very rapidly the number of species falls as 'aggressive' plants take over. At the same time the bulk of plants increases very rapidly. Given time, the community will get back to its 'normal' line of succession and species number will start to increase again, but there is a real danger that the weed-cutting programme will be repeated at some point between 'X' and 'Z' before the diversity has recovered. As a result, the community is kept in check in a species-poor state.

Nature conservation values sites which have reached late or stable stages of succession for reasons including:

– they are *species-rich*, and likely to contain more uncommon and rare species than less diverse communities: an objective of conservation is to prevent loss of species and thus action tends to be directed to those which are scarcer and hence, in general, most at risk.

– the interactions between organisms in diverse communities are, for the most part, little known and their study may reveal information of value, perhaps applicable to the management of systems or to the sustained cropping of natural systems.

– it is intrinsically more efficient to conserve one site with a large number of species rather than several with only a few.

Nature conservation also values highly large sites, rather than small ones. Other things being equal it is preferable to protect one site of area x rather than three separate sites each of area $x/3$. There are two main reasons for this – the large spatial requirements of top predators and the risks of extinction of species within small sites.

As has been shown, predators at the ends of food chains require a large biomass of plant producers to sustain them because, at each trophic level where energy is passed to and between consumers, there is an energy loss. Thus heron, otter and pike, for example, must all have much larger feeding territories than moorhen, water vole and roach. It follows that, to achieve their conservation, large areas of suitable habitat must be maintained. In fact, as a rule-of-thumb conservation judgement, it can be assumed that if the top predator populations are flourishing, a site or habitat is in good health and will sustain all the other species which form the community. This is why the monitoring of predator populations and their protection as 'monitoring tools' assumes some importance in conservation work.

Even though the composition of a diverse community may remain stable over time, there will still be detailed changes in numbers and locations of its component species – perhaps because of changes in available food or nutrient supply, as a result of disease or of sudden changes in the physical environment, such as a tree falling or a meander loop cutting through. Where a habitat is very extensive, the probability is that it will always provide, somewhere within itself, an adequacy of suitable niches for every species in the community. Because of this, though an individual species may suffer loss in one spot, it will find a new opportunity in another. There is little danger of it becoming extinct within the site. Overall, the community exists in a state of *dynamic equilibrium*, with short-term changes in abundance or location of individual species but long-term stability.

Human management of lowland Britain increasingly directs energy flows in ways which enable a larger proportion to be 'harvested' for human use. Areas in low-intensity exploitation, capable of maintaining diverse and abundant wildlife, become fewer and smaller, the fragments existing like islands in a sea. In general, the smaller the site, the fewer the species it will be able to sustain. Thus, nature conservation places a high priority on the protection of such large, diverse sites as remain.

Rivers have two qualities which make them more resistant to local catastrophe than are isolated terrestrial sites. One is their continuous, linear nature, which provides the potential opportunity for colonists to move within them, and the other is that

many river organisms have evolved strategies for dealing with sudden and potentially harmful change. This is because river communities, perhaps more than any other, naturally have to cope with frequent changes in their physical conditions, such as winter spates, which disrupt them annually to a greater or lesser extent. Many water plants have floating seeds or regenerative parts, so that they can readily recolonise lost habitat downstream. Movement upstream is a slower process but may be aided by animals – many seeds resist digestion. Many aquatic invertebrates are winged and can disperse widely. Others instinctively swim upstream in order to combat the effects of current. Fish, birds and mammals all have the potential to move over long distances, more or less rapidly, in order to recolonise lost ground.

The linear nature of a river system means that individual habitats are rarely totally isolated from each other. Perhaps water quality is the most important inhibiting influence on organisms which move within the river itself. The input of pollutants may reduce levels of dissolved oxygen, inhibit plant growth or actually poison invertebrates, fish and other animals, but provided pollutant inputs are controlled, the river demonstrates a remarkable capacity for rapid recovery. However, machines – hydraulic excavators, draglines, Bradshaw buckets and weed-cutting boats – are capable of causing more thorough and more frequent disruption of the system than any natural phenomenon. As a result, the powers of recovery of plant and animal populations are defeated, so that only species from the pioneer or early successful stages – such as 'blanket weed' – can survive. The community is impoverished, and its ability to withstand even natural changes in conditions is weakened. Fluctuations from year to year may set in; alien plants such as Japanese knotweed can take over.

Within limits, rivers can adjust, both physically and biologically, to the changes caused by man, as long as the changes are not too radical, too fast or too destructive. How much is 'too radical', how fast is 'too fast' varies with every system and with the changes imposed! Experience and experiment can give a guide. The desired alternative *can* often be accomplished with less damage to the wildlife community – the techniques reported in this Handbook are some of the ways in which flood alleviation and land drainage have been achieved with less disruption of the river system than would have been the case with some conventional practices.

Rivers are living systems, are a community, and, whilst in a small island like Britain, with 60 million people and a high standard of living, they cannot be unaffected by human activity, they should be respected in their own right. With this ethic, it is appropriate that parts or the whole of some river systems should be demarcated as special and efforts made to conserve them in a natural state. Meanwhile, the approach to river management elsewhere must be that as much as possible is conserved, and where disturbance is unavoidable, reinstatement is built into the programme of work.

'That land is a community is the basic concept of ecology: but that land is to be loved and respected is an extension of ethics.'

Aldo Leopold, 1949.

SUMMARY

1 Plants are the *producers* on which all animals depend. The more abundant and productive the plant life of a river, the more animals will be able to live there.

2 All living creatures are *specialists*, adapted to exploit one particular type of environment.

3 Plants and animals cannot alter their special *adaptations* except in the very long-term. Thus, if the conditions to which they are adapted disappear (from natural causes or as a result of human intervention), they too must disappear from the site or area concerned.

4 A particular set of conditions for a species is its *habitat*. Many species will share any given habitat, each using it in a different way and each interacting with the others. The whole set of species within a habitat is its *community*.

5 Removal of one member of a community will affect others. In general, the fewer species in a community, the more unstable it is. Unstable communities change; their members gradually alter the habitat, providing opportunities for more and different species. The community becomes more *diverse*, supporting more species, and more *stable*, changing more slowly. Thus the rate at which new species join the community slows.

6 Communities which contain many species are relatively old. They are valued by conservationists because they include rare species, and because they are important to research.

7 The larger the site, the less likely it is that any species will become extinct from it; inimical conditions are less likely to affect the whole area.

8 Top predators require large areas of suitable habitat. If the predator populations are stable, then it is probably true that their habitat and its component wildlife community is in good health.

9 Thus, large sites with well-developed, mature wildlife communities, including many species both common and rare, are highly valued for nature conservation.

10 Individual species on rivers have living strategies which enable them to cope with sudden natural changes such as spates and low flows. Thus, they are generally resistant to change. However, repeated destruction of specialist conditions, as by frequent maintenance cycles, will cause extinction.

On the other hand, their ability to recolonise is great, given the chance.

11 River engineering should seek to maintain or create physical diversity in river form, so providing opportunities for the development of diverse and stable wildlife communities.

REFERENCES

Holmes, N T H, 1980. Preliminary results from the river macrophyte survey and implications for conservation. Nature Conservancy Council, Chief Scientist Team Note 24.

Holmes, N T H, 1983. Focus on nature conservation No 4: typing British rivers according to their flora. Nature Conservancy Council.

SELECT BIBLIOGRAPHY

General Ecology

Armstrong, P H, 1978. Discovering ecology. Shire.
King, T J, 1980. Ecology. Nelson.
Owen, D F, 1980. What is ecology? (2nd edition). Oxford University Press.
Ricklefs, R E, 1978. The economy of nature: a textbook of basic ecology. Blackwell Scientific.

Freshwater Ecology

Clegg, J, 1974. Freshwater life. Warne.
Macan, T T, 1974. Freshwater ecology. Longmans.
Maitland, P S, 1978. Biology of freshwaters. Blackie.
Townsend, C R, 1980. The ecology of streams and rivers. Edward Arnold.
Whitton, B A, 1979. The natural history of Britain and North Europe. Rivers, lakes and marshes. Ed J Ferguson-Lees and B Campbell. Hodder and Stoughton.

PART II: THE BIOLOGY OF RIVER WILDLIFE

INTRODUCTION

This part comprises a series of essays, each of which looks at a particular type of river wildlife. Each describes the importance of rivers for that wildlife group; the habitat requirements of the species concerned; and the impact of river engineering works on them. As far as possible, detailed information is presented in tabular form. This section is not intended to provide information about identification – instead, a select bibliography directs the reader to key texts.

BIOLOGICAL 1: PLANTS

Prepared by Gill Lewis from data supplied principally by Dr N T H Holmes, Chief Scientist Team, Nature Conservancy Council, Huntingdon.

1. INTRODUCTION

Algae, mosses, liverworts, lichens, herbs, grasses, sedges, trees – an infinite variety of plants live in and alongside rivers. For hundreds of plants, running fresh water is the only habitat in which they can survive. For others, it is one of a range of habitats where they can be found.

For the community as a whole, the plants are the producers of organic matter and the fixers of solar energy. Just as vital is their role in the physical structure of the community. On top of the variety of physical habitats provided by variations in channel bed and bank form, the larger plants offer innumerably more intricate variations – the surfaces of stems above or below water, the undersides of leaves, crevices in bark, holes in tree trunks, inside flowers, amongst root mats. Plants modify the physical characteristics of the site, its flow velocity, silt accumulation, temperature regime, light availability, oxygen concentration and humidity. Most algae in silty rivers, for example, are attached to the stems and leaves of water plants; invertebrates in turbulent rocky streams can be found in great numbers in the shelter of moss clumps. The plants in a river system are the major biotic factor which modifies physical conditions.

From the human point of view, the plants in and beside water can make or mar the beauty of the river scene.

There is an enormous diversity in the form and life cycles of river plants which have evolved to take advantage of the variety of conditions in river systems. From source to mouth, and in any natural cross section, the variation of water depth, flow velocity, and substrate size, as well as bank height, slope, aspect, period of inundation and soil-type, forms an intricate pattern of zones which different types of plants may inhabit. In addition, as the process of succession progresses, starting with the colonisation of bare areas, different types of plants can occupy the same patch. River plant communities are restricted by the absence of light, very high velocities or extreme turbulence, permanently unstable substrates or gross pollution.

In reality there is a continuum of habitat variation, but as an aid to understanding the very complex river ecosystem, it is useful to subdivide the river into **mid-channel**, **channel edges**, **banksides** and **banktops**. The cross-section of a 'typical' small lowland river illustrates these divisions and the broad 'type' of plants associated with each (Figure 1). Other types of rivers can be similarly divided, but of course the relative area available for colonisation in each zone will be different.

Mid-channel – Aquatic: no plants at all if scour prevents the channel bed from stabilising. In turbulent rivers with a stable bed, only lichens, mosses and encrusting algae will be able to inhabit this zone. If the flow velocity is moderate but the substrate stable, rooted, submerged streamlined plants and attached algae are present. Broad-leaved and floating-leaved species will predominate if the flow velocity is low.

Channel edges – Aquatic: no plants at all if scour prevents the bed stabilising, or if heavily shaded by overhanging bank plants. Otherwise this is the richest zone for plants; where flow is slowed by shoals, bays or stands of robust emergent plants, pond-like conditions may develop – at least

Figure 1: Cross-section of a typical lowland river, divided by habitat types.

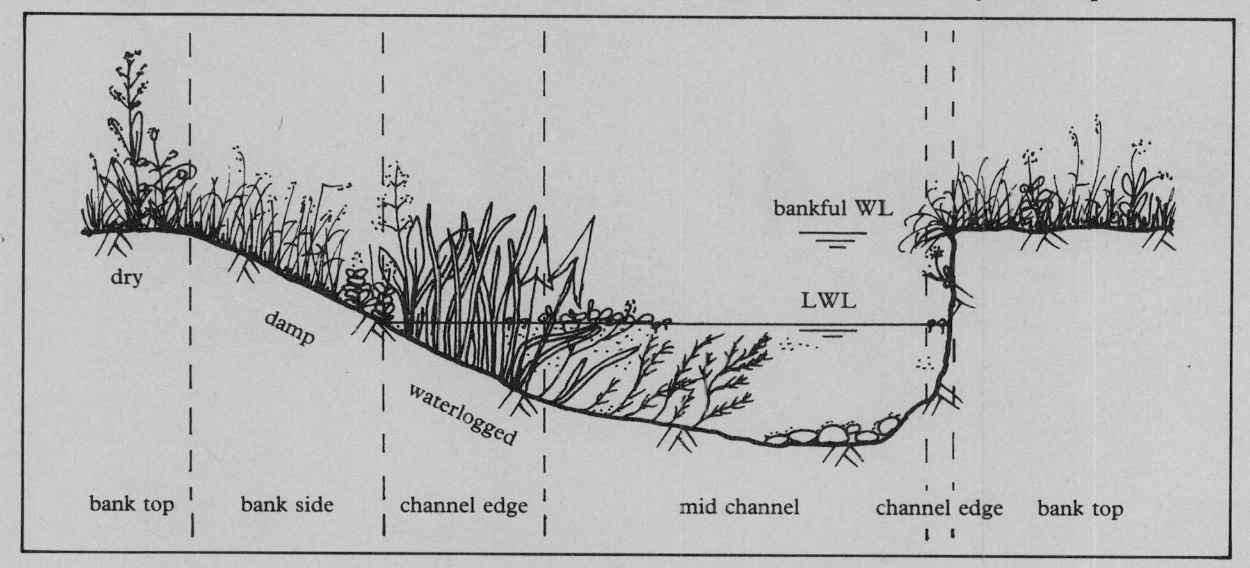

temporarily – in summer. Emergent broad- and narrow-leaved plants may dominate, with floating-leaved rooted plants towards the edges or in deeper water. Floating, unrooted plants may be found amongst emergents, or in still bays and back-waters. Attached algae on fixed plants are the primary food source for many aquatic invertebrates. Most higher plants are perennial, dying back in winter, to regrow from overwintering buds and root stocks. This zone is the one most likely to be damaged by river management work.

Banksides – Predominantly 'dry': no higher plants at all if the slope is very steep, gorge-like or densely shaded. This is a transition zone between the channel and floodplain, with a gradation of soil moisture content and length of submersion by floods. Both river plants and less specialised dry land plants may be found here. Amphibious species are characteristic at the interface of bank and channel, where they grow on the shallowest, muddiest edges. Herbs and grasses may be rooted on the bank but they straggle out over the water into the channel. Alders and some willows may grow in this zone, shading and influencing the adjacent channel and banktop.

Most plants on stable banks are perennial: many form clumps or dense stands which remain dense throughout the winter, others die back to root stocks. Plants of temporary shoals and unshaded river edges, usually annuals, often have bright flowers and seed prolifically – important food sources for insects and seed-eating birds. The potential diversity of plant types is greatest in this zone, but may be restricted severely by both river management and adjacent land-use (eg grazing, herbicide spraying, burning).

Figure 2: Plan diagram of the habitat sub-divisions.

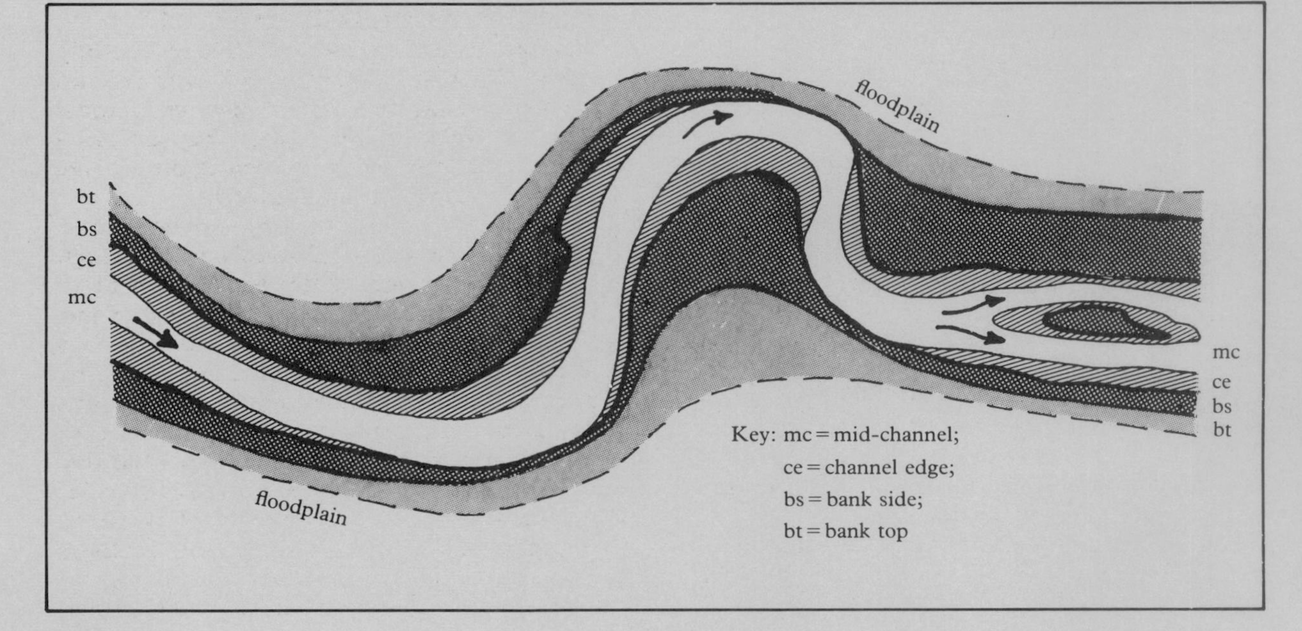

Banktop – Predominantly 'dry'. The vegetation depends primarily on adjacent land-use. Most plants here can also be found in woodlands or field-edges, but a few are rare and riversides are the only habitat in which they thrive. Plants of wet seepages or bare, dry clay banks fall into this latter category. Trees, scrub, herbs, sedges and grasses as well as ferns, mosses, lichens and liverworts can be found in this zone. In old woodlands the humid zone along the riverside may have an especially fragile plant community of lichens, mosses and ferns. Otherwise, under trees, the plant cover may be sparse because of shade. In theory the banktop is indistinguishable from the rest of the floodplain; in practice the boundary of the wild community is determined by field edges or built-up areas.

Because each of these sub-divisions is 'defined' by water-levels and bank slopes – all attributes of channel forms – in 'natural' rivers they occur as irregular zones and patches in the linear/sinuous river corridor (Figure 2). The mid-channel and channel edge zones are particularly mobile, changing as erosion and deposition alter river form. At any one cross-section one or more zones may be absent. Edge or bankside zones may be missing where the slope between the deep-water channel and banktop is so great that there is no space for them to develop. In naturally meandering channels this will be compensated for by shallow banks elsewhere. In rivers that have been straightened or graded to uniform depth, the pattern of zones will also be uniform, paralleling the channel. Unless deliberate steps are taken to build in variety of depths and slopes, the natural and essential variety of vegetation will be lost.

The vast range of habitats present on rivers is reflected in a wide variety of aquatic and bank plants. We have attempted to summarise the habitat requirements of these plants below. Data

are given on native plants only – so giant hogweed, Himalayan balsam and Japanese knotweed are not listed, even though they may be abundant on rivers.

The tables seek to group plants by their obvious physical similarities and are intended to be a guide to:-

a) What may be found in a reach – but because of regional differences, geographical isolation, and the effects of past management, only field survey can show what actually *is* there.

b) Which plants might disappear as a result of river works – deepening, widening, regrading banks, increasing velocity, change in sediments, increase in shade, may change conditions so significantly that the plant community changes, and a different one may take its place (with repercussions on the animal community).

c) Which plants are suitable to be replanted – so that the community can recover as quickly as possible from disturbance. This is linked to **219** (Aquatic Plants). Establishing in the technical section which details examples from sites where this has been done; see also **238** bank plants, and **258** tree planting.

2. KEY TO PLANT HABITAT TABLES

The Keble Martin plate number refers to Keble Martin, 1969, a useful illustrated guide to British plants, most of them in colour.

● – preferred conditions, most frequently found/high tolerance.
○ – very commonly found/fair-good tolerance
∘ – occasionally found/moderately tolerant
∅ – when several species have been amalgamated, some prefer this condition and others shun it.
• rarely found

blank	– absent/intolerant	
NP	– no preference	
L	– lowland only	altitude of site
U	– upland only	
T	– transitional only	
Thr	– throughout	
A	– annual/biennial	life-cycle
P	– perennial	
*	– uncommon plant, recorded in fewer than 100 national kilometre grid squares, out of circa 2,600.	
34	– the plant may grow both in the channel and on the bank.	
[....]	– very common, likely to rapidly re-colonise unaided, not suitable for replanting.	

3. USE OF THE PLANT HABITAT TABLES

The data can be read laboriously along the lines, noting which species' habitat requirements coincides with the proposed or existing conditions. An easier technique for access to the information is to use a slotted guide-card (figure 3).

A card is cut with a slot at right and left, and with tabs marked and cut in line with each column in the table. Tabs are turned down to correspond with the conditions in the river site. As the card is slid down the tables the plants which have all or nearly all large black circles or large open circles in the turned-down spaces are associated with those conditions. Note that tables 1-7 (channel plants) have different column headings to tables 8-12 (bank plants).

If the intention is to redevelop a natural plant cover, then a selection can be chosen from the associated species according to the requirements of the scheme – for rapid cover, improvement of fish and invertebrate habitat, food for wildfowl or small birds, or just for an attractive river's edge community.

Figure 3: Slotted guide-card for use with the plant habitat tables.

4. PLANTS AND THEIR HABITATS

a. Mosses and Liverworts. These are the majority of aquatic plants in turbulent reaches where there is some hard, stable substrate for them to grow on – rock or tree roots. They are often overlooked but they play a vital role in the ecology of the upper reaches of many rivers.

They are the first colonisers of rivers where few other plants can grow. Turbulence and high velocities of spates, and/or the presence of boulder and bedrock substrates prevent flowering plants from growing, except in very sheltered pockets with silt. Within cushions and tight, low-lying mats of mosses, many invertebrates shelter and feed. Caddis, mayfly and stonefly larvae in particular use clumps of moss on rocks and tree roots. The only alternative sites are the undersides of boulders, and in spaces in gravel beds – so mosses increase the available living space for these creatures.

Mosses are characteristic of upland rivers (over

200 metres), as well as of the upper reaches of some lowland rivers. In reaches where silt accumulates, mosses and liverworts are smothered. However, weirs and falls interrupting this type of reach will have a covering of mosses if the water is unpolluted. The willow moss, *Fontinalis antipyretica* is very common in such situations.

As well as being found submerged, the same or related species can be found in the splash zones around falls and rapids, on walls which are only submerged in spates, and in damp situations nearby on rocks and trees.

Moss-dominated reaches tend to be affected only rarely by river works, because many are not designed as main river. Those that are main river are often fast-flowing and require little maintenance weed-cutting or dredging. They are susceptible, however, to land-use changes in the catchment. For example, forestry or upland drainage and ploughing can cause rocky stretches to silt up, changing the character of the vegetation. Pioneer tree clearance in deeply shaded stretches will increase light levels on the river bed and allow other plants to grow – filamentous algae usually being the first invaders. Where gravelly channels are drastically disturbed – say for realignment in road works – the resulting instability will prevent mosses recolonising for many years; meanwhile the loss of shelter for invertebrates and fish can be compensated for by installing current deflectors and small weirs (see pages **118** and **126**).

Transplanting mosses and liverworts is not feasible except with the boulders they are growing on, and then should only be put in the main flow, not on the edge where deposition of silt may smother and kill the plants. Ordinary household bricks in fast-flowing rivers often become densely covered with mosses and algae, and can be 'transplanted' to new sites as a source of recolonising material.

b. Free-floating, unrooted plants (Table 1)

These will only flourish in backwaters, cut-off channels and still bays in any river. Where flow velocity is moderate they may also occur, held by rooted emergent plants. They form a rich habitat for aquatic invertebrates where, for example, snails, some mayfly larvae and beetles will feed on bacteria and algae on the underside of the floating mat. Many species are also valuable sources of food for wildfowl. Non-native plants such as the water-fern have a similar mat-like habit. However, in ideal conditions of unshaded, still, clean, nutrient-rich water, some free-floating species can become a nuisance, carpeting the surface and reducing oxygen concentrations. Duckweed and water-fern can be particularly troublesome and eradication is difficult. Although herbicides will kill them, they leave the problem of disposal of a rotting plant mass.

Table 1: Free-floating, unrooted plants

K.M. NUMBER	SPECIES	ALTITUDE	SUBSTRATE						FLOW			DEPTH				WIDTH				CHEM.			WATER QUAL.			SHADE TOLERANCE	DISTURBANCE TOLERANCE	LIFE CYCLE
			Clay	Silt	Peat	Sand	Gravel-Pebble	Cobble-Boulder	Nil-Slow	Moderate	Fast-Rapid	>1 m	0.5-1 m	0.1-0.5 m	0.1-dry	>20 m	10-20 m	5-10 m	<5 m	Base poor	Base neutral	Base rich	Clean	Moderate	Polluted			
34	Hornworts	L	○	●		◦	◦		●			●	◦	•		○	○	○	•		◦	●	○	●	◦	●	●	A/P
88	[Duckweeds]	L	○	○	•	•			●	●		◦	●	●	•	•	◦	●	○	•	●	○	○	◦			●	A
59	*Fringed water lily	L	●	●					●			●	●	◦		○	○	○	◦			●	○	○			◦	P
66	Bladderworts	Thr	•	◦	●	•			●			◦	○	○		•	○	○	○	○	○	○	●			●	●	A/P
79	Frogbit	L	○	○	•	•			●			●	◦			○	○	○	•			●	◦	●			◦	A/P

c. Submerged, narrow-leaved plants (Table 2)

The narrow leaves of this group are often an adaption to enable them to withstand high flow velocities. Most are flexible and conform to the flow, waving in turbulent conditions – crowfoots and pondweeds may grow into long, trailing clumps up to five metres long. These may be a nuisance in shallow channels in mid-summer, raising water levels. Mare's tail, bulbous rush and shoreweed are smaller, stiffer plants that resist flows and grow upright underwater.

This flexibility or lack of it does not mean that they are all undamaged by the high velocity and turbulence of flow in spates. Crowfoots tend to be brittle and break up, especially in late summer, so dispersing fragments from which new plants grow.

If rooted into temporary accumulations of silt they are more easily washed out than if rooted into consolidated clay on the river bed. In such silty rivers, the species present are very different from those found in rivers with gravel substrates.

Some of these plants are only submerged for part of the year, in spates, otherwise growing upright as emergents. Arrowhead and unbranched bur-reed are examples. Others (eg bulbous rush, shoreweed, and mare's tail) grow successfully out of water on shoals or at the water's edge, emerging as water levels fall in summer. Still others may form floating mats of plants, anchored to the bottom.

For the animal community, submerged plants and attached algae increase the habitable surface area for many invertebrates and also provide food sources. In many rivers they are particularly important to coarse fish for egg-laying and food. In turbulent rivers, the only submerged plants are generally narrow-leaved species and so they are particularly valuable in increasing habitat diversity for animals.

When transplanting these, whole plants should be moved with a good ball of sediment round the roots. They should be planted in sections or reaches of low to moderate flow velocity with a stone on the rootball to prevent wash-out.

Table 2: Submerged, narrow-leaved plants
(some are part-emergent, some others have floating leaves)

K.M. NUMBER	SPECIES	ALTITUDE	SUBSTRATE						FLOW			DEPTH				WIDTH				CHEM.			WATER QUAL.			SHADE TOLERANCE	DISTURBANCE TOLERANCE	LIFE CYCLE
			Clay	Silt	Peat	Sand	Gravel-Pebble	Cobble-Boulder	Nil-Slow	Moderate	Fast-Rapid	>1 m	0.5-1 m	0.1-0.5 m	0.1-dry	>20 m	10-20 m	5-10 m	<5 m	Base poor	Base neutral	Base rich	Clean	Moderate	Polluted			
34	Mare's tail	L	○	◦	•	◦	●		◦	●	•	◦	●	●	•	◦	●	●	◦		◦	●	●	◦	•		◦	P
87	Bulbous rush	U/T	•		•	○	●	•	◦	○	●	•	○	●	•	•	●	●	◦	●	◦		●	•		●	●	P
71	Shoreweed	U	•			◦	●	◦	•	●	◦	•	○	○	○	○	○	○	•	●	○	•	●	•		●	◦	P
34	*Water milfoils	Thr	○	●	•	•	○	•	●	○	○	○	○	•		○	○	○	•	○	•	●	○	○	•	◦	◦	P
39	*River water dropwort	L	●	◦		◦	◦		◦	●	•	•	○	●		○	○	○	•		•	●	○	○			◦	P
90	Small pondweed	L	○	○		◦	◦		●	○		•	○	○		◦	○	○	◦	○	○	○	○	○	◦	●	◦	A/P
90	[Fennel pondweed]	Thr	○	○		○	○	•	○	●	◦	◦	●	○		○	○	○	◦		◦	●	•	○	●	◦	●	P
90	Flat-stalked pondweed	L	◦	●					●			◦	●	◦		◦	○	○	○		○	○	○	○	○	◦	◦	P
2	Cmn. water crowfoot	Thr	•	•	•	•	●	◦	○	○	◦	•	◦	●	◦	•	○	○	○	○	○	•	●	○	•		●	A/P
2	Fan-leaved water crowfoot	L	●	●					●	•		○	●	•		○	○	○	•			●	○	○	•	●	◦	P
2	River water crowfoot	T/L	○	•		◦	●	◦	◦	●	○	○	●	●	•	●	○	○	•	•	●	○	●	•				P
—	Pond water crowfoot	T/L	◦	•	•	◦	●	•	◦	●	◦	•	◦	●	◦	•	○	●	○	•	○	●	●	○	◦		◦	A/P
2	Thread-leaved water crowfoot	T/L	○	•		◦	○		○	○	•	◦	○	○	•	◦	○	○	○	•	◦	●	●	◦		◦	●	A/P
79	Arrowhead	L	●	●		•			●	◦		•	◦	●		○	○	○	○		○	●	○	○	○		●	A/P
91	Floating clubrush	U	◦	•	○	◦	◦	•	•	●	•		•	●	•	•	◦	○	○	●	•		●				◦	P
88	Unbranched bur-reed	L	○	○	•	•	•		○	○	•	•	○	○	•	○	○	○	○	•	○	○	○	○			●	P
90	Horned pondweed	L	•	●		●	◦		●	○		•	◦	●		○	○	○	○		◦	●	○	○	•		●	P

d. Submerged, broad-leaved plants (Table 3)
The pondweeds are always submerged, but lesser water parsnip and starworts can also grow as emergents – the first as an upright, bushy plant, the latter as a prostrate mat on mud.

This group is less streamlined than the narrow-leaved submergents, and may cause more obstruction to water flow. The plants provide a varied underwater habitat for many invertebrates, attached algae and fish. Curled pondweed is the most widespread species in this category since it tolerates organic pollution. In some polluted rivers this and/or common club-rush may be the only plants growing in mid-channel.

Starworts – of which there are many species, a few of them rare – are worth introducing to any site. They never grow large enough to hinder flow and are broken up and washed out by spates. Narrow-leaved water parsnip, similarly, usually grows in limited clumps, and is a useful 'habitat improver' for invertebrates.

Provided they are well-anchored, both narrow-leaved and broad-leaved submerged plants could be used to stabilise a channel bed – as velocity increases the plants flatten against the bed and hydraulic resistance decreases. Curled pondweed and fennel pondweed are good candidates for this role, although either may spread and be a nuisance to fishermen when water levels drop. In addition, by taking light and nutrients, submerged plants prevent the explosive summer growth of filamentous algae which, in some channels, can be a far greater hindrance to flow, and much harder to eradicate.

Table 3: Submerged, broad-leaved plants

K.M. NUMBER	SPECIES	ALTITUDE	SUBSTRATE						FLOW			DEPTH				WIDTH				CHEM.			WATER QUAL.			SHADE TOLERANCE	DISTURBANCE TOLERANCE	LIFE CYCLE
			Clay	Silt	Peat	Sand	Gravel-Pebble	Cobble-Boulder	Nil-Slow	Moderate	Fast-Rapid	>1 m	0.5-1 m	0.1-0.5 m	0.1-dry	>20 m	10-20 m	5-10 m	<5 m	Base poor	Base neutral	Base rich	Clean	Moderate	Polluted			
38	Narrow-leaved water parsnip	L	◦	◦	•	○	●	•	•	○	●	•	◦	●	○	•	◦	○	●		•	○	●	•		◦	◦	P
34	Starwort species	Thr	○	○	•	•	○	◦	○	●	•	•	●	●	•	◦	○	○	○	∅	●	∅	●	○	•	◦	◦	A/P
89	Opposite leaved pondweed	U	○	•		◦	◦		●	◦		◦	●	◦		◦	●	●	◦		◦	●	○	○				P
90	Curled pondweed	T/L	○	◦	•	◦	○	•	○	○	◦	•	○	●		○	○	○	○	•	●	○	○	○	○	◦	●	P
89	Shining pondweed	L	○	○		•	•		●			○	●	●		○	○	◦			◦	●	○	○			●	P
89	Perfoliate pondweed	T/L	○	○		◦	○	•	●	○		◦	○	○		○	○	○			○	○	●	◦			◦	P
79	[Canadian pondweed]	T/L	○	○		○	○		○	○	•	○	○	○		○	○	○	○		○	○	○	○	◦		●	A/P

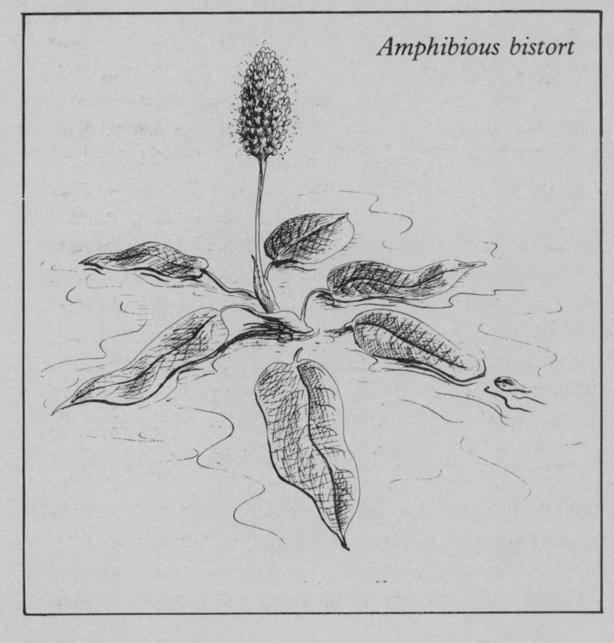
Amphibious bistort

e. Rooted, floating-leaved plants (Table 4)
This small and very specialised group has leaves which float flat on the surface, but in spates swirl below water level and become streamlined. Their hydraulic resistance, even so, is likely to be greater than that of submerged, narrow-leaved plants (Table 2). Studies with broad-leaved pondweed has shown that its hydraulic resistance decreases as it is pulled under. Yellow water-lily, with permanently submerged, cabbage-like leaves as well as floating ones, is a severe problem in dykes in some parts of Britain. It is tolerant of organic pollution, but its growth is checked by higher flow velocities. White water lily is rarely found in rivers, preferring cleaner water and still conditions in lakes, gravel pits and pools. This and amphibious bistort can be planted in cut-offs and bays.

Floating leaved plants are often used as resting and breeding sites for aquatic insects, especially damselfly and dragonfly species.

Table 4: Rooted, floating-leaved plants

K.M. NUMBER	SPECIES	ALTITUDE	SUBSTRATE: Clay	Silt	Peat	Sand	Gravel-Pebble	Cobble-Boulder	FLOW: Nil-Slow	Moderate	Fast-Rapid	DEPTH: >1 m	0.5-1 m	0.1-0.5 m	0.1-dry	WIDTH: >20 m	10-20 m	5-10 m	<5 m	CHEM.: Base poor	Base neutral	Base rich	WATER QUAL.: Clean	Moderate	Polluted	SHADE TOLERANCE	DISTURBANCE TOLERANCE	LIFE CYCLE
5	[Yellow water lily]	L	●	◦					●	◦		○	○	◦		○	○	○	◦		●	◦	○	○	◦	◦	●	P
5	White water lily	Thr	●	◦	○				●			○	○	◦		○	○	○	◦	○	○	◦	●			◦		P
89	Bog pondweed	U/T	○	○	●	◦		◦	○	○	◦		•	●	◦	•	◦	◦	●	●	◦		●				◦	P
89	Broad leaved pondweed	Thr	○	○	○	◦	◦	◦	○	○	◦	◦	●	◦		○	○	○	◦	○	○	○	○	○	•	•	●	P

f. Emergent, narrow-leaved plants (Table 5)
This category of plants is commonly lumped together as 'reeds' in colloquial terms (ie upright, green water plants, as opposed to 'weeds' which are horizontal green water plants!). Botanically this is quite wrong, and misleading. The only true reed is the common reed *Phragmites australis*; all the others in this list, except the water horsetail which is a primitive, non-flowering plant, are types of grass, sedge, rush or herb linked only by belonging to a very large plant group called monocotyledons.

They are all perennial plants which grow in clumps from underground stems (termed 'rhizomes') from which they spread sideways and out into the channel until checked by deep water, high velocity flow or unstable substrate. Narrow leaves help them to withstand spates, but only the common club rush can withstand continuous moderate flow velocities; it often invades mid-stream shoals, and may aggravate sedimentation. At the channel edge, where these plants invariably grow because of the low flow velocity, they themselves reduce the velocity further to create local pond-like conditions. Sediment accumulating in and at the edge of beds of emergent plants may allow them to encroach further into the channel, hence the need for invasive species to be kept in check by weed-cutting and periodic desilting. *However, not all these species are invasive.* The water plantains occur as small patches within beds of other plants, or singly on the edges of channels. They are attractive plants with showy flowers and seed heads, and quite distinctive broader leaves. In deep water, however, only submerged leaves may be formed and rarely will flowers be produced. The flowering rush is probably the most attractive and most often overlooked river plant. It occurs in small patches, often on the edge of patches of bur-reed, and is never a weed problem. Its delightful heads of pink flowers appear in July above nondescript 'rush-like' leaves. Spike rush may invade shallows from a marshy edge, but is always kept in check by deep water and moderate flow velocity.

All these plants, except common clubrush, can also grow on the immediate bankside, in permanently wet soils. This, plus their permanence, tough growth and tendency to slow flows and encourage local silt accumulation, makes them useful living materials for bank protection against scour. Techniques are described in Part III sections *2* and 4 for planting on shallow-water berms, **175**, **219** and in various man-made bank protection systems **186**.

Stands of emergents are havens for aquatic invertebrates – sheltering and feeding on accumulated organic matter and on algae attached to the underwater stems. Emergents form a vital link between air and water for aquatic insects, such as many caddisflies, damselflies, and dragonflies, as the mature nymphs or larvae crawl up out of the water to emerge as adults clinging to stems and leaves. Some damselflies lay their eggs *in* the stems of water plants, others on stem and leaf surfaces underwater.

Table 5: Emergent narrow-leaved plants
("reeds" in colloquial terms)

K.M. NUMBER	SPECIES	ALTITUDE	SUBSTRATE						FLOW			DEPTH				WIDTH				CHEM.			WATER QUAL.			SHADE TOLERANCE	DISTURBANCE TOLERANCE	LIFE CYCLE
			Clay	Silt	Peat	Sand	Gravel-Pebble	Cobble-Boulder	Nil-Slow	Moderate	Fast-Rapid	>1 m	0.5-1 m	0.1-0.5 m	0.1-dry	>20 m	10-20 m	5-10 m	<5 m	Base poor	Base neutral	Base rich	Clean	Moderate	Polluted			
79	Water plantain	L	●	◦					●	◦		•	•	○	●	•	•	○	○	•	◦	●	○	○			●	P
79	Flowering rush	L	●	◦		•	○	•	●	○	•	•	◦	●	◦	◦	●	●	•		•	●	○	○				P
91	Spike rushes	Thr	○	○	○	•	◦	◦	○	○	◦		•	○	●	○	○	○	○	◦	●	◦	○	○			◦	P
—	Water horse-tail	Thr	○	○	○	•	•		●	•		•	•	●	◦	○	○	○	○	◦	○	○	●	◦		◦	◦	P
95	Common reed	L	○	○	○	•			●			◦	○	○	●	◦	◦	○	○		○	○				◦		P
91	Common club-rush	T/L	●	○	•				○	●	•	•	◦	●	◦	○	●	●	•		○	●	○	○			●	P
88	[Branched bur-reed]	T/L	●	●					●	◦			◦	●	○	○	○	●	●		○	○	○	○	◦		●	P
88	Reedmace	L	●	◦		•	•		●					•	●	○	○	○	○		○	○	●	◦			◦	P

g. Emergent, broad-leaved plants (Table 6)
These also grow on wet banks as well as in the channel edge. With the exception of water dock, these plants differ from the narrow-leaved emergents in that they are low-growing and form mats of foliage at the water's edge or on the edge of reedbeds. The watercresses can form quite dense, floating mats of leaves, and in narrow, silty channels they may be a nuisance. Blue water speedwell is a medium-sized but delicate plant, with attractive spikes of small flowers. Water dock can form dense, upright stands of tall plants in fens, but is more commonly found as single plants on the channel edge, limited by flow velocity and deeper water from encroaching further. Hemlock water dropwort is an emergent broad-leaved plant, but is not included in Table 6 because it is not advisable to plant it as it is poisonous and can cause skin rashes. It is a large plant and is widely distributed.

These emergent broad-leaved plants have a greater hydraulic resistance and are more easily washed out than narrow-leaved emergents. They are therefore no use as bank protection against scour. The cresses break up into fragments and regrow easily from these in late summer or early winter, overwintering as small plants. Water dock dies back to large root stocks, and can be transplanted and grown from pieces of these. All these species (including hemlock water dropwort) are valuable to invertebrates, providing additional habitat in the channel's edge. The cresses in particular form a sheltered environment favoured by many beetles, snails, fly larvae and emerged fly adults, and are therefore good feeding areas for waterbirds and ducklings. Planted on channel edges, in bays and at the edge of 'reedbeds', these are excellent 'habitat improvers'.

Table 6: Emergent, broad-leaved plants
(note that all of these plants behave differently when growing on banks)

K.M. NUMBER	SPECIES	ALTITUDE	SUBSTRATE						FLOW			DEPTH				WIDTH				CHEM.			WATER QUAL.			SHADE TOLERANCE	DISTURBANCE TOLERANCE	LIFE CYCLE
			Clay	Silt	Peat	Sand	Gravel-Pebble	Cobble-Boulder	Nil-Slow	Moderate	Fast-Rapid	>1 m	0.5-1 m	0.1-0.5 m	0.1-dry	>20 m	10-20 m	5-10 m	<5 m	Base poor	Base neutral	Base rich	Clean	Moderate	Polluted			
37	[Fool's water cress]	L	●	○		•	•		●	○		•	•	○	●	•	∘	○	○		●	○	○	○		∘	∘	A/P
7	Watercress	L	○	○		•	•		●	∘				○	●	•	∘	∘	●		∘	●	○	○		∘		P
74	Water dock	L	●	○	•	•	•		●					∘	●	○	○	○	•		•	●	○	∘				P
84	Blue water speedwell	L	○	●		•	•		●	○			•	○	○	•	○	●	∘		∘	●	○	○	∘	∘	●	A/P

h. Encroaching plants (Table 7)
These are plants of marsh, mud or silty edges – on silty shoals, in cattle drinking-bays and where marshes and seepages lie adjacent to the channel. Their growth pattern makes them ideally suited to shallowly sloping river banks, but given very shallow water and low flow velocities they may be invasive. There is a wide variety of plant forms in this category: the sedges and grasses are narrow-leaved, the others are broad-leaved. Only perennials are listed here, but there are many annuals which also could be included, such as blinks and marsh bedstraw. Greater and lesser pond sedge, whorlgrass and reed sweetgrass can form dense stands of a single species. Great yellow cress and pink water speedwell are more usually in small

Table 7: Encroaching plants

K.M. NUMBER	SPECIES	ALTITUDE	SUBSTRATE						FLOW			DEPTH				WIDTH				CHEM.			WATER QUAL.			SHADE TOLERANCE	DISTURBANCE TOLERANCE	LIFE CYCLE
			Clay	Silt	Peat	Sand	Gravel-Pebble	Cobble-Boulder	Nil-Slow	Moderate	Fast-Rapid	>1 m	0.5-1 m	0.1-0.5 m	0.1-dry	>20 m	10-20 m	5-10 m	<5 m	Base poor	Base neutral	Base rich	Clean	Moderate	Polluted			
93	*Water sedge	U	∘	○	○	•		•	●	∘	•			•	●		ND			○	○	•	●	∘			●	P
94	Lesser pond sedge	L	●	○	•	∘		•	●	○	•			○	●		ND				○	○	○	○	○	•	●	P
94	Greater pond sedge	L	○	○	○	•		•	●	•				○	●		ND				○	○	○	○	○	∘	●	P
94	Bottle sedge	U/T	○	○	○	∘		∘	●	○	•			○	●	○	○	○	∘	●	∘		○	○	∘		●	P
94	Bladder sedge	U/T	∘	∘	●	•			○	•				○	●	○	○	○	∘	○	○	∘	○	○		●	∘	P
97	Whorl grass	L	○	●	•	∘	•		●	•				○	●	∘	○	○	○		∘	●	∘	○	∘	∘	∘	P
97	[Reed sweetgrass]	L	○	●	•	•			●	∘		•	●	●	●	○	○	○	∘		○	●	○	○	○	∘	●	P
89	Bog bean	Thr	○	○	○	•	•		●			•	∘	●	○	∘	∘	∘	○	○	○	○	●	•			∘	P
93	Amphibious bistort	L	○	○	•	○			○	∘					●		ND				○	○	○	○	○	∘		P
7	Great yellow-cress	L	○	●					●	•				○	●	•	○	○	○		•	●	○	○	∘		●	P
64	Pink water speedwell	T/L	○	○	•	•	•		●	○			•	∘	○	•	○	○	○	•	○	○	●	○	•		∘	P

patches mixed with other plants.
The sedges and grasses tend to be long established in the middle stages of a succession, whereas the others are invaders into open areas. Therefore, when bog bean, amphibious bistort, yellow cress and pink water speedwell are planted, their patch may be overgrown by other species within a decade or so. Reed sweetgrass is the most aggressive of all emergent plants, and eliminates other species from an area. It quickly dominates small channels and dykes. It is not advisable to plant it anywhere. Despite this, it is a rich habitat for invertebrates, is favoured by cattle, and seeds and leaves are eaten by wildfowl, coot, moorhen and swans. The smaller sweetgrass species – such as small, floating and plicate sweetgrass – are not so aggressive but have similar 'plus' features (see Table 9).
Greater and lesser pond sedge have been planted very successfully in shallow water to encourage sedimentation and prevent scour (see Part III, **171** and **219**).
Bogbean and amphibious bistort can both be invasive in lake margins, and may choke small ponds, but in rivers are limited by flow and depth, and so are not troublesome. Bogbean has characteristic large trifoliate leaves and spikes of showy, pink, fringed flowers which appear briefly in May. Amphibious bistort has two forms (hence the name) – either with floating leaves when growing in water, or forming a straggling, non-woody 'bush' to half a metre high, on banks. Both of these, and the cress and pink water speedwell are attractive species to plant with others as habitat improvers.

j. Narrow-leaved, upright bank plants
(Table 8)
This category lists only native plants particularly

Table 8: Narrow-leaved, upright bank plants

K.M. NUMBER	SPECIES	ALTITUDE	SUBSTRATE						FLOW			BANK SLOPE			HGHT.			CHEM.			WHERE PLANT							LIFE CYCLE
			Clay	Silt	Peat	Sand	Gravel-Pebble	Bedrock	Nil-Slow	Moderate	Fast-Rapid	>60°	30-60°	<30°	>1 m	0.5-1 m	<0.5 m	Base poor	Base neutral	Base rich	Just submerged	At water level	Just above	>30 cm above	SHADE TOLERANCE	STABILIZING ABILITY	SCOUR RESISTANCE	
79	Water plantain	L	○	○	•	•		•	●	◦			•	●	•	○	○		○	○		●	●				◦	P
93	Slender tufted sedge	L	○	◦	•	◦		•	●	◦	•	•	◦	●	•	●	•		●	○		●				●	●	P
94	Lesser pond sedge																											
93	*Water sedge	U/T	◦	○	○	•		•	●	◦	•		◦	●	•	●	•	○	○	•	○	●				●	●	P
93	Tufted sedge	L	◦	◦	●				●	•				●	◦	●	◦			●	○	●				◦	◦	P
93	Common sedge	U/T	•	◦	○	•		○	○	○	○	○	○	◦		○	○	◦	●	◦		○	○		◦	●	●	P
92	False foxsedge	L	●	•		•		•	●	◦		○	○	•		○	○		○	○			●		◦	◦	◦	P
92	Greater tussock sedge	L	◦	◦	◦				●	•				○	●	○		•	○	○	○	○			●	◦		P
94	Pendulous sedge	L	●			•			●	◦		●	◦	•		●		○	○					●	●			P
91	Common spike rush	Thr	○	○	•	◦	•	○	●	○	•			●		•	●	•	●	◦	○	○		○	◦	●	●	P
83	Yellow Iris	T/L	○	○	•	◦	•	•	●	○	◦	•	◦	●	●	◦			○	○	●	●			◦	●	●	P
87	Sharp-flowered rush	U	○	•	○	◦	•	○	○	○	○	○	○	•	•	○	○	●	○	•	◦	●		◦	●	●	●	P
87	Jointed rush	U/T	○	◦	◦	○	•	•	○	○	•	○	○	•				●	◦	•				●	◦	●	●	P
87	Bulb rush	U/T	○	•	•	○	•		•	○	○			○			●	●	•		●	●		◦	◦	◦	◦	P
86	Soft rush	U/T	●	•	◦	•		•	○	○	◦	○	○	•		○	○	●	○	•					◦	●	●	P
86	Hard rush	T/L	●	•		◦		•	●	○		○	○	•		○	○		○	●				●		●	●	P
95	Reed canary grass	T/L	○	○	•	○	•	○	○	●	○	•	○	○	○	○			○	○		○	○			●	●	P
95	Common reed	L	○	○	○	•			●				•	●	●				○	○		●			◦	◦		P
88	Branched bur-reed	T/L	○	●	•	•		•	●	◦			•	●	●	○			○	○	○	○	○			●	●	P
88	Narrow-leaved reedmace	L	○	●	◦				●	•			•	○	●				○	○		◦	●			●	◦	P
88	Reedmace	L	○	○	◦	◦			●	•				●	●			•	○	○		◦	●			●	◦	P

associated with rivers. The 26 species listed here are found in open sites, often marshy, or else in woodland. The only ones which will withstand grazing are tufted hair grass, hard and soft rush and yellow iris. Islands in rivers may have stands of pendulous sedge and wood rush which on the adjacent banks have been grazed out (especially in upland rivers with wooded banks). Some are invasive into the channel edge and grow as single species stands – ie reedmace, narrow-leaved reedmace, common reed and branched bur-reed. Most of these plants, however, grow as clumps or tussocks mixed in patches with others at the water's edge. Their distribution depends largely on their tolerance of submergence and need for damp or waterlogged soil. Some of the marsh species cannot tolerate high flow velocities while flooded, but others, such as reed canary grass, are more tolerant and so are common beside moderately fast rivers subject to spates.

The common reed is often mistakenly thought of as purely a water plant – as it is found growing in up to two metres of water in lakes and ponds. However, it has been found that it always establishes on the damp soil of lake and river margins, and only gradually invades deep water in the late stages of succession, when a large amount of organic matter has accumulated. It cannot withstand wave-wash or current, and so is rare in rivers except in shallow bays and backwaters (see Part III, **219**).

As with narrow-leaved emergent plants, these narrow-leaved bank plants are important 'habitat improvers' for insects, providing cover and food for birds and mammals and sheltered sites where other plants can grow. Common reed and reed canary grass are essential for sedge and reed warblers to breed, and can form day resting sites for otters. Grasses and sedges overhanging the water contribute organic matter to the river system, as food for invertebrates and fish.

Grasses and sedges are useful for bank protection against scour. Both their fibrous or fleshy roots and tussocky, perennial leaves and stems protect the soil. They have been deliberately planted as toe protection in a number of sites (see Part III, **171** and **219**).

Very often the drier banks are dominated by plants that could occur in a wide variety of other habitats eg nettles, hemlock, false oat grass – tough perennial plants associated generally with 'wastelands'. Such plant communities are particularly common on rivers that are disturbed by dredging, or where the natural plant cover has been kept in check by herbicides. Non-natives such as Himalayan balsam, monkey flower, Japanese knotweed and giant hogweed have taken over many miles of ungrazed banks, and excluded native plants.

Branched bur-reed

k. Narrow-leaved straggling bank plants (Table 9).

These are grasses of open situations, which tend to float as mats across the water's edge, though still

Table 9: Narrow-leaved, straggling bank plants

K.M. NUMBER	SPECIES	ALTITUDE	SUBSTRATE						FLOW			BANK SLOPE			HGHT.			CHEM.			WHERE PLANT							LIFE CYCLE
			Clay	Silt	Peat	Sand	Gravel-Pebble	Bedrock	Nil-Slow	Moderate	Fast-Rapid	>60°	30-60°	<30°	>1 m	0.5-1 m	<0.5 m	Base poor	Base neutral	Base rich	Just submerged	At water level	Just above	>30 cm above	SHADE TOLERANCE	STABILIZING ABILITY	SCOUR RESISTANCE	
95	[Creeping bent]	T/L	○	◦	•	○	•	•	●	○	•	○	○	○		•	●	•	○	○			●	●	●	◦	●	P
95	*Orange foxtail	L	○	◦	•	○	•		●	◦			•	●			●		○	○				●	◦	◦	◦	A
95	Marsh foxtail	T/L	○	◦	•	○	•	•	●	○	•		•	●			●		●	○		●	◦		●	●	◦	P
97	Small sweet-grass	L	○	●	•	•		•	●	•				●		●		•	○	○	○	○			◦			P
97	Floating sweet-grass	U/T	○	○	○	◦	•	◦	○	○	○	•	◦	○		○	○	○	○	○			○	○	◦	●	●	P
97	[Reed sweet-grass]	L	○	○	◦	◦			●	•			•	●	○	○	•		○	○	○	○	○		◦	●	◦	P
97	Plicate sweet-grass	T/L	○	○	•	◦		•	●	◦			•	●		○	○		○	○		○	○		◦	◦	◦	P

rooted in the bank, at or above water level. Except for reed sweet-grass, they are low-growing plants, generally soft and less securely rooted than the stiffer upright grasses and sedges.

Reed sweet-grass is an aggressive, fast-growing plant that takes over an area, excluding other plants from it. Creeping bent is often an early coloniser in the edges of dredged channels, but may remain in later stages of colonisation as well. All these grasses are good cover for aquatic and marsh invertebrates; both seeds and shoots are food for wildfowl. The low-growing species rarely provide sufficient breeding cover for birds but they may be of importance for small mammals.

Grasses tend to increase where cattle have access to the river's edge, since taller growing or broad-leaved plants are grazed out or damaged by trampling.

1. Broad-leaved, upright bank plants
(Table 10).

Most of these are the showy flowers that brighten the banks of lowland rivers in summer. They may tolerate light shade, but are absent under continuous tree cover. Stretches where the bank vegetation is a mixture of dense tree cover and patches of open, flower-rich tall plants will have a very high overall diversity of both plants and animals.

Because of their prolific seed output, many of these colonise shoals and beaches in summer, and are washed out in winter months. On banksides they are more permanent when mixed in amongst stands of reeds and grasses.

The flowers of many are important nectar sources for a variety of butterflies and other insects. On warm, sunny, sheltered banks patches of purple loosestrife, water mint and hemp agrimony can attract large numbers of butterflies in July and August.

If being planted, the roots of whole perennial plants should be taken with a generous amount of soil, in late winter or spring.

In addition, plants that are common 'weeds' in rough grassland and field edges share the same habitat. Thistles, and docks are obvious candidates, but teasel, common mallow and burdock are frequent and contribute flowers, seed heads, stems and leaves to the community's food sources. They also significantly increase the variety of habitats for terrestrial invertebrates.

Nettle and hemlock can often dominate a bank,

Table 10: Broad-leaved, upright bank plants

K.M. NUMBER	SPECIES	ALTITUDE	SUBSTRATE						FLOW			BANK SLOPE			HGHT.			CHEM.			WHERE PLANT							LIFE CYCLE
			Clay	Silt	Peat	Sand	Gravel-Pebble	Bedrock	Nil-Slow	Moderate	Fast-Rapid	>60°	30-60°	<30°	>1 m	0.5-1 m	<0.5 m	Base poor	Base neutral	Base rich	Just submerged	At water level	Just above	>30 cm above	SHADE TOLERANCE	STABILIZING ABILITY	SCOUR RESISTANCE	
37	Fools watercress	T/L	●	•	•	•		•	○	○	•	•	◦	●	•	○	○		○	○		●			◦	●	●	P
38	Lesser water parsnip	L	○	○	•	•		•	○	○	○			●	•	○	○		•	●	●	●			◦	●	●	P
67	Water mint	T/L	○	◦	•	○	○	○	○	○	◦	●	◦	•		○	○		○	○			●		●	●	●	P
63	Water figwort	T/L	○	◦	•	○		•	●	○		○	○	◦		●	•	•	○	○			○	○	●		◦	P
4	Marsh marigold	U/T	○	•	○	•		•	○	○	•		○	●		○	●	•	●	◦			●	●	●			P
26	Meadow sweet	Thr	○	•	○	◦	•	◦	○	○	◦	◦	○	●	•	●	•		○	○			●		●	●	●	P
34	Purple loosestrife	L	○	○	◦	○			●	◦		◦	○	○		○	○		◦	●	◦	●	◦		◦	◦		P
67	Gipsy wort	L	○	◦	•	○	•	•	●	○		○	◦			○	○		○	○			○	●	◦	◦	◦	P
39	[Hemlock water dropwort]	Thr	◦	◦	○	◦	◦	○	•	◦	●	●	○	◦	◦	●	◦	●	◦						◦	●	●	P
69	Marsh woundwort	T/L	○	◦	•	○	•	•	○	○	•	○	○	•		○	○		○	○				●	◦	●	•	P
46	Butterbur	T/L	◦			○	○	◦	◦	●	◦	○	○	•	○	○	•		●	◦		◦	●		●	●	●	P
46	Coltsfoot	Thr	◦			○	●	◦	•	◦	●	•	•	●			●		○	○				●	◦	●	●	P
45	Bur marigold	L	●	○					●					●		•	●		●	○				●				A
60	Common comfrey	L	●	○	•	◦			●	○		○	○	•	◦	●	◦		○	○			●	●	◦	●	●	P
44	Hemp agrimony	T/L	○	◦	•	○	•	◦	●	◦		●	○	◦	○	○	•		○	○			●	●	●	●	●	P
35	Great willowherb	T/L	●	•		●	◦	◦	○	○	•	●	○	•		○	○		●	○			●	●		●	●	P
	Royal fern	T/L			○	○	•	•	•	●	•	◦	◦	◦	●			◦	◦	•				●	●	●	◦	P

especially after disturbance, or if herbicides have killed their competitors. Although nettles are useful as food plants for small tortoiseshell and peacock butterflies, and both hemlock and nettles give some cover for small mammals, large expanses of either reduce the habitat value of banks for wildlife. They can be eradicated, where necessary, by slashing several times a year for two years, or by applying a systemic herbicide.

Table 11: Broad-leaved, straggling bank plants

			SUBSTRATE						FLOW			BANK SLOPE			HGHT.			CHEM.			WHERE PLANT							
K.M. NUMBER	SPECIES	ALTITUDE	Clay	Silt	Peat	Sand	Gravel-Pebble	Bedrock	Nil-Slow	Moderate	Fast-Rapid	>60°	30-60°	<30°	>1 m	0.5-1 m	<0.5 m	Base poor	Base neutral	Base rich	Just submerged	At water level	Just above	>30 cm above	SHADE TOLERANCE	STABILIZING ABILITY	SCOUR RESISTANCE	LIFE CYCLE
7	Large bitter cress	T/L	○	•	○	•		•	○	◦	•	○	○	○		•	●		●	◦			●	●	●	◦	◦	P
42	Common marsh-bedstraw	T/L	○	○	○	◦	•	◦	●	◦	•	○	◦	◦			●		○	○				●	◦		◦	P
29	Water avens	Thr	○	●	●	•	•		○			•	•	○		◦	●	•	◦	●	●	◦			●	●	◦	P
60	Water forget-me-not	T/L	○	○	○	○	◦	◦	○	○	◦	○	○	◦		◦	●	◦	●	○			●		◦	●	●	P
15	Water chickweed	L	○	○	•	○		○	●	◦		○	○	◦		○	○		◦	●			●		●			P
73	Amphibious bistort	L	○	○	•	○			●	◦		◦	◦	○		○	○		○	○			●		◦	◦		P
3	Lesser spearwort	Thr	◦	•	○	•		○	•	●	○	•	○	○			●	◦	●	◦					◦	◦	●	P
3	Greater spearwort	T/L	◦	◦	●				●	◦			•	●			○		○	◦	○		●		•	◦	◦	P
3	Celery-leaved buttercup	L	○	●		•			●	•				●		◦	●		◦	●		●			◦	◦	◦	A
2	Ivy-leaved crowfoot	U	◦	○	○	•			●	•				●			●	●	•			○	○		◦			A/P
2	Round-leaved crowfoot	U	◦	○	○	◦			●	•				●			●	●				○	○					A
7	Great yellow-cress	L	●	●		•			●	•			•	●	•	●	•		○	○	•	●	◦		◦	◦		P
7	Watercress	T/L	○	●	•	◦	•	•	○	○	•		•	●		○	●		•	●	●	●			◦		◦	P
7	Marsh yellow-cress	T/L	○	○	•	•		•	○	○	•	•	•	●			●		○	○				●				A
7	Creeping yellow-cress	T			•	○	●	○	•	○	●	•	•	●			●		●	◦				●	◦	●	●	P
61	[Bitter sweet]	T/L	○	○	•	○	◦		●	•		○	○	◦	●	○			○	○		○	○	○	●	◦	◦	P
64	Brooklime	Thr	●	◦	◦	○	◦	◦	●	○	•	•	◦	●			●	•	●	•			●	◦	◦	◦	◦	P

m. Broad-leaved, straggling bank plants

(Table 11).

Although some of these can be found straggling out over water (ie they are amphibious), such as amphibious bistort, water forget-me-not, and watercress, they are more commonly found amongst other, taller plants, climbing over or through them to the light. They are characteristic of very mixed, species-rich plant patches. None of them is invasive or grows large enough to increase the flood hazard.

As a result of habitually growing amongst taller plants, they are moderately shade tolerant. They grow on the edges of reedbeds, willow scrub, bramble patches and in damp soil at the foot of steep banks. They flourish even more in full sunlight, and contribute attractive flowers to the riverscape.

Growing individually or in small patches amongst other plants, little is known about their direct value for invertebrate, fish or bird life. However, as additional plants in an otherwise species-poor site, they contribute to its variety, and therefore increase the diversity of wildlife habitats.

Table 12: Bankside trees and shrubs

K.M. NUMBER	SPECIES	ALTITUDE	SUBSTRATE: Clay	Silt	Peat	Sand	Gravel-Pebble	Bedrock	FLOW: Nil-Slow	Moderate	Fast-Rapid	BANK SLOPE: >60°	30-60°	<30°	HGHT.: >1 m	0.5-1 m	<0.5 m	CHEM.: Base poor	Base neutral	Base rich	WHERE PLANT: Just submerged	At water level	Just above	>30 cm above	SHADE TOLERANCE	STABILIZING ABILITY	SCOUR RESISTANCE	LIFE CYCLE
77	Alder	T/L	○		•	○	•	•	◦	●	◦	●	○	•	●			•	○	○			●	●		●	●	P
42	Ash	T	○		•	○	•	•	○	○	•	●	○	•	●				○	○				●		●	●	P
77	Common oak	T/L	●			○			◦	●		●	○	•	●				○	○				●		●	●	P
77	White willow	Thr	○	○	◦	◦	•	•	●	○	◦	•	◦	●	●			•	○	○	◦	◦	○	●		●	●	P
77	Common osier	T/L	●	●	○	•	◦	•	●	○	◦	•	○	●	●			•	○	○	○	○	○	○		●	●	P
77	Goat willow (sallow)	Thr	●	●	◦	•	◦	•	●	○	◦	◦	○	●	●			◦	○	●	○	○	○	○		●	●	P
20	Alder buckthorn	L	○	•	●				○	○			○	○	●			●	◦				○	○		●	●	P
78	Native poplars	T/L	●	•	◦	•						○	○	○	●				○	○			○	●		●	●	P

n. Bankside trees and shrubs (Table 12).
Centuries ago most British rivers had wooded margins. Under the resultant shade developed specialised communities and showy flowering plants were mostly confined to a few sunny gaps. A survey of the Tone and Yeo in Somerset showed that the predominantly tree-covered Tone had an average of 27.6 river plant species and 76.2 bank plant species per half-kilometre, while the Yeo, similar except for less tree cover, had 23.5 river plants and only 59.1 bank plant species per half-kilometre. A mosaic of dense tree cover and open patches seems to give maximum plant diversity (Lewis 1980).

The habitat requirements of most trees found on river banks are much as in non-river situations. Most can withstand short periods of inundation, but few can tolerate permanently damp or waterlogged conditions. The trees included in the table are most common on riversides because of their tolerance of wet soils. Alder and willow species are the characteristic riverside trees. Ash is extremely common on banktops, especially in the north. Oak is ubiquitous on dry banktops, just because it is found throughout Britain – often with hazel, hawthorn or sycamore. Alder buckthorn is generally sparse, but found on damp soils, and deserves to be more widely planted. Native poplars are typical of damp or waterlogged soils, are handsome trees and deserve more attention in planting schemes – they should never be confused with non-native hybrids such as the black Italian poplar, planted for matchwood. Bramble and gorse are included as examples of scrub species which create thickets of dense, low cover, extremely valuable to wildlife.

In a natural succession, trees are typical of the later, more stable stages. Ash, oak and alder may dominate for very long periods. Willows may invade at quite an early stage, but be present in later communities as well.

Generally, willows are a very complex group, and their long history of use by man has complicated the picture further with a variety of different common names. Although not strictly correct, in general, tall, single trunked trees are referred to as 'tree willows' (eg crack and white willow), multi-stemmed, long-leaved willows are 'osiers', and multi-stemmed, round-leaved willows are 'sallows' (eg goat and eared willow). As native trees that have been here since before the Ice Ages, they have a great number of insects adapted to live in and on them. They also provide a multitude of places for birds, mammals and even other plants to breed and find cover. Willows are therefore prime 'habitat improvers', to be protected during management work and planted afterwards if necessary. Fortunately they regrow easily from branches and truncheons (see Part III **265**) and can be managed to prolong their life-span (see Part III **249** and **252**). Some of their many traditional uses in bank protection are described in Part III **158, 165** and **166**.

Alder, of which there is only one native species, is the other characteristic riverside tree. It is common by rivers almost everywhere except on peat and well-drained gravels, as it germinates only in wet conditions. Young trees, however, can be transplanted to drier sites quite easily.

A long-established native tree, alder is well integrated into the river ecosystem. Its roots are fine, penetrating well below water level and

probably naturally played a crucial role in preventing bank scour, thereby maintaining streams in narrower, deeper, swifter channels than they have adopted since trees have been cleared. The roots have nitrogen-fixing bacterial nodules. As a result the leaves are nitrogen-rich and increase the fertility of base-poor waters. The roots are rich habitat for invertebrates, especially caddisfly larvae and some damselfly nymphs, and are good fish cover. It is a food plant for several moths such as the lime hawkmoth, pebble hook-tip and the alder moth, and the seeds are winter food for siskins and goldfinches. Alders, therefore, are excellent as 'habitat improvers' and should be protected and replanted wherever possible. They have been deliberately planted for shade and bank protection in a few schemes (see Part III, **154** and **214**).

5. PROTECTED PLANTS

Section 13(1)(6) of the Wildlife and Countryside Act 1981 makes it an offence for any person (unless authorised – ie the owner or occupier or any person authorised by the owner or occupier or authorised in writing by a local authority) intentionally to uproot any wild plant. Section 13(1)(a) extends this protection, making it an offence to pick, uproot or destroy plants listed in Schedule 8. In both cases, however, a person shall not be found guilty of an offence if his action was the incidental result of a lawful operation which could not reasonably have been avoided. The following *selection* from Schedule 8 lists the plants likely to be affected by land drainage:

Fen violet	– *Viola persicifolia*
Triangular club-rush	– *Scirpus triquetrus*
Brown galingale	– *Cyperus fuscus*
Water germander	– *Teucrium scordium*
Fen orchid	– *Liparis loeselii*
Ribbon-leaved water plantain	– *Alisma gramineum*

Palmer and Newbold, 1983 contains an assessment of the distribution and rarity of wetland plants in relation to water authority and river purification board areas. It highlights the unequal distribution of nationally rare plants around Britain, and indicates which authorities and boards have important sites for rare plants in their areas.

6. REFERENCES

Keble Martin, W, 1969. The Concise British Flora in Colour. Michael Joseph.

Lewis, G, 1981. Somerset Rivers Survey: a survey of the rivers Tone, Yeo, Cary and Northmoor Drain, to map and describe their flora and fauna. Somerset Trust for Nature Conservation/Wessex Water Authority. Unpublished report.

Palmer, M and Newbold, C, 1983. Wetland and Riparian Plants of Great Britain. Nature Conservancy Council.

7. SELECT BIBLIOGRAPHY

General accounts

Dony, J G, Perring, F H and Rob, C M, 1980. English Names of Wild Flowers. The Botanical Society of the British Isles.

Haslam, S M, 1978. River Plants. Cambridge University Press.

Haslam, S M, Sinker, C A, and Wolseley, P A, 1975. British Water Plants. Field Studies 4/243-351.

Haslam, S M and Wolseley, P A, 1981. River Vegetation: its identification, assessment and management. Cambridge University Press.

Sculthorpe, C D, 1967. The biology of aquatic vascular plants. Arnold.

Identification

Clapham, A R, Tutin, T G and Warburg, E F, 1962. Flora of the British Isles. Cambridge University Press.

Clapham, A R, Tutin, T G and Warburg, E F, 1981. Excursion flora of British Isles. Cambridge University Press.

Hubbard, C E, 1968. Grasses. Penguin.

Jermy, A C, Chater, A O and David, R W, 1982. Sedges of the British Isles. Botanical Society of the British Isles, Handbook No 1.

Phillips, R, 1977. Wild flowers of Britain. Pan Books.

Phillips, R, 1980. Grasses, ferns, mosses and lichens of Great Britain and Ireland. Pan.

Rose, F, 1981. The wild flower key: British Isles – N W Europe. Warne.

Tutin, T G, 1980. Umbellifers of the British Isles. Botanical Society of the British Isles. Handbook No 2.

BIOLOGICAL 2: INVERTEBRATES

Margaret Palmer, Chief Scientist Team, Nature Conservancy Council, Huntingdon

1. INTRODUCTION

A river corridor forms a complex mosaic of flowing and still waters, marsh, grassland, woodland and bare earth habitats. Within this mosaic is a network of microhabitats, each exploited by a particular invertebrate fauna. A silty, sandy or gravelly river bed has its community of burrowers. The interfaces between water and river bed, water and aquatic plants, water and air each have their own clinging, creeping, hanging or skating invertebrates. In slow-moving sections of rivers, the water column is inhabited by planktonic and free-swimming species; the splash zone and the wet mud of river banks are characterised by an entirely different, semi-terrestrial community; and the drier, grassy or wooded river margins provide a large variety of microhabitats for fully terrestrial species at different times in their life histories.

2. INVERTEBRATE DIVERSITY AND ABUNDANCE

There are an estimated 30,000 species of terrestrial and aquatic invertebrates, excluding marine species, in Britain; over 1,000 species exploit the water's edge location and more than 3,500 species spend all or part of their life cycles in fresh water. Almost all the aquatic animals occur in running water, a few are confined to rivers and streams and many groups reach their maximum expression in flowing water. More than half the freshwater invertebrate species in Britain are insects. Although insects as a class are essentially terrestrial, air-breathing animals, some orders, for example the mayflies, stoneflies, dragonflies and caddis flies, have aquatic larvae, whilst other bugs and beetles spend most of their adult life, as well as their immature stages, under the water. Another sizable class of freshwater invertebrates is the Crustacea, which includes crayfish, shrimps, water skaters and water 'fleas' (eg *Daphnia*), and in

Figure 1: Two flatworms, Dugesia polychroa *(left) and* Dendrocoelum lacteum *(right).*

Britain comprises over 300 aquatic species. There is a similar number of water mites, over 100 species of aquatic oligochaete worms, and about 80 species of freshwater molluscs. Most of the other groups of aquatic macroinvertebrates are represented by fewer species. However, some small groups, for instance the triclad flatworms (12 species) and leeches (16 species), may contribute large numbers of individuals to a river community.

In two 50-metre lengths of the River Lambourn in Berkshire, studied by the Freshwater Biological Association, at least 190 species of aquatic invertebrates have been found. These include 148 insects, five crustaceans, 10 oligochaete worms, six leeches and four flatworms. The best represented insect families are the chironomid midges (46 species) and the caddis flies (37 species).

The density of invertebrates in rivers can be surprisingly large and, consequently, invertebrates are very important as food for vertebrate animals, especially fish. In a slow-flowing mill stream in Dorset, it has been estimated that each year about 20 million individual invertebrates, with a combined dry weight of 14 kilograms, drift past a single point (Crisp and Gledhill, 1970). A square metre of mud in this stream harbours up to 30,000 individuals, with 85 per cent of the standing crop being made up of chironomid midge larvae, worms and molluscs. In the Bere Stream, a Dorset chalk stream, a square metre of submerged watercress has been shown to hold over 150,000 individuals with a biomass of nearly 40 grams, and a square metre of gravel can produce 7,000 individuals with a biomass of four grams (Westlake et al, 1972). Worms are the most numerous animals in both situations, but the shrimp *Gammarus pulex* makes the largest contribution to the biomass. Upland systems are far less productive. The top five centimetres of gravel in one Welsh mountain stream contains between 20 and 1,300 individuals per square metre, depending on the time of year (Hynes, 1961, 1968). The peak biomass of invertebrates in the River Lambourn occurs in late autumn/early winter, with a subsidiary peak in late spring/early summer (Wright et al, 1983).

3. THE DISTRIBUTION AND HABITAT REQUIREMENTS OF INVERTEBRATES

Invertebrates, like all animals, need food, oxygen and shelter from predators and unfavourable elements of the environment. Many species have very precise requirements and are minutely adapted to particular microhabitats, whereas others are less specialised and therefore more widespread. The distribution of invertebrates in different types of waters and throughout different zones of a single river reflects these requirements and adaptations. The pale, eyeless, highly-specialised water slater *Asellus cavaticus*, for instance, is confined to cave systems and wells, whereas the closely related *Asellus aquaticus*, which possesses both eyes and pigment, is widely distributed in still and flowing productive waters throughout Britain.

Figure 2: Water hog-louse or water slater, Asellus aquaticus.

a. Longitudinal zonation

Often relationships between species are complex and competition may play a part in restricting distribution. The flatworm *Crenobia alpina* is generally associated with high altitudes and water temperatures below about 15°C and is usually found in headwaters, whereas a similar species, *Polycelis felina*, appears to be more tolerant of high temperatures and usually occurs further downstream. However, there is also evidence suggesting that *Crenobia alpina* is more able to withstand turbulent flows than *Polycelis felina*, and that it may be unable to compete successfully with *Polycelis felina* in less turbulent, downstream waters (Lock and Reynoldson, 1976).

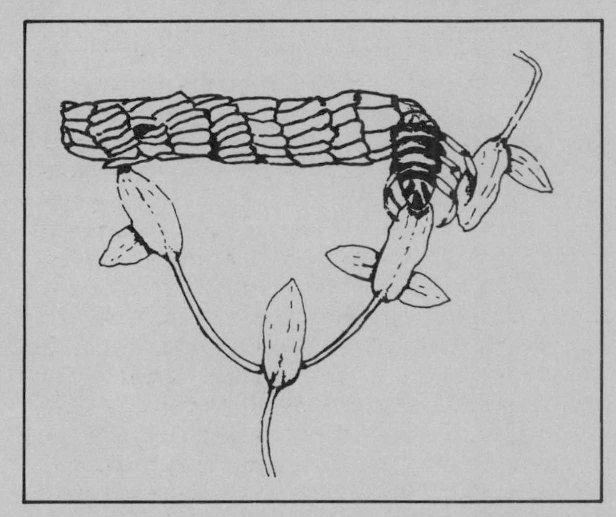

Figure 3: Caddis fly-larva, Phryganea striata, *feeding on ivy-leaved duckweed,* Lemna trisculca. *Its case is made up of pieces of leaf, cut and glued together.*

Certain caddis flies are characteristic of springs and intermittent streams, but the great majority breed in permanent waters. Fifty three species and species-aggregates recently recorded as larvae from rivers in southern England can be grouped into five categories according to their preference for intermittent and upstream sites, middle sites, lower sites or combinations of these sites (Cooling, 1982). However, there is considerable overlap between the groups and the causes of the zonation have yet to be explained.

b. Swift water and sluggish water animals

One of the most important ecological factors controlling the distribution of riverine invertebrates is the current. Although the mean velocity of an unimpounded river is steady throughout its length (see 'Introduction 2: River Processes and Form') there are obvious local differences in flow velocity and turbulence depending on slope, roughness of bed and banks, water depth and incidence of spates. Torrential rocky headwaters and stony lowland riffles accommodate very different faunas from deep, quiet, silty pools and oxbows.

Figure 4: Mayfly larva, Rhithrogena sp.

In fast-flowing water with little vegetation, most invertebrates must cling to stones or seek out crevices where turbulence is reduced. Many of these animals are flattened or streamlined. Flattened forms include nymphs of the mayfly genera *Rithrogena*, which live exposed on stones, and *Ecdyonurus*, which cling to the underneath of stones. Streamlining is seen to perfection in the mayflies *Baetis* and *Centroptilum*. These nymphs are often very numerous in stony streams, where they stand head-on to the flow, with their long tails acting as vanes, swinging their bodies from side to side in the eddies. Other animals, such as the spiky maggots of the fly *Atherix ibis*, are far from streamlined, having long projections which probably serve to wedge them into crevices between stones. Many of the case-building caddis larvae which live in fast-flowing water incorporate heavy stones in their cases which act as ballast.

Some invertebrates, for instance leeches, maintain their positions in streams by means of suckers. The mayfly *Rithrogena* has its front gills modified to form friction pads. The river limpet *Ancylus fluviatilis* has a broad foot by means of which it adheres to stones, and the flexible membrane at the edge of its shell fits closely into irregularities, making an effective seal. The free-living larva of the caddis fly *Rhyacophila* has a pair of strong posterior claws which it uses as grapples. Larvae of black-flies Simuliidae hang in exposed places in high velocity flow. Each makes a silken mat as an anchorage to which it adheres by means of a circlet of hooks at the end of the abdomen. If displaced by the flow the larva lets out a silk 'life-line' up which it climbs to regain its anchorage. The pupal stage of the blackfly is spent inside a shoe-shaped case of silk, glued firmly to a solid surface.

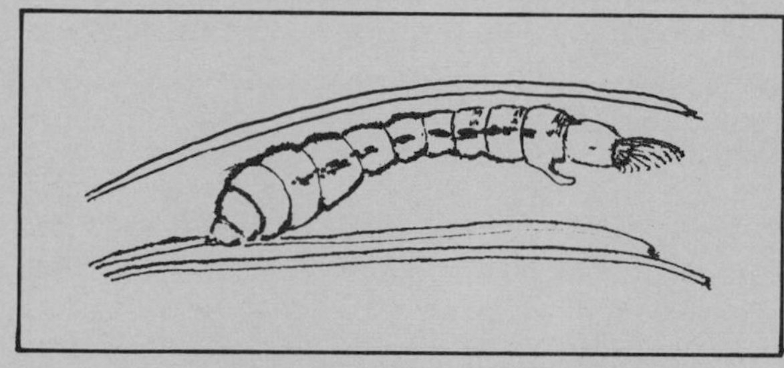

Figure 5: Blackfly larva, Simulium sp, *attached to a water crowfoot leaf segment.*

Stream animals which lack well developed attachment organs often show behavioural adaptations to life in moving water. The shrimp *Gammarus*, a very successful stream-dweller, shows a strong tendency to swim against the flow and to shelter beneath stones. Many insects, both during their aquatic larval stages and as flying adults, tend to move upstream, thus compensating for the continual drift which occurs as animals lose their hold and are swept downstream. The long narrow nymphs of the stonefly genus *Leuctra* avoid the current by burrowing into sandy parts of the stream bed. Some animals, such as the shrimp *Niphargus*, live a subterranean existence deep in the gravel.

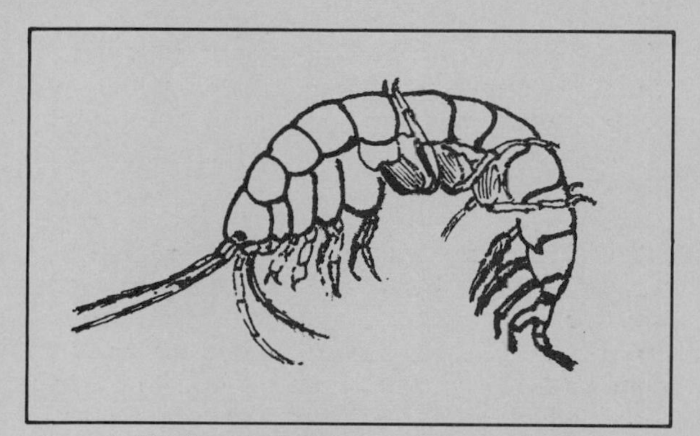

Figure 6: Freshwater shrimp, Gammarus pulex.

In turbulent water there is no shortage of oxygen. Many stream-dwelling invertebrates, including the damselfly *Calopteryx virgo*, some mayfly nymphs, blackfly larvae and many stonefly nymphs, cannot live in still water because they need high levels of dissolved oxygen. Plastron respiration, in which a layer of air, acting as a gill, is trapped on the body surface in a pile of water repellant hairs, works only in well aerated water. The riffle beetles Elmidae and the river bug *Aphelocheirus* use this method and so can breathe air without continually rising to the surface.

In swift headwater reaches and lowland riffles, invertebrates must either creep cautiously in search of food, maintaining a precarious hold with claws and suckers, or they must remain stationary and allow the current to bring food particles their way. Snails and many mayflies move about on the stones grazing on algal films; shrimps are scavengers; flatworms, most leeches, damselflies and some stoneflies are active predators. Caddis larvae, such as *Hydropsyche*, construct silk nets in which they lie waiting for food particles to be trapped. The stationary blackfly larvae have 'mouth brushes' which they use to strain small particles from the water as it passes.

In areas of slow-moving water, especially if the bed is predominantly silty and aquatic plants are abundant, there is ample cover and less need for anchorage in the flow. Free-swimming and burrowing animals abound and surface tension is exploited by shoals of water-skaters (*Gerris*).

In the absence of swiftly-flowing, well-oxygenated water, many invertebrates have to create their own small currents to obtain sufficient oxygen. Mayflies of the genus *Baetis* are confined to running water because their nymphs cannot move their gills effectively, but the genus *Ephemerella*, which can create respiratory currents by strong gill movements, is common in the mud of depositional reaches of river. Most dragonfly and damselfly nymphs live in mud or on plants in still or slowly-flowing water. Dragonfly nymphs create respiratory currents by pumping water in and out of the rectum, and they can also use this mechanism for 'jet-propelled' locomotion. The plastron-breathing riffle beetles are scarce in sluggish waters, but the diving beetles, which constantly return to the surface to renew air bubbles carried beneath their wing cases, are common. Mosquito larvae, which hang from the surface film and breathe air, are only found in still water. A muddy bottom may contain large numbers of burrowing worms and chironomid midge larvae ('bloodworms'), which are able to obtain oxygen even if it is present in very low concentrations, because of the haemoglobin in their blood. The organic mud is a rich source of food for such animals.

A study of a section of the River Wye (Scullion et al, 1982) has shown that, although there is a greater

density of invertebrates in a riffle than in a pool, species-richness is similar in both situations. Mayflies, caddis flies, stoneflies and black-flies are all more abundant in the riffle than in the pool, whereas chironomid midge larvae make up over 70 per cent of the animals in the pool.

c. The role of water plants

Water plants are extremely important to invertebrates for shelter and attachment sites. Very few aquatic invertebrates eat living aquatic plants, although the fly genus *Hydrellia* includes species whose larvae feed on submerged leaves. Many invertebrates utilise epiphytic algae covering the surfaces of submerged leaves and stems, and some caddis fly and aquatic moth larvae bite off pieces of leaf which they use in constructing their cases. Numerous invertebrates consume detritus derived from decayed plant material, but much of this originates from fringing bankside vegetation, especially in upland streams.

Perhaps because of their very large, stable surface area, as well as the cover which they provide, water plants support a more varied and dense invertebrate community than gravel or silt. In the River Lambourn study it has been shown that there are more invertebrate families and higher densities of most invertebrates on submerged plants than in sediments. Exceptions are the cased caddis *Agapetus*, which is most abundant in gravel, and the pea-shell cockle *Pisidium* which favours silt (Wright et al, 1983). In stony rivers with little vegetation, submerged tree roots take the place of water plants in providing shelter for animals such as caddis larvae.

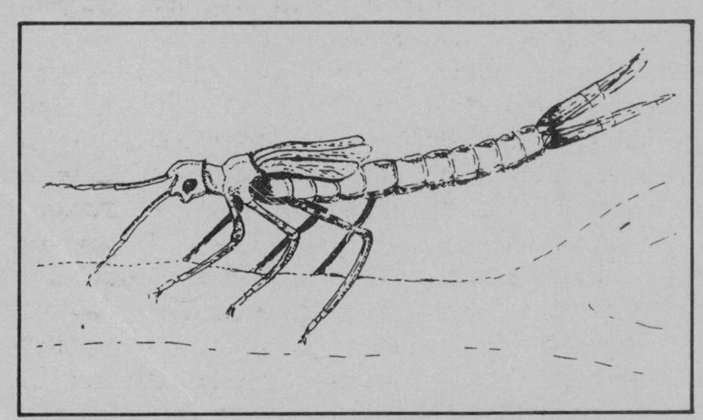

Figure 7: Nymph of the demoiselle agrion, Agrion virgo, *prior to emergence.*

Emergent vegetation is essential for the existence of certain invertebrates. Many dragonflies, for instance, need reed stems or other emergent parts of water plants up which to crawl from the water before completing the final moult which releases the adult insect. Tall, emergent plants such as flowering rush *Butomus umbellatus*, reed sweet-grass *Glyceria maxima*, bur-reed *Sparganium erectum* and common club-rush *Scirpus lacustris*, support their own individual assemblages of terrestrial and semi-terrestrial insects.

d. Peripheral habitats

The water's edge invertebrate community, like the aquatic community, is complex, with plant-feeding species, decomposers, predators and parasites all interdependent.

The herbs, bushes and trees making up river bank vegetation support a great variety of invertebrates. Some, such as bees and adult hoverflies, butterflies and moths, are nectar or pollen feeders, dependent on flowers. Many butterfly caterpillars have specific food plants, for example, bird's-foot-trefoil and rest harrow for the common blue, buckthorn for the brimstone and elm for the white-letter hairsteak. Dead wood is an important habitat for invertebrates such as woodlice and many families of flies and beetles. Numerous invertebrates, for example earthworms and springtails, are decomposers which feed on decaying leaves and other plant debris in the soil. Predatory invertebrates include spiders, centipedes and many insects, notably ladybird beetles and hoverfly larvae which are economically important because of the vast number of aphids that they consume. Parasites include the snail-killing flies Sciomyzidae whose larvae attack both aquatic and terrestrial snails.

Tall vegetation creates a sheltered environment for flying insects. Dragonflies, such as the nationally scarce club-tailed darter *Gamphus vulgatissimus*, favour the tree-lined stretches of rivers, where they beat up and down hunting small insects and establishing their territories. Butterflies, too, are most common in sheltered, sunny situations such as well-vegetated river banks.

Areas of shingle, sand and mud at the water's edge are important for certain groups of invertebrates, for instance wolf spiders and predatory beetles and bugs. Shingle islands with some alder or willow and a fringe of grasses and sedges are particularly rich in invertebrates. Many ground beetles Carabidae, including 25 of the 58 British species of the genus *Bembidion*, are associated with shingle, sand or mud on banks and islands. The saucer bugs Saldidae hunt their prey in similar situations, and *Cryptostemma alienum*, a tiny dipsocorid bug, is highly specialised, living under stones and gravel on the edges of the upland streams and rivers. South-facing, slowly-eroding, bare, sandy banks are used by burrowing solitary bees and wasps for nest construction. The wasp *Crossocerus walkeri*, a river bank specialist, provisions its cells only with adult mayflies.

Wet, overgrown river valley habitats, seepages and the shallow remnants of oxbows for example, are also extremely important for many invertebrates. Some of our rarest damselflies, including the scarce blue-tail *Ischnura pumilio* and the southern damselfly *Coenagrion mercuriale*, breed in boggy margins of streams in places such as the New Forest.

Many flies, including crane-flies Tipulidae and shore-flies Ephydridae, are dependent on water's edge habitats. They live in a variety of substrates and may be confined to sections of river with a particular flow regime, or to open or shady situations. Some riparian invertebrates have even more specialised requirements. The rare snail *Perforatella rubiginosa* is found in flood refuse among tree roots along the Thames, and needs annual inundation to provide fresh leaf litter and twigs.

e. Water quality

The concentration of dissolved and suspended minerals and of organic compounds in river water depends mainly on the geology of the catchment and on the degree to which man has modified natural water chemistry by inputs of sewage or industrial and agricultural effluents.

Invertebrates vary in their tolerance to pollution. Certain groups, notably most stoneflies, many mayflies and some caddis flies, have larvae which are very sensitive to organic pollution, probably because they have high oxygen requirements. Other invertebrates, such as shrimps and mussels, are moderately susceptible to pollution, whereas some groups, including many chironomid midges, worms and air-breathers such as rat-tailed maggots, can exist in grossly polluted water.

The fauna of many waters, especially lowland rivers, has been impoverished because of man's use of natural watercourses as sewers. In Germany, for instance, there is evidence that sewage pollution has enriched river water and increased algal growth in the interstices of gravel beds to the extent that young pearl mussels are smothered and killed. The orange-spotted emerald dragonfly *Oxygastra curtisii* became extinct in Britain when its last stronghold on the Moors River in Dorset was affected by sewage pollution *within* the permitted public safety limits.

Because invertebrates show a range of sensitivity to pollution and are continuously 'sampling' the water in which they live, the invertebrate fauna can be used as the basis of a 'biotic index' which reflects the overall water quality of a stretch of river. Numerous biotic indices have been devised, the most recent and most convenient being the Department of the Environment/National Water Council 'Biological Monitoring Working Party Score' (Table 1), which was used in the 1980 national river quality survey. The higher the score, given by totalling scores for the individual families represented, the cleaner the water. The BMWP score does, however, tend to reflect habitat diversity as well as water quality. In the 1980 survey the scores ranged from 0 in part of the Trent to over 200 in some southern chalk streams.

f. National distribution patterns

Generally the upland rivers of northern and western Britain are less alkaline and have steeper gradients than the lowland rivers of southern and eastern England. These differences are reflected in the national distribution of invertebrate species and communities.

Half the British freshwater mollusc species are rarely found in water with less than 20 parts per million of calcium (Boycott, 1936). These are the 'hard water' species, and include the great pond snail *Lymnaea stagnalis* and the great ramshorn *Planorbarius corneus*. 'Hard water' species are generally restricted to south-east England and the Midlands. Most of the other species, the 'soft water' species, can tolerate low calcium concentrations but are also found in calcium-rich water and are, therefore, much more widely distributed. A notable exception to this rule is the pearl mussel *Margaritifera margaritifera* which occurs only in fast, cool waters, low in calcium, and is confined to northern and western Britain.

As a result of a recent survey which covered over 300 sites on about 50 relatively unpolluted rivers (Wright et al, in press) a national classification of river invertebrate communities has been evolved. Several environmental factors, including alkalinity, substrate particle size and discharge, show a high correlation with the type of invertebrate community. Sites with alkaline water, low discharge and silty beds, have communities of invertebrates such as the water slater *Asellus*, whereas sites with low alkalinity, high discharge and stony beds are typified by animals such as stoneflies, and the flattened mayfly *Ecdyonurus*. Most stonefly species therefore occur principally in upland areas of Britain, and the stonefly fauna is especially poor in the Midlands and East Anglia, even in unpolluted waters.

One further factor controlling national invertebrate distribution appears to be climate. The number of dragonfly species recorded shows a decrease from the south to the north of Britain. Twenty-four species are southern in distribution, being absent from or rare in Scotland, 10 species are widespread or common throughout Britain and four are confined to Scotland. Species such as the southern hawker *Aeshna cyanea* and the azure damselfly *Coenagrion puella* are very common in southern England, become progressively scarcer at higher latitudes and are very rare in Scotland.

4. THE IMPACT OF RIVER MANAGEMENT

River management procedures have an impact similar to that of natural catastrophes upon the flora and fauna. Biological communities have an inbuilt resilience which enables them to recover after environmental stress resulting from events such as flood or drought, but the ability to cope with man-made 'catastrophes' is limited by the frequency, intensity and extent of such events. Moreover, natural upheavals such as floods often tend to maintain habitat diversity, by scouring out beds of emergent plants which may have clogged a channel, by recreating bare vertical banks which have become overgrown, or by forming new riffles and pools. By contrast, man's attempts to tame rivers invariably lead to uniformity and loss of habitat diversity, which in turn tends to reduce the numbers of species which a river can support.

If a section of river bed is denuded, animals recolonise the area from four directions; they come downstream by drift, upstream by migration, vertically upwards from within the substrate and downwards from aerial sources, for instance through egg-laying. Williams and Hynes, 1976 have shown that, in a denuded section of stream in Canada, drift contributed over 40 per cent of the new colonisers, aerial sources were next in importance and upstream migration and movement from within the substrate each made smaller, but nevertheless significant, contributions. Many groups of organisms have preferred routes for recolonisation, so if one route is blocked the new

Table 1: The amended DoE/NWC 'Biological Monitoring Working Party' Score System

	Families	Score
Mayflies	Siphlonuridae Heptageniidae Leptophlebiidae Ephemerellidae Potamanthidae Ephemeridae	10
Stoneflies	Taeniopterygidae Leuctridae Capniidae Perlodidae Perlidae Chloroperlidae	
River bug	Aphelocheiridae	
Caddis	Phryganeidae Molannidae Beraeidae Odontoceridae Leptoceridae Goeridae Lepidostomatidae Brachycentridae Sericostomatidae	
Crayfish	Astacidae	8
Dragonflies	Lestidae Agriidae Gomphidae Cordulegasteridae Aeshnidea Corduliidae Libellulidae	
Caddis	Psychomyidae Philopotamiidae	
Mayflies	Caenidae	7
Stoneflies	Nemouridae	
Caddis	Rhyacophilidae Polycentropidae Limnephilidae	
Snails	Neritidae Viviparidae Ancylidae	6
Caddis	Hydroptilidae	
Mussels	Unionidae	
Shrimps	Corophiidae Gammaridae	
Dragonflies	Platycnemididae Coenagriidae	
Bugs	Mesoveliidae Hydrometridae Gerridae Nepidae Naucoridae Notonectidae Pleidae Corixidae	5
Beetles	Haliplidae Hygrobiidae Dytiscidae Gyrinidae Hydrophilidae Clambidae Helodidae Dryopidae Eliminthidae Chrysomelidae Curculionidae	
Caddis	Hydropsychidae	
Craneflies Blackflies	Tipulidae Simuliidae	
Flatworms	Planariidae Dendrocoelidae	
Mayflies	Baetidae	4
Alderflies	Sialidae	
Leeches	Piscicolidae	
Snails	Valvatidae Hydrobiidae Lymnaeidae Physidae Planorbidae	3
Cockles	Sphaeriidae	
Leeches	Glossiphoniidae Hirudidae Erpobdellidae	
Hog louse	Asellidae	
Midges	Chironomidae	2
Worms	Oligochaeta (whole class)	1

community may be different in composition from the original one, or may take a long time to re-establish itself.

a. Weed cutting

Few long-term studies have been undertaken concerning effects of river management on aquatic invertebrates. Events following cutting of submerged vegetation have been studied in a Danish lowland stream (Kern-Hansen, 1980), and in the River Hull, a Yorkshire chalk stream (Pearson and Jones, 1978). During cutting of the total plant cover in the Danish stream, the number of animals drifting downstream increased 173 times, and for several days after cutting the drift-density of many species remained significantly higher than before the disturbance. However, if half of the plants were left as bars across the stream, only a slight increase in drift was detected because the displaced invertebrates quickly found new refuges and the stream bottom was more stable than in the areas where all the plants were removed. In the River Hull study it was shown that cutting and dragging out the vegetation resulted in the removal of large numbers of animals from the water and caused increased drifting of plant-dwelling species and an upsurge in the activity of invertebrates on the river bottom. Recovery in the five months following cutting appeared to be rapid and the invertebrate community seemed to be little affected in the long-term. However, weed cutting on the River Hull was a regular annual activity and this may have already removed susceptible species from the community, leaving only those able to tolerate disturbance. Thus, the long-term effects of such a procedure might be more dramatic when carried out in a previously unmanaged river.

b. Channel modification

Several recent monitoring exercises have indicated a wide range of recovery times for invertebrate communities following gross disturbance of the river bed. A December dredging operation on the River Hull, during which 30 to 40 centimetres of gravel were removed from the bed, appeared to produce only short-term effects, as most species had recovered their normal strength within five months (Pearson and Jones, 1975). Flood protection works carried out on the River Derwent, Derbyshire, produced little detectable effect on the invertebrate community, as recolonisation behind the excavators, which were working slowly upstream, was rapid (Rees, 1980). A two-year study of a Dorset millstream after draining and dredging indicated that recovery was fairly complete one year after the operation, but that several years might be needed for full recovery (Crisp and Gledhill, 1970).

A study by the Anglian Water Authority (1982) demonstrated a significant decrease in invertebrate quality following dredging of the Great Ouse. There was a decrease in numbers of animals and in species-richness, and the invertebrate communities at separate affected sites became very similar. Dredging reduced habitat diversity and caused silt deposition on formerly firm beds because of the erosion of modified banks. Deterioration in invertebrate quality occurred, despite the fact that the effects of the dredging operations were ameliorated by leaving parts of the channel and banks untouched. One sampling site did show considerable recovery in invertebrate quality after 17 months, probably because of a reduction in filamentous algae and the appearance of a riffle.

A Welsh Water Authority investigation (Brooker, 1982) of the colonisation of re-instated submerged gravel beds in a dredged section of the Afon Gwyrfai showed that the colonisation rate for new, stable gravel beds was about one invertebrate species or group every five days, and that it would take at least a year for the maximum complement of species to be attained. If the gravel were fine and shifting, both the number of species and the population density would still be below normal after four years. However, the provision of gravel beds in a dredged channel did increase the abundance of invertebrates and led to greater species-richness.

The decline of some invertebrate species may be due, at least in part, to dredging operations. The pearl mussel's recent decline appears to be largely attributable to overfishing, but in some rivers in Scotland canalisation has changed the nature of the gravel bed, or salmon pools have been created, and the mussels have disappeared. Pearl mussels are very slow-growing and do not breed until they are about 12 years old (Young and Williams, 1953) so if a population is depleted it will take a long time to recover. Similarly, some dragonflies and stoneflies take several years to mature, and if a stream is frequently dredged these are probably the species which suffer most. Animals such as chironomid midges and blackflies, which have very short generation times and effective dispersal mechanisms, are the first colonisers of denuded areas and quickly become numerically dominant. As drift is a very important source of recolonising animals, dredging in an upstream direction is likely to be less catastrophic than working downstream.

c. Bank modification

The loss of bankside vegetation caused by river improvement schemes has several effects on the aquatic community. Because the primary food source of most streams is organic material supplied from non-aquatic sources, the removal of surrounding vegetation reduces the productivity of the aquatic ecosystem. Reduction of shade can result in a raising of maximum water temperatures and an increase in the abundance of aquatic plants. Both these factors are fundamental changes in the character of a river, and can have profound effects on aquatic animals.

The destruction of tall emergent vegetation leads to the loss of specialist plant-feeding invertebrates. Tree removal eliminates shelter provided for aquatic invertebrates by submerged roots and impoverishes the riparian fauna. In contrast, reprofiling of eroding banks and the consequent growth of vegetation on the new, more gently-sloping banks, eliminates the bare surfaces needed by burrowing solitary wasps and bees.

d. Timing of operations

The timing of river management operations is an important factor influencing the recovery of the invertebrate community. If weedcutting is carried out in early summer before the hatch of abundant weed-dwelling groups such as mayflies and chironomid midges, these groups could be severely reduced in numbers for the whole of the summer. On the other hand, several studies, including the Welsh Water Authority investigation on the Afon Gwyrfai, have suggested that the least damaging time for dredging is late spring/early summer, because this would allow the bare bed to be recolonised by egg-laying from neighbouring insect populations during July and August.

e. The impact of field drainage improvements

The improvement of agricultural land made possible by arterial land drainage and flood alleviation schemes often leads to previously permanent grassland coming under the plough. The water quality of the river may then suffer because of changes in the river's regime, higher turbidity and increased run-off of fertilizers, and possibly pesticides. Enrichment of the water by plant nutrients can cause algal blooms, which may smother the larger aquatic plants or cause deoxy-

Table 2: The effects of river management on aquatic and water's edge invertebrates. A tick indicates possible impacts on invertebrates due to the action specified.

		Aquatic weed cutting	Channel works	Bank works
1.	Removal of part of the invertebrate population from the water or riverbank.	√	√	√
2.	Disturbance, leading to increased activity, drift of aquatic invertebrates and dispersal of populations.	√	√	√
3.	Reduction in cover provided by aquatic and bankside plants, leading to increased predation, also drift of aquatic invertebrates and dispersal of population.	√	√	√
4.	Loss of emergence sites (eg reed stems) for insects.	√	√	√
5.	Removal of food plants, leading to the elimination of specialist plant-feeding invertebrates	√	√	√
6.	Instability of river bed and consequent loss of firm attachment sites for aquatic invertebrates.	√	√	
7.	Reduction in habitat diversity (eg loss of riffles, meanders, trampled margins, beds of aquatic plants) causing impoverishment of invertebrate communities.	√	√	√
8.	Increased suspended solids loading and siltation, which may clog gills, smother eggs and young stages, or decrease the oxygen concentration of the water.	√	√	√
9.	Localised reduction in flow, leading to lower oxygen concentration.		√	
10.	Reduction in shade because of the removal of trees etc, leading to increased insolation, higher water temperatures and increased submerged plant growth.		√	√
11.	Reduction in food supply for aquatic and water's edge invertebrates because of the removal of bankside vegetation.		√	√
12.	Nutrient enrichment, siltation and pollution with pesticides following drainage of surrounding land and intensification of agriculture.		√	√
13.	Loss of wet peripheral habitats because of lowering of water table and reduction of flooding, leading to elimination of whole invertebrate communities.		√	√

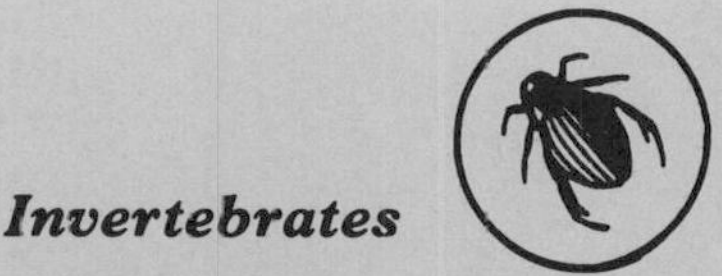

genation problems. Moreover, under-drainage, lowering of the water table and decreased incidence of flooding can all have a profound effect on wet river valley habitats such as flood meadows, marshes, fens and pools. The disappearance of these features means a permanent loss of wetland invertebrate communities.

f. The impact of arterial river engineering works

The major impacts of river management on invertebrates are summarised in Table 2. Probably the most damaging long-term effect of large-scale river engineering works is the loss of habitat diversity caused by such activities. The foregoing discussion has implied that invertebrate communities only attain their full potential in rivers with varied substrates, flow-rates and depths; well-developed riffle and pool patterns; diverse margins with features such as shingle banks, muddy edges and eroding banks; vegetation, including trees and substantial beds of water plants; and a variety of associated wetland habitats, such as flushes and reedswamp. Heterogeneous systems are innately stable. The taming of a river imposes a uniformity which may engender physical and biological instability and can distort or impoverish its invertebrate community.

5. REFERENCES

Anglian Water Authority, 1982. Report on studies of the ecological and hydrological effects of dredging on the River Great Ouse at Thornton, Buckinghamshire, 1976 to 1979. Joint report of the Scientific Directorate and Great Ouse River Division.

Boycott, A E, 1936. The habitats of freshwater molluscs in Britain. J Anim Ecol, **5**, 116-186.

Brooker, M P (ed), 1982. Biological Investigations in the Welsh Water Authority. Proceeding of seminar held in Brecon on 9 March, 1982. IV. An assessment of macroinvertebrate colonisation of two reinstated salmonid spawning gravel beds in the Afon Gwyrfai, Snowdonia: an interim report by R J Hemsworth.

Cooling, D A, 1982. Records of Trichoptera from rivers in Southern England. Ent Gaz, **33** (2), 123-134.

Crisp, D T and Gledhill, T, 1970. A quantitative description of the recovery of the bottom fauna in a muddy reach of a mill stream in Southern England after draining and dredging. Arch Hydrobiol, **67**, 502-541.

Hynes, H B N, 1961. The invertebrate fauna of a Welsh Mountain stream. Arch Hydrobiol, **57**, 344-388.

Hynes, H B N, 1968. Further studies on the invertebrate fauna of a Welsh mountain stream. Arch Hydrobiol, **65**, 360-379.

Kern-Hansen, U, 1980. The effect of macrophyte-cutting on the invertebrate fauna in a Danish lowland stream. Poster lecture presented at XXI S I L Congress, Kyoto, August 1980.

Lock, M L and Reynoldson, T B, 1976. The role of inter-specific competition in the distribution of two stream-dwelling triolads, *Crenobia alpina* (Dana) and *Polyelis felina* (Dalyell), in North Wales. J Anim Ecol, **45**, 581-592.

Pearson, R G and Jones, N V, 1975. The effects of dredging operations on the benthic community of a chalk stream. Biol Conserv, **8**, 273-278.

Pearson, R G and Jones, N V, 1978. The effects of weed-cutting on the macro-invertebrate fauna of a canalised section of the River Hull, a northern English chalk stream. J Environ Man, **7**, 91-97.

Rees, S, 1980. Rivers and Wildlife. A review of the importance of rivers for wildlife and methods to integrate nature conservation and river management. 5. River communities, their value and the effects of different management practices: iii Invertebrates. Report of seminar held by RSNC and RSPB, 13 November 1980.

Scullion, J, Parish, C A, Morgan, H and Edwards, R W, 1982. Comparison of benthic macroinvertebrate fauna and substratum composition in riffles and pools in the impounded River Elan and the unregulated River Wye, mid-Wales. Freshw Biol, **12**, 579-595.

Westlake, D F, Casey, H, Dawson, F H, Ladle, M, Mann, R H K and Marker, A F H, 1972. The chalk ecosystem. Productivity problems of freshwaters (eds Z Kajak and A Hillbricht-Ilkowska). Proceedings of the IBP-UNESCO symposium on productivity problems of freshwaters, pp 615-635. Kazimierz Dolny Poland.

Williams, D D and Hynes, H B N, 1976. The recolonisation mechanisms of stream benthos. Oikos **27**, 265-272.

Wright, J F, Hiley, P D, Cameron, A C, Wigham, M E and Berrie, A D, 1983. A qualitative study of the macroinvertebrate fauna of five biotopes in the River Lambourn, Berkshire, England. Arch Hydrobiol, **96**, 271-292.

Young, M and Williams, J, 1983. The status and conservation of the freshwater pearl mussel *Margaritifera margaritifera* Linn in Great Britain.

Biol Cons, **25**, 35-52.

6. FURTHER READING

Hynes, H B N, 1972. The Ecology of Running Waters, Liverpool University Press.

Macan, T T, 1959. A guide to Freshwater Invertebrate Animals. Longman, London.

Macan, T T, 1974. Freshwater Ecology. 2nd ed. Longman, London.

Macan, T T and Worthington, E B, 1974. Life in Lakes and Rivers. Third ed, Collins (New Naturalist Series), London.

Mellanby, H, 1975. Animal Life in Freshwater: a Guide to Freshwater Invertebrates. Chapman and Hall Science Publications, London.

Swales, S, 1982. Environmental effects of river channel works used in land drainage improvement. J Environ Man, **14**, 103-126.

Whitton, B A (ed), 1975. River Ecology. Studies in Ecology, Vol 2. Blackwell Scientific Publications, London.

BIOLOGICAL 3: AMPHIBIANS AND REPTILES

Dr A Cooke, Chief Scientist Team, Nature Conservancy Council, Huntingdon.

1. INTRODUCTION

There are 12 species of amphibians and reptiles which are native to Britain and these are listed below. Guides for identification are recommended in the reference list.

2. AMPHIBIANS

Despite the fact that amphibians need water for breeding and many species spend their lives in moist surroundings, rivers tend not to provide good habitat for amphibians. Reasons for this include: (1) the warm shallow conditions preferred by many species to spawn in are better provided by pools rather than rivers; (2) spawn and tadpoles are washed downstream; (3) predatory fish, which are more likely to be encountered in rivers, have a catastrophic effect on the tadpoles of frogs and newts (toad tadpoles appear to be unpalatable and are left alone). The best places on a river for amphibians are the more shallow, sheltered and well-vegetated edges. Outside the breeding season, amphibians may be found on land during the daytime hiding under logs, stones or manmade objects such as corrugated iron sheeting or slabs of concrete.

Amphibian species: habitat requirements and census techniques

Great crested newt (warty newt) *Triturus cristatus*. The most aquatic of our newts, breeding in still or slow flowing water. It tends to be found in water bodies with much fringing submerged vegetation but with open deepish centres. A hard water species, it tends to be absent from the north and west. It is the rarest newt in Britain and is declining at a greater rate than any other amphibian; it is totally protected by the Wildlife and Countryside Act 1981.

Warty newts are most active after dark, and populations are best estimated by torchlight on an evening in the breeding season (April-June). Counts of more than 100 in a 100 metre stretch of bank would be quite exceptional, and the Nature Conservancy Council would like to be informed of any such concentrations. Counts of more than 10 indicate a good population. The legal protection afforded to this species means that it is an offence to harm or disturb the newts or their habitat.

Smooth newt (common newt) *T vulgaris*. This species prefers still, hard water. It has a similar distribution to the warty newt, but is much more abundant. Any site with warty newts will almost certainly have smooth newts, generally in greater numbers, breeding in plants in the shallows. Newts lay their eggs individually and tend to stick them onto leaves of water plants. Torchlight counts or daytime netting counts of more than 100 indicate an exceptional population, and of more than 10 a good population.

Palmate newt *T helveticus*. The palmate newt tends to be found in still, soft water, but it sometimes breeds in flowing water. It is common in the west and north of Britain, but is quite rare in central England and East Anglia. For census techniques, refer to the smooth newt.

Common toad *Bufo bufo*. Perhaps the amphibian most likely to be found in rivers. It spawns in relatively deep water for an amphibian: 30-40 centimetres is typical, but breeding toads have been found at depths of several metres in Lake Windermere. Nevertheless, even the toad is more at home in still or slow-flowing water. Wide, fast-flowing rivers are likely to present barriers to migration to more suitable sites. Thus, at one breeding site in a lake near the River Great Ouse in Cambridgeshire, toads appear to risk being crushed by traffic by crossing the river over a narrow bridge rather than swimming. Toads require plants, usually emergent species, around the submerged stems of which they entwine their strings of spawn. Toads are virtually impossible to census accurately by quick simple methods. But if the site is fairly open, a count of breeding animals (largely males) may be meaningful. A count exceeding 5,000 individuals would be exceptional, while a count of more than 500 indicates a good population.

Natterjack toad *B calamita*. The rare natterjack does not occur in rivers in Britain.

Common frog *Rana temporaria*. The frog is a familar animal of both still and flowing water, but a recent population decline in the countryside, coupled with the conservation efforts of the public,

Great crested newt

have tended to turn this into a species dependent on suburban garden ponds over much of England. The frog typically breeds in warm, shallow edges, but will breed in steeply shelving sites if there are dense mats of submerged vegetation on which to lay its spawn. When laid, the spawn is sticky and is often adhered to vegetation. Once anchored, it is usually able to survive substantial increases in water velocity or depth. The relative abundance of a frog population can be readily assessed by counting the clumps of frog spawn: 500 clumps indicates an exceptional population and 50 clumps a good population.

Effects of river and ditch management on amphibians.

The most likely riverine situation to have breeding populations of amphibians are small meandering streams with shallow well-vegetated edges. Any attempt to straighten the course, steepen the sides, make the cross section more uniform down the length of a stream or remove vegetation is likely to be detrimental. Arterial works to improve drainage and/or irrigation, such as have taken place on the fens, have a dramatically detrimental effect on amphibians. The introduction and use of pumps for drainage can also do harm by permanently lowering the water table or perhaps by affording greater control of water level, so that otherwise suitable ditches are too dry during the amphibian breeding season. One should not forget that amphibians also require different terrestrial habitats. The toad is adapted to withstand a dry environment, but the newts and the frog are more restricted to moist surroundings. A change in use of adjacent land from pasture to arable is detrimental, as is the total removal of nearby trees and scrub.

Amphibians prefer a varied habitat: too many trees mean too much shade and cool conditions, but areas with a total lack of scrub or trees seem to be avoided. Scrub and woodland presumably provide shelter, foraging areas and hibernation sites. If the adjacent land is rendered totally unsuitable, then amphibians would be more or less confined to the freshwater habitat and the banks, so exposing them to the hazards of maintenance, such as dredging or herbicide spraying, that the adults at least might otherwise avoid. As some amphibians, particularly frogs, will hibernate in mud under water, dredging operations should not take place during the hibernation season in areas in which frogs are suspected to be hibernating. The hibernation season varies between regions, but as a generalisation it may be taken as mid-October to the end of February. Herbicides are relatively non-toxic to amphibia and other vertebrates, but may have drastic indirect effects by removing plant life used as egg-laying sites, cover or food. They should not be used where good populations of amphibians are known to occur. Some species are able to tolerate brackish conditions: toad tadpoles, for example, can survive in 10 per cent sea water. Higher concentrations, however, cause mortality of all species.

3. REPTILES

Reptiles are less aquatic than amphibians, although four of the six species are often found in moist damp habitats of a kind that are frequently associated with rivers. It is, however, the adjoining land rather than the river itself which is more important for reptiles. Reptiles generally like habitat with much structural diversity, comprising deep vegetation in which to forage and shelter, with open unshaded areas nearby in which to bask. As they do not gather in the water to breed, they tend to be much less conspicuous than amphibians and are correspondingly more difficult to census. Casual observation can at best only indicate which species are present, so census techniques are not discussed in this account. The best places to look for reptiles are basking in open areas or under pieces of wood, metal, stone, concrete etc, which may provide an essential component of the habitat. Reptiles tend to be at their most conspicuous when basking in the spring (mid-March to May) following emergence from hibernation. All the reptile species in Britain have suffered recent population declines, mainly as a result of loss or modification of habitat.

Reptile species: habitat requirements

Sand lizard *Lacerta agilis*. The sand lizard is confined to heaths and sand dunes in Britain and is not associated with rivers.

Viviparous lizard (common lizard) *L vivipara*. This species is often found in moist well-vegetated habitats. It is a good swimmer and has been observed hunting in the water. It is found in suitable areas throughout Britain.

Slow worm *Anguis fragilis*. The slow worm is also found in damp habitats. It tends to be the most secretive of our reptiles and is most frequently found by turning over stones, etc. It is found throughout Britain, but is rather rare in Scotland.

Grass snake *Natrix natrix*. The name '*Natrix*' means water snake and this is the most aquatic of our reptiles. It is often found in damp places and can be seen hunting tadpoles and other prey in the water. It is an egg-laying species and because of this it is very rare in the north of Britain where the climate is cooler. Its dependence on suitably warm egg-laying sites, such as compost heaps or sawdust piles, may limit its numbers in some areas.

Smooth snake *Coronella austriaca*. The rare smooth snake is restricted to heathland in the south of England.

Adder (viper) *Vipera berus*. The adder is

found quite often in moist habitat, such as banks and streams. It swims well. It occurs throughout Britain.

Effects of river management on reptiles.
Reptiles are more dependent on the survival of suitable bankside habitat than on changes in the freshwater itself. Nevertheless, management of a stream which results in the loss of amphibians could be detrimental to a population of predatory grass snakes. In the Fens of East Anglia, changes in freshwater and terrestrial habitat have led to the virtual extermination of both frogs and grass snakes. In order for a riverside habitat to remain suitable for reptiles there should be dense patches of deep vegetation interspersed with open areas. Refuges provided by logs, manmade debris etc are important, as are warm incubation sites for grass snakes. Reptiles and amphibians are often found on marginal or derelict land and the loss of such land since the 1930s because of 'improvements' of many kinds has been the principal reason for their decline.

4. SELECT BIBLIOGRAPHY

General accounts

Arnold, E N, Burton, J A and Ovenden, D W, 1978. A Field Guide to the Reptiles and Amphibians of Britain and Europe. Collins, London.

Frazer, J F D, 1983. Reptiles and Amphibians in Britain. Collins, London.

Street, D, 1979. The Reptiles of Northern and Central Europe. Batsford, London.

Distribution

Arnold, H R, 1973. Provisional Atlas of the Amphibians and Reptiles of the British Isles. Biological Records Centre, Abbots Ripton.

Habitat requirements and impact of habitat changes

Beebee, T J C, 1980. Habitats of the British Amphibians. (3): river valley marshes. Biol Cons, **18**, 281-287.

Beebee, T J C, 1981. Habitats of the British Amphibians. (4): agricultural lowlands and a general discussion of requirements. Biol Cons, **21**, 127-139.

Cooke, A S, 1975. Spawn site selection and colony size of the frog (*Rana temporaria*) and the toad (*Bufo bufo*). J Zool Lond, **175**, 29-38.

Cooke, A S, & Ferguson, P F, 1976. Changes in status of the frog (*Rana temporaria*) and the toad (*Bufo bufo*) on part of the East Anglian Fenland in Britain. Biol Cons, **9**, 191-198.

Cooke, A S and Frazer, J F D, 1976. Characteristics of newt breeding sites. J Zool Lond, **178**, 223-236.

Prestt, I, Cooke, A S and Corbett, K F, 1974. British Amphibians and Reptiles. In the Changing Flora and Fauna of Britain: 229-254. Hawksworth, D L (Ed), Academic Press, London.

Identification

Buckley, J, 1982. A Guide for the Identification of British Amphibians and Reptiles. British Herpetological Society, London.

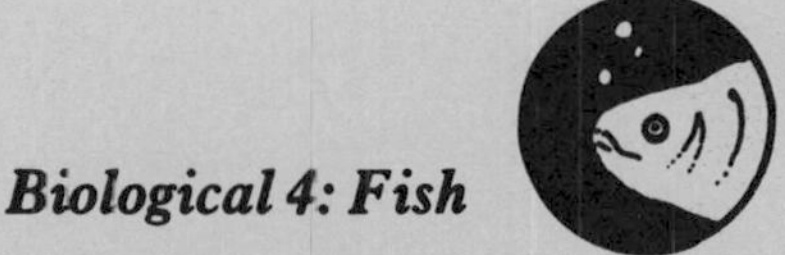

BIOLOGICAL 4: FISH

Dr N Milner, Senior Fisheries Scientist, Welsh Water Authority.

1. INTRODUCTION

Rivers vary widely in appearance from steep, confined moorland streams to large floodplain rivers, and each type has a characteristic fish fauna adapted to the habitat which it offers.

The valuable recreational and economic asset provided by river fisheries is constantly threatened by interference with the habitat. An understanding of the relationships between fish populations and their natural habitat is fundamental, therefore, to the sensible management of this resource.

This section briefly discusses the principles underlying the use of habitat by fish and considers some specific examples. It is intended as an introduction for those with little background in fisheries biology.

2. THE LINK BETWEEN FISH POPULATIONS AND PHYSICAL HABITAT FEATURES

Fish maintain their populations by the four biological processes of reproduction, feeding, growth and self protection, each of which is linked in various ways with environmental features (Table 1).

The physical features of a river are determined by the complex interactions of erosive and depositional processes, themselves related to topography, geology and river discharge. Water velocity is the major factor linking channel-forming activities and also represents the dominant feature of river habitat as far as fish are concerned. The distribution of fish between and within river systems is mainly related to their ability to cope with water velocity. A gradation can be seen from the salmonids (including salmon and trout) which live in cool, turbulent waters of coastal streams or upland reaches of larger rivers, to species such as roach and bream which are typically found in the warmer, less turbulent lowland reaches.

3. HABITAT REQUIREMENTS OF BROWN TROUT

Brown trout and most other salmonids spawn between October and January in the upper reaches of river systems, where they lay their eggs in holes (termed redds) which they excavate in gravel beds. Specific conditions are necessary for spawning and incubation to be successfully completed. By responding to certain cues, trout select a gravel composition with a low silt content that allows water to percolate over the eggs, supplying oxygen and removing metabolic wastes. Penetration of water into the gravel is more effective with a convex bed profile. Thus, trout spawning usually occurs at the boundary where the tail of a pool curves over into a downstream riffle. Some typical habitat parameters for trout spawning are: velocity range 22-38 centimetres per second; water depth 14-28 centimetres; particle size 70 per cent of gravel within range 6-76 mm; fines (eg over one

Table 1: Principal habitat features important to fish

Biological process		Governing habitat features
1. REPRODUCTION		
(i) access to spawning areas	–	provision of suitable depths and water velocity, absence of barriers to movements
(ii) spawning	–	suitable spawning substrate
(iii) incubation of eggs	–	stability of substrate, provision of adequate temperature, oxygen supply and water movement
2. FEEDING AND GROWTH		
(i) availability of food organisms	–	bankside and aquatic vegetation, substratum suitable for invertebrate production, supply of allochthonous organic material
(ii) best use of energy for maintaining position and food gathering	–	cover and shade, eg rocks, tree trunks, diversity of flow type, riffle-pool sequences (in trout streams), aquatic and bankside vegetation, appropriate temperature range
3. SELF PROTECTION		
(i) from physical displacement by current	–	shelter and visual isolation, eg varied bed profile undercut banks, rocks, tree trunks, roots, accumulated debris, aquatic vegetation and, for fry and juveniles, weedy shallow marginal slacks, backwaters.
(ii) from predation		
(iii) from competition with their own and other species		

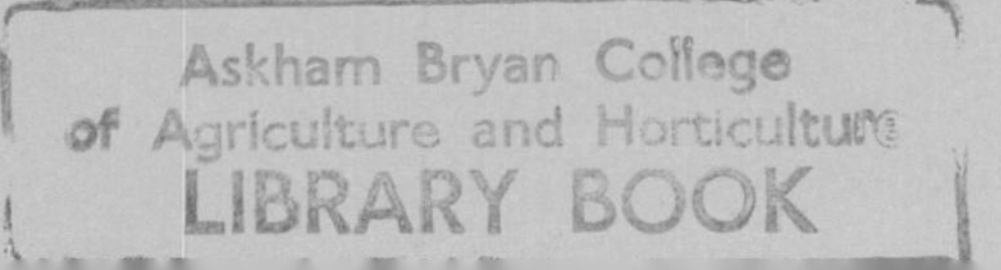

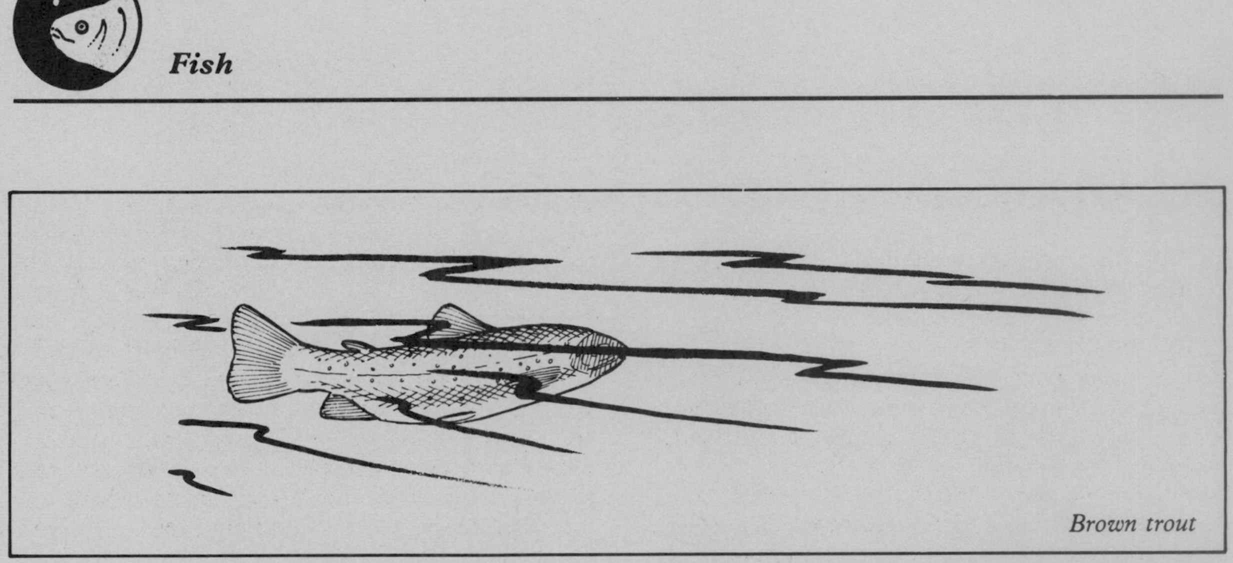
Brown trout

mm dia) not to exceed 10 per cent.

Habitat requirements change as trout grow. On emerging from the gravel, some time between March and April, the young fish stay close to the stream bed, using its roughness to protect them from predation and displacement. As they disperse from the spawning area, territorial behaviour, which is particularly strongly developed in salmonids, ensures that each fish occupies and defends its own patch. Territorial aggression is initiated by the perceived presence of other fish. Therefore, under conditions of adequate food supply, the number of territories is directly related to the abundance of cover items that provide visual isolation (Table 1).

Trout feed on invertebrates obtained from the stream bed or brought down by water flow. Access to areas of high water velocity improves food availability, but this must be balanced against the need to reduce energy expenditure in position holding. Consequently trout take up positions sheltered from direct high velocities but within easy reach of drifting prey.

Bankside vegetation is also important as a habitat feature because it provides a source of roots and fallen branches for instream cover, stabilises banks, provides a source of insects for food and shades the stream, keeping temperatures low in summer and giving overhead cover to fish.

4. INTERSPECIFIC VARIATION IN HABITAT REQUIREMENTS

Salmonids (including salmon, brown and sea trout, and grayling) occupy a comparatively restricted zone in the river systems of Britain. The majority of other fish species come under the general heading of coarse fish: a group which includes eel, dace, chub, barbel, perch, pike, roach, rudd, bream, tench and carp. In addition there are small, but often abundant, 'forage' species such as minnows, bullhead and stoneloach. Many coarse fish (and also grayling) are shoaling species and, compared with trout, are less closely associated with individual habitat features by territoriality. The most specific requirements of coarse fish are those associated with reproduction and survival of newly hatched fry.

No coarse fish excavate redds, but several species which can live in the faster flowing sections of rivers deposit eggs which stick to gravel surfaces, eg grayling, barbel, dace, chub, bullhead and loach. The other species typically lay their eggs in weed beds or debris located in shallow backwaters and marginal slacks, ditches and oxbows; habitats that also serve as nursery areas for fry and juveniles (Table 2). An adequate oxygen supply, some water flow and an absence of silt are required for successful incubation. As they grow, the young fish move to increasingly deeper and faster water, but within reach of protective cover such as weed beds, submerged tree trunks and roots. Different species are adapted to various ranges of velocity and bed material composition (Table 2), although there is a considerable overlap, particularly in slower sections or reaches. The shoaling behaviour of many coarse fish is a protective device in itself and they can roam freely over large areas of open water. Habitat selection varies seasonally and in the winter most species seek out the protection of slow deep water, tree roots and undercut banks.

Coarse fish are more catholic in their diet than salmonids. Many are omnivorous and use invertebrates, plants and detrital matter as food: weed beds and depositing muddy areas are necessary habitat components for such species.

Temperature, oxygen and turbidity are important habitat-related factors that influence fish abundance, growth and distribution. Temperature is initially determined by altitude, latitude and water source, but can be altered radically at site level by river regulation, thermal effluents and bankside tree removal. Tolerance to temperature corresponds closely with water velocity selection, thus lethal temperatures for the salmonids are generally over 25°C compared with over 34°C for carp and tench. Optimum growth temperature for brown trout is about 13°C and spawning requires temperatures of under 10°C. Tench and carp spawn at over 15°C. Trends in oxygen requirements follow those for temperature. For salmonids incipient lethal levels lie between 4 and 8 milligrams of oxygen per litre and for coarse fish between 2.5 and 5.5 milligrams of oxygen per litre. Oxygen is related to physical habitat insofar as

Table 2: Some basic habitat preferences of different species

Species	**Spawning**			**Water Velocity**				**Bed Material**			
		Substrate									
	Time	*Gravel*	*Weed*	*V.Slow*	*Slow*	*Moderate*	*Fast*	*Mud*	*Sand*	*Gravel*	*Boulders*
Trout/ Salmon	Oct-Jan	***			*	**	***			**	**
Grayling	March-May	***			*	***	**		*	***	**
Dace	March-July	**	**		*	***	**	*	**	**	*
Chub	May-June	**	**	*	**	**		*	*	**	
Barbel	May-July	***			*	**	*		*	***	*
Perch	April-June		***		*	**		*	**	*	
Pike	March-May		***	**	**	**	*	**	**	*	
Roach	April-June		***	**	**	**		*	**	**	
Rudd	April-June		***	**	*			**	*		
Bream	May-June		***	***	*			**	*		
Carp	May-July		***	***	*			***			
Tench	May-Aug.		***	***				***			

*** *Preferred*
** *Common*
* *Present*

water velocity, plant growth and decay can have a major impact on the oxygen regime of a river section. Shading by bankside vegetation indirectly affects the balance between oxygen supply and uptake, by modifying plant growth rate and water temperature. In unpolluted trout zones, oxygen is rarely a limiting factor, but is an important consideration in slow flowing lower reaches where temperatures are usually higher and plant growth may be extensive.
Turbidity from suspended matter can inhibit plant growth by reducing light penetration. Direct effects on fish are thought to be negligible provided that concentrations of suspended solids do not exceed 80 milligrams per litre. However, excessive silt deposition can interfere with egg development and production of food organisms.

5. CONCLUDING REMARKS

Habitat requirements are the result of a complex interaction between fish and their environment. A continuum of adaptation is apparent over the range of habitats afforded by river systems, but two dominant principles emerge. First, for all species, it is the spawning and fry stages which are most tightly linked to habitat and which are most vulnerable to environmental degredation. Second, diversity of habitat is most important because it ensures a range of sizes and species of fish. This is a valuable feature in a fish community because it contributes to the stability of the ecosystem.

6. SELECT BIBLIOGRAPHY

Fish Biology and habitat requirements
Hynes, H B N, 1970. The ecology of Running Waters, Liverpool University Press, 555pp.

Nikolsky, G V, 1963. The Ecology of Fishes. Academic Press. London and New York, 352pp.

White, R J, 1973. Stream channel suitability for coldwater fish. Proceedings, 28th Annual Meeting of the Soil Conservation Society of America, Hot Springs, Arkansas, pp61-79.

Fish Identification
Maitland, P S, 1972. A key to the Freshwater Fishes of the British Isles. Freshwater Biological Association. Scientific Publication No 27.

Wheeler, A, 1969. The Fishes of the British Isles and North-West Europe, London, Macmillian Press.

Impact of river works
Keller, E A, 1976. Channelization: environmental, geomorphic, and engineering aspects. *In* D R Coates (Ed). Geomorphology and engineering, Dowden Hutchinson and Ross, Stroudsberg, Pa, 1976.

Kennedy, G J A, Cragg-Hine, D, Strange, C D & Steward, D A, 1983. Effects of a land drainage scheme on the salmonid populations of the River Camowen, Co Tyrone. J Fish Man, **14**, 1-16.

Mills, D, 1980. The management of forest streams. Forestry Commission Leaflet No 78, London HMSO, 19pp.

Swales, S, 1982. Environmental effects of river channel works used in land drainage improvement. J Environ Man, **14**, 103-126.

BIOLOGICAL 5: MAMMALS

Gill Lewis and S M Macdonald, The Vincent Wildlife Trust, Baltic Exchange Buildings, 21 Bury Street, London.

1. INTRODUCTION

Otters, water voles and water shrews are the native mammals most dependent on rivers for their livelihoods. In addition, coypu and American mink, which originally escaped from fur farms, have become well established in riparian habitats. The majority of other British mammals regularly use bankside habitats although they are not restricted to them.

Vegetation is of particular importance to mammals, since it offers food and cover from predators, including man. Such cover may be in the form of patches of scrub, tall herbaceous vegetation, reedbeds or bankside trees and hedgerows. Heavily managed rivers, lacking these features, support impoverished mammal populations. Some animals have more specific habitat requirements and these are detailed below.

2. SPECIES ACCOUNTS

Otter

Otters declined sharply in numbers during the late 1950s and early 1960s and, in some places, the decline continues today. The pesticide dieldrin was strongly implicated in the crash but, since then, habitat destruction has helped prevent a recovery. Otters need dense cover for daytime refuge and females in particular need secure holt sites. Mature bankside trees, especially ash, sycamore and oak, which have eroded cavities within their root systems, are often favoured. Otters are shy of human disturbance, but can tolerate it best where they have abundant cover: as habitat is removed they become increasingly vulnerable.

Because an otter ranges over many miles of river, a conservation strategy for this species should be considered in terms of the entire catchment. The protection of only small pockets of habitat is likely to be inadequate for the long-term survival of a population. As many mature trees as possible should be conserved and regeneration should be encouraged to provide the holts of the future.

It has been suggested that mink compete with otters for food, and that this has limited the recovery of otter populations. Contrary to this belief, however, recent studies have shown that otters feed mainly on fish, whereas mink have a much more catholic diet, including a substantial amount of small mammals and birds. Mink are also more tolerant of habitat degradation and human proximity than otters. At their present low population levels, food availability is not thought to be limiting otter numbers and any competition with mink is, therefore, insignificant. Otters and management for their conservation are described in more detail in Part III, pages 277-82.

Water shrew

Water shrews are found throughout Britain, in unpolluted streams and ponds. They prefer slow-flowing water where aquatic invertebrates are abundant, and are especially common in water-cress beds. They need cover at the water's edge to conceal them from predators. Their prey includes insects and other invertebrates, small fish and amphibians. Although highly adapted for aquatic life, water shrews can be found at considerable distances from water – often in woodland and scrub.

Water vole

Water voles are found throughout Britain, on lowland rivers, ponds, canals and drainage ditches. Their preferred food is grass, but emergent plants, willow leaves and ground elder are also frequently taken. Most feeding takes place on land.

Each male water vole usually has a home range of 100 metres or so, and the female about half this, the precise length depending on the quality and suitability of the habitat. The home ranges of individuals frequently overlap. Usually at least one main burrow is built, located near their feeding grounds and constructed with entrances above and below water level and on top of the bank. Feeding burrows are also built, to provide protective 'bolt holes' close to the feeding grounds

Otter swimming in river

and to give access to these areas from the water. The only day-active mammal confined to rivers, the water vole is the species most likely to be seen. But it is thought it is probably in decline due to river management works reducing the suitability of rivers as habitat and possibly making the species more vulnerable to predation from rats and mink. In some areas reductions in water quality may also have had a detrimental impact.

Bats

Of the 13 species of bats found in Britain, two are particularly associated with rivers, the Natterer's and Daubenton's bats. Bat populations, overall, have crashed in the last few years and it is unlikely that these two species are exceptions. They require mature trees with cracks and hollow trunks or timber as roost sites, at least in the summer. They catch the flying insects that are abundant over aquatic and bankside plants on lowland rivers. Their food sources may be reduced by large-scale weedcutting in early summer, but loss of roosting-trees is probably the greater hazard to their survival. Bat conservation measures are detailed in Part III, pages **283-4**.

Table 1 summarises the habitat requirements of mammals particularly associated with rivers.

3. SELECT BIBLIOGRAPHY

General accounts

Chanin, P R F, and Jefferies, D J 1978. The decline of the otter *Lutra lutra L* in Britain: an analysis of hunting records and discussion of causes. Biol J Linnean Soc **10**: 305-328.

Corbet, G B, and Southern, H N, 1977. The handbook of British mammals. Blackwell Scientific Publications.

Gosling, L M, 1974. The coypu in East Anglia. Transactions of the Norfolk and Norwich Naturalists' Society **23**: 49-59.

Linn, I, and Chanin, P, 1978. Are mink really pests in Britain? New Scientist 77, No 1092, 2nd March 560-2.

Macdonald, S M, and Mason, C F, 1983. Some factors affecting the distribution of otters (*Lutra lutra*). Mammal Review **13**: 1-10.

Mason, C F, and Macdonald, S M (in press). Some factors affecting the distribution of mink (*Mustela vison*). J Zool.

Royal Society for Nature Conservation, 1980. Focus on otters – a guide to their natural history and conservation. RSNC.

Stebbings, R E, and Jefferies, D J, 1982. Focus on bats: their conservation and the law. Nature Conservancy Council.

Stoddard, D M, 1970. Individual range, dispersion and dispersal in a population of water voles (*Arvicola terrestris L.*) J Anim Ecol **39**: 403-25.

Yalden, D W, and Morris, P A, 1975. Biology of bats. David and Charles.

Distribution

Macdonald, S M, 1983. The status of the otter (*Lutra lutra*) in the British Isles. Mammal Review **13**: 11-23.

Food

Churchfield, J S, 1979. A note on the diet of the European water shrew, *Neomys fodiens bicolor*. J Zool **188**: 294-6.

Wise, M H, Linn, I J, and Kennedy, C R, 1981. A comparison of the feeding biology of mink *Mustela vison* and otter *Lutra lutra*. J Zool **195**: 181-213.

Water vole

Table 1: Requirements and distribution of mammals particularly associated with rivers

Common Name	Habitat	Distribution	Food Sources	Comments
Otter	Rivers and wetlands exclusively. Need cover of marginal vegetation, trees and reedbeds. Secure breeding sites essential.	Now largely absent from Central & S England & S Wales. Only abundant in NW Highlands & Islands of Scotland.	Predominantly fish, particularly eels. Frogs and occasionally young birds and mammals.	*Protected Species.* Nocturnal.
Mink (non-native)	Rivers and wetlands, with cover of marginal vegetation and/or trees.	Became established in late 1950s, now widespread and still expanding.	Crayfish, fish, birds and their eggs, small mammals, large insects.	Now thought not to be competing with otter. Mainly nocturnal.
Coypu (non-native)	Slow rivers and grazing marsh with fen, reedbeds, and marshes.	Confined to East Anglia, escaped in 1930s.	Grasses at all times of year, also water plants and willow shoots.	Pest species, because of large burrows in banks. Nocturnal.
Water shrew	Clear, unpolluted streams and wetlands, with plant cover.	Throughout.	Insects predominantly, also small fish, snails and frogs.	Small burrows in banks, near surface. Active day and night.
Water vole	Lowland rivers, canals, ponds and drainage ditches with clay banks and good marginal vegetation.	Throughout.	Water plants – very selective feeder.	Small burrows in banks (and pastures) near surface. Semi-colonial. Day-active.
Natterer's bat	Open woodland and grassland, particularly over rivers.	Throughout, no longer common.	Moths, dusk-flying insects.	*Protected species.* Nocturnal. Summer roosts in old trees, and sometimes in winter.
Daubenton's bat	Over reedbeds and rivers, with marginal vegetation and trees.	Throughout, no longer common.	Moths, dusk-flying insects.	*Protected species.* Nocturnal, roosts in hollow trees.

BIOLOGICAL 6: BIRDS

Dr L H Campbell, Senior Research Biologist, Royal Society for the Protection of Birds, Sandy.

1. INTRODUCTION

Although at some time or other the majority of the bird species found in Britain may make some use of rivers, whether it be for breeding, feeding or simply as a route through the countryside, their dependence on the riverine environment obviously varies considerably. The little grebe, whose nest is only centimetres from the water surface, and the kingfisher sitting, fish in beak, beside a riverbank nest hole are both closely associated with rivers for much of the year. The heron and cormorant, each in their own way typical river-birds, use the river mainly for feeding or roosting, whilst the blackcap and whitethroat, independent of the river's aquatic characteristics, may breed in woodland or scrub on or near the river's edge.

The richness of the bird community which makes use of British rivers is a clear pointer to the fact that rivers have an importance beyond their simple aquatic role. As pressures because of changing land-use have increased, rivers have tended to become the last resorts for communities or individual species which were formerly more widespread or numerous. With their aquatic characteristics supplemented by a variable and patchy band of associated terrestrial habitats, rivers have assumed the role of mixed-habitat corridors within the countryside and it is the importance and use of this river corridor for birds which is discussed in the following paragraphs.

2. PATTERNS OF BIRD USAGE

Although various species make use of rivers in autumn and winter and some of these may be very numerous, particularly in associated wetland habitats, the greatest diversity of species is present in spring and summer. These can be roughly divided into four groups according to the sort of use they make of the river and its flood plain (Table 1). The groups are not rigid and from region to region the same species may change its grouping. Similarly the lists shown for groups 3 and 4 are not comprehensive, showing only the more interesting species that may occur.

In winter the river channel is used by mallard, teal or other waterfowl although conditions for feeding are usually less than ideal because of high water levels, turbulence and turbidity. When lakes and ponds freeze over rivers can provide open water reaches and safe refuges for wildfowl which feed on fields by night, and persistent rough cover, trees and berry-bearing bushes will attract and shelter resident birds and migrant visitors like siskin, redwing and fieldfare. As a result of flooding, adjacent areas can assume importance for feeding wildfowl. Washland areas, such as the Ouse Washes in Cambridgeshire, hold huge numbers but even small flooded areas may be locally important.

Table 1: Categories of birds making use of river corridors during the breeding season

Category 1

Birds which breed in close association with rivers or riverine habitat features:

Great crested grebe	Common sandpiper
Little grebe	Kingfisher
Mallard	Sand martin
Tufted duck	Dipper
Red-breasted merganser	Reed warbler
Goosander	Marsh warbler
Mute swan	Sedge warbler
Moorhen	Grey wagtail
Coot	Reed bunting

(Ringed plover, little ringed plover, bittern, water rail, bearded tit, gadwall, oystercatcher, common tern, pied wagtail may all occur on occasions in this category).

Category 2

Birds, chiefly waders, which breed in wetland areas adjacent to and associated with rivers:

Oystercatcher	Black-tailed godwit
Lapwing	Redshank
Snipe	Ruff
Curlew	Yellow wagtail

Category 3

Birds which breed in non-riverine habitats found within the river corridors:

Little owl	Lesser whitethroat
Grasshopper warbler	Spotted flycatcher
Blackcap	Pied wagtail
Garden warbler	Canada goose
Whitethroat	

(The species listed above are some of the more interesting of the many common species which may occur).

Category 4

Birds using the rivers for feeding or resting but not breeding there:

Cormorant	Shelduck
Grey heron	Greenshank
Teal	Dunlin
Wigeon	Gulls
Shoveler	Common tern
Pochard	Swallow
Goldeneye	House martin

(Many other species, including those in categories 1, 2 and 3, may be classed in this group on particular individual river systems).

3. GENERAL HABITAT REQUIREMENTS

The general ways in which rivers may be exploited by birds have been outlined above. As with any other habitat, the value of the river corridor for birds is closely related to the diversity of the habitat features which it contains. Reduction in river habitat diversity will be reflected in species higher up the food chain. Because birds are near the top of the food chain, they provide a good indication of the general health of the river corridor.

But what are the particular aspects of the river environment which are most important to birds? In many respects birds are non-specialist in their requirements since few species are totally dependent on any single habitat feature. Instead they require a particular type of habitat structure within which individual components can vary considerably. Accordingly, when considering the habitat requirements of river birds it is usually most appropriate to describe the overall structure of the preferred habitat and not simply to produce a list of individual physical features or plant species with which the birds appear to be associated.

Over and above the individual species' requirements there are, of course, several general factors which may limit population size or restrict distribution, irrespective of the presence of otherwise suitable habitat. For instance, some birds are at the extreme limits of their normal breeding ranges in Britain and may be absent from a river simply because it is outside their range. Thus, despite extensive reedbeds in the north, reed warblers only breed in the southern half of the country.

Water quality is also important for all those species that feed on rivers. Major pollutants such as pesticides, oil or lead can have a direct effect and there are well documented cases of the impact of lead shot or fishing weights on mute swan and other wildfowl. However, pollution may also indirectly affect birds by reducing or destroying the aquatic plant and animal populations upon which they feed. In this respect fish-eating species such as the kingfisher or invertebrate specialists like the dipper are sensitive and conspicuous indicators of water quality.

Altitude also appears at first sight to limit river bird distribution. Indeed some species, such as common sandpiper or grey wagtail, and others like coot or moorhen, are often thought of as upland or lowland species. In fact this relationship is probably spurious and merely reflects the fact that the preferred habitat of these species tends to be found in the upper or lower reaches of most rivers. Where for geological reasons these features occur in other parts of the rivers, the associated birds are also likely to occur.

4. SPECIFIC HABITAT REQUIREMENTS

In this section no attempt has been made to describe the specific requirements of all the species in Table 1, although Table 2 includes a summary of some of the main species-habitat associations for those birds most closely linked with rivers. Instead three species – dipper, coot and kingfisher – have been selected to illustrate the different ways in which rivers are important for birds:

a. Dipper

With their white belly, bobbing stance and rapid direct flight, dippers are conspicuous and characteristic birds of the upland river. Throughout northern and western Britain they are likely to be found wherever turbulent, well oxygenated water flows over rocky or stony substrates, high in the headwater streams or close to sea-level. Although tending to avoid dense conifer plantations, they are equally at home on open or wooded stretches. Exposed rocks and boulders within or beside the river are used as perches from which to feed or as markers which help to establish territories. Uniform unbroken stretches of water are avoided.

The main food items are aquatic invertebrates, such as the larvae of caddis and stoneflies. They capture these from or below the water surface by wading in shallow pools or, in deeper parts, by walking underwater. With their heavy dependence on aquatic prey, dippers are inevitably sensitive to water quality conditions.

Dipper nests, which are usually constructions of moss and grass, may be built on ledges or crevices in riverside rock faces, on sheltered shelves behind waterfalls or amongst the overhanging roots of large trees. In more open situations a nest may be

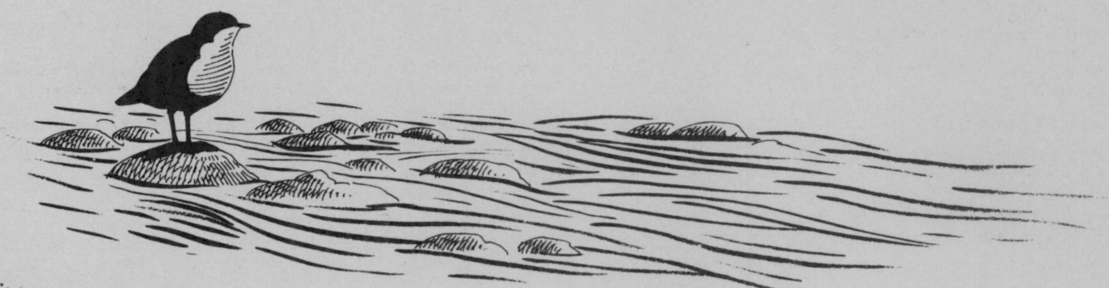

Dipper

Table 2: Characteristics of major species breeding in close association with rivers.

Species	Status	'Good Density' Prs/ 10 km	River Type	Habitat Characteristics	Food	
GREAT CRESTED GREBE	Uncommon; mainly in south	2	LOWLAND	Deep; lakelike; quiet; well developed fringing emergent vegetation especially reeds.	Fish; aquatic invertebrates	Nests of vegetation attached to reeds or trailing branches
LITTLE GREBE	Widespread and sometimes numerous especially in south	10+	LOWLAND Backwaters, oxbows, canals	Luxuriant aquatic, emergent and marginal vegetation, overhanging branches, bushes and scrub.	Insects; molluscs; tadpoles; small fish	Floating nest platforms attached to emergent vegetation, trailing branches
MALLARD	Very common and widespread	30+	LOWLAND UPLAND	Emergent vegetation; bankside scrub; rank herbage; old willows. Very adaptable.	Omnivorous and opportunistic	Where habitat on riverbanks is not ideal will freely nest at distance from water up ditches, in hedges or scrub. Young then brought to water
TUFTED DUCK	Rather scarce but sometimes at high density	5+	LOWLAND	Open lakelike sections with good marginal emergent vegetation.	Omnivorous: fish, aquatic invertebrates, green plant material	Nests in tussocks or dense aquatic vegetation. Apparent territories on rivers may involve birds actually nesting on nearby lakes, pools or gravel pits
RED-BREASTED MERGANSER	Widespread north and west of Scotland; also Northern Ireland and spreading in northern England and Wales		UPLAND Coastal lochs	Well oxygenated, unpolluted upland rivers, with boulders, riffles and sand banks. Banks with dense vegetation such as heather, scrub or woodland.	Fish	Preference for coastal areas. Nests in dense ground cover
GOOSANDER	Highlands; SW Scotland and Northern England. Spreading in Wales		UPLAND Lochs	Clear, unpolluted, upland rivers, particularly where well wooded	Fish	More inland and montane than merganser. Prefers to nest in tree holes over or close to water
MUTE SWAN	Widespread in lowland areas; numerous in south	5-10	LOWLAND Canals, oxbows	Wide or open channels with islands, backwaters, spits or stands of emergent vegetation, eg reeds.	Mainly aquatic vegetation; also emergent plants and seeds. Also graze on land, particularly early in season	Declines on rivers in parts of England have been attributed to the effects of lead. Local distribution changes attributable to effects of navigation or increased availability of other habitat (eg gravel pits)
MOORHEN	Very common and widespread	25+	LOWLAND Canals, backwaters, oxbows, ditches	Abundant emergent vegetation, bankside scrub, overhanging trees, bushes or hedgerows.	Omnivorous; may feed within river but also often in adjacent pasture	Nests in emergent vegetation, trailing branches or in bushes. May nest well away from river if suitable habitat is lacking
COOT	Common and widespread in south; more scarce in north	20+	LOWLAND Canals	Moderately wide, open channels, with extensive marginal emergent vegetation such as reeds and bulrushes. Overhanging and trailing scrub or branches important for early nests.	Omnivorous; plants predominant	Nests floating or over water in rushes, reeds or trailing branches. Adjacent wet pasture may be important for feeding early in season
COMMON SANDPIPER	Widespread in upland areas north of a line from Humber to Severn estuaries	5-10	UPLAND Streams, lakes	Well oxygenated; rocky, shingle shores, banks and islands; rough vegetation on or near to river.	Aquatic invertebrates	Nests in rough cover on the river bank, islands or some distance away, usually well above normal flood levels
KINGFISHER	Widespread and quite common except in Scotland where scarce and mainly found south of the Highlands		LOWLAND, to lesser extent upland. Canals	Exposed earthbanks, usually overhanging water; requires perches (eg branches, coarse vegetation) from which to fish. Usually in relatively open sections	Mainly fish but also tadpoles and aquatic invertebrates	Nests usually in earthbanks; may nest away from river or in tree roots
SAND MARTIN	Widespread; less so in south	(Colonial)	UPLAND/ LOWLAND	Vertical earth and sand banks soft enough for burrowing. Open areas without woodland.	Aerial insects	Colonies vary from year to year, sites being unstable and liable to become unsuitable. Opportunistic and may nest in pipes in walls
DIPPER	Widespread in north and west; absent from England east of line Humber – Isle of Wight	5-10	UPLAND	Turbulent, well oxygenated streams and rivers; rocks, boulders, shingle, waterfalls; rock outcrops; earthbanks. Open moorland or wooded sections.	Aquatic invertebrates taken on or below water surface	Nests naturally on rock outcrops or in earthbank overhangs and tree rocks; regular use of man-made structures such as bridges and weirs

Species	Status	'Good Density' Prs/ 10 km	River Type	Habitat Characteristics	Food	
REED WARBLER	Widespread in south; absent north England, Scotland, Ireland and much of Wales		LOWLAND	Beds of reed; reed fringe or other rough bankside vegetation (willowherb, hawthorn).	Predominantly insectivorous	Large numbers usually confined to extensive reedbeds but scattered pairs elsewhere. Nests typically attached to reed stems, well above ground or water level
SEDGE WARBLER	Widespread and numerous throughout lowland Britain	10-15	LOWLAND	Reeds, willow carr, hawthorn thickets, rough scrub and bushes.	Insectivorous	Nests low down in dense vegetation
GREY WAGTAIL	Widespread, though absent in much of central and eastern England	5-10	UPLAND (Lowland)	Turbulent upland streams; weirs; mill races. Rock outcrops.	Insectivorous	Nests on rocky ledges; in tree roots; also on man-made structures
REED BUNTING	Widespread and common	10	LOWLAND	Marshy areas; reedbeds; fringing emergent vegetation; hedgerows and ditches; rank vegetation.		Nests in thick vegetation. Formerly largely restricted to marsh or riverine areas – have now spread widely into rough ground in agricultural areas

under the overhanging lip of an earth bank or, where such natural features are absent, on structures such as bridges, weirs or mill buildings. The main common feature seems to be that the nest opening should be over running water.

Dippers remain on the rivers in autumn and winter, although they may desert the less hospitable reaches. Communal roosts form which are most evident on structures such as bridges.

b. Coot

In marked contrast, coots, equally conspicuous with their white foreheads, are characteristic of the less turbulent, often turbid, lowland river where it is vegetation rather than physical features that lend variation to the channel. Coots prefer water depths of one to two metres and avoid narrow streams or ditches. They mainly eat plants and depend for much of the year on aquatic plants and water weeds. However, in winter and early spring they may feed extensively on riverside fields and meadows.

Vegetation is also of major importance for breeding, providing suitable nest sites and protection for the young. The nest platforms are built on or just above the water surface, within or attached to a wide range of different sorts of vegetation. Particularly early in the season, coots may use trailing branches of willow or hawthorn scrub, whilst elsewhere they may nest within stands of common reed or fringing bur-reed and club rush. The actual plant species does not seem to matter, the most important factor being the presence of sufficient persistent vegetation to hold and protect the nest structure. Inevitably, with nests near to the water surface, coots are highly susceptible to the effects of flooding.

Like dippers, coots are territorial during the breeding season but, whilst some may remain on rivers in autumn and winter, the majority tend to gather on lakes and reservoirs nearby or further afield.

c. Kingfisher

Whilst dippers and coots are closely associated with features which can conveniently be classed as upland or lowland, kingfishers, perhaps the most spectacular of riparian birds, are much more obviously dependent on a single feature, vertical earthbanks. Scarce in Scotland, their apparent preference for lowland rivers is probably a reflection of the greater frequency of earthbanks on such rivers. Although kingfishers mainly eat fish, especially minnows and sticklebacks, they will also feed on insects, tadpoles and small molluscs or crustaceans. This dependence on aquatic prey also means that, like dippers, kingfishers are sensitive to water quality.

Their nest entrances are found towards the top of vertical earthbanks, usually between 75cm and two metres from the water surface, where they may be vulnerable to flooding. Each nest has a tunnel of up to 1.5 metres long which is excavated by the kingfishers, and there are usually tree roots, overhanging branches or similar suitable perches

Coot

Kingfisher

close to the entrance, which are used when the tunnel is being built or for subsequent resting or fishing.

Kingfisher populations are known to be severely affected by harsh winter weather conditions and this factor, coupled with their dependence on earth banks and good water quality, has led to them being one of the river bird species most threatened by man's use of rivers.

5. UPLAND AND LOWLAND BIRD HABITATS

Turning from this close look at three characteristic river birds, it is possible to take a wider view by considering two hypothetical stretches of river, one upland and one lowland, their associated habitats and bird communities (Figure 1).

A diversity of physical features is conspicuous on an ornithologically-rich upland river. Aquatic and emergent vegetation is not obvious and the river corridor is often narrow. In the steeper parts, turbulent and well oxygenated water passes through waterfalls, pools and rapids between rocky banks with boulders and stones. This mosaic of shallows and pools, slack and faster flowing water supports rich aquatic invertebrate populations which are food for grey wagtails and dippers.

Where the gradient is less the river may meander through valley pastures, with relatively long sections of deeper water (pools) broken by rock or shingle bars (riffles) where the water is more shallow and turbulent. Here, dippers and grey wagtails may have to nest on man-made structures or more natural sites on adjacent tributary streams. Shallow, shingle areas and the margins of pools provide feeding areas for common sandpipers which, like oystercatchers or ringed plovers, may nest on shingle islands or in rough vegetation at greater distances from the river channel.

These wider and deeper upland sections also support fish populations on which breeding red-breasted mergansers and goosanders can feed. Mergansers nest in dense heather, grass or scrub close to the water's edge but goosanders prefer wooded stretches where they can find tree-holes or root cavities by the water. Where there are exposed earthbanks, sand martins and kingfishers may nest.

In the lowlands in summer, it may be difficult to distinguish a length of river rich for birds from a poor one, since emergent and bankside vegetation may be dense on both. But in spring, the river presents a very different face. Winter floods and weather have battered and flattened the vegetation leaving only robust features such as scrub, hedges or trees, especially those trailing in the water, as suitable nest sites. In backwaters or at the mouths of drainage ditches, reeds and other potential nest site plants may also have survived.

Thus ornithologically-rich lowland river sections contain a variety of persistent habitat features. Reeds in a ditch, the fallen branch of an overhanging willow or the trailing branches of bankside hawthorn bushes provide not only suitable sites for the nest platforms of coots, moorhens, and little grebes, but also cover and protection from predators for both adults and their chicks. Mute swans nest on islands or spits which can hold their massive nest structures as well as offer a degree of protection from disturbance. On wider, more lake-like sections where sizeable beds of reed have developed, great crested grebes and water rails can nest and the first reed warblers and sedge warblers take up their singing positions. If there are suitable earth banks, kingfishers and sand martins will nest.

As the season progresses, water levels fall and aquatic and emergent plants grow rapidly, breeding coot and moorhen have a much wider choice of

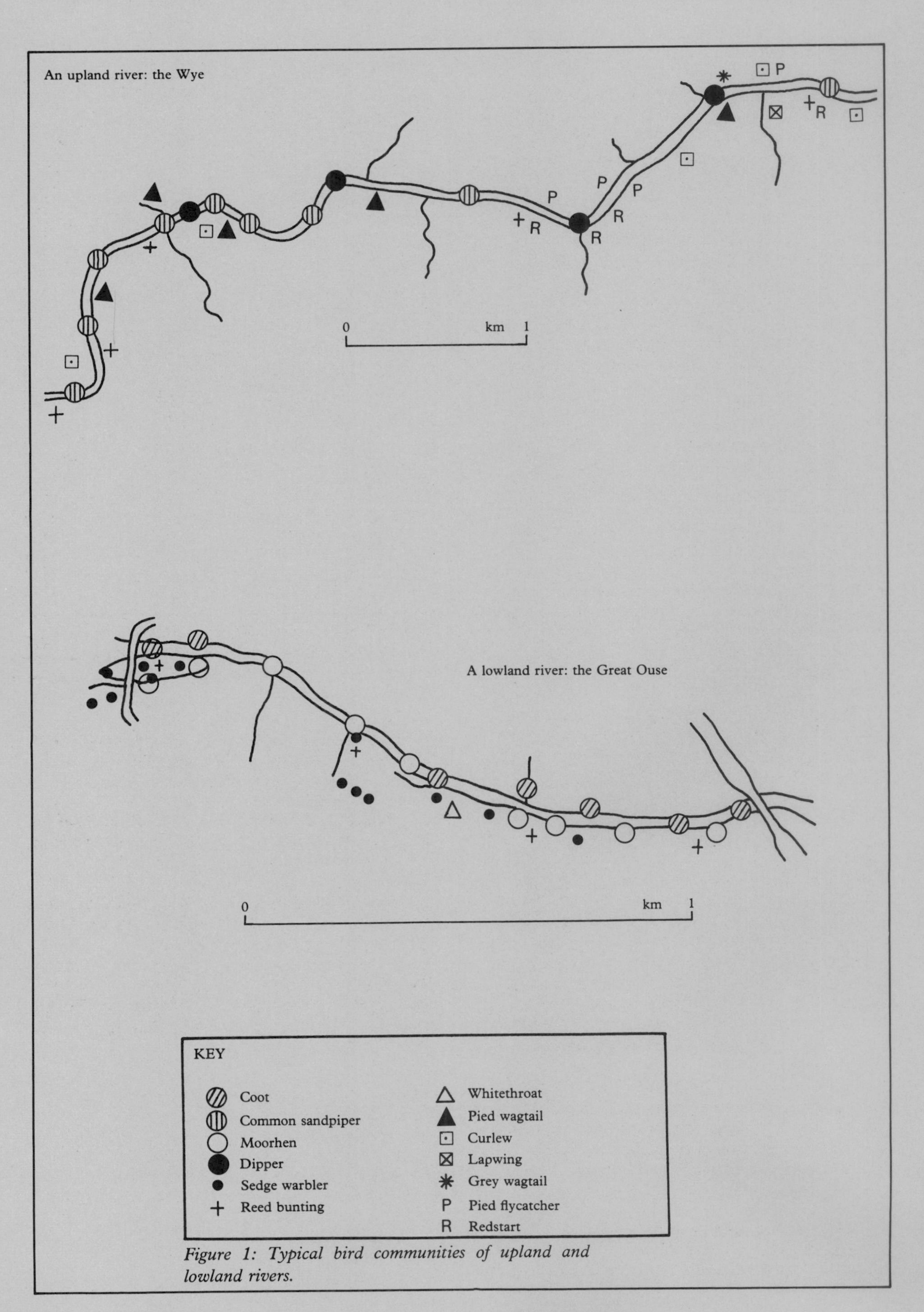

Figure 1: Typical bird communities of upland and lowland rivers.

sites to lay their second or replacement clutches. Nests may be found in even the narrowest bands of emergent reeds, bur-reeds or bullrushes. As beds of aquatic weeds develop, moorhens, coots and mute swans, which may have previously been feeding in adjacent fields, are able to move onto the river itself to feed on aquatic plants or invertebrates.

Riverside habitats tend to be of greatest importance in lowland areas, largely because land-use changes have been much more dramatic there. But in the uplands most of the characteristic, non-riverine species, such as golden plovers and ring ouzels, depend on large, open tracts of moorland or rough pasture. Where such habitat has been replaced, for example by forestry, residual patches along the river corridor are unlikely to be sufficiently extensive. However, persistent over-grazing or burning may now have restricted native woodland to the riverside slopes and the upland river corridor may be the only local areas for passerines such as willow warblers and pied flycatchers. Larger species like merlins and hooded crows may also rely on river corridor trees or rank heather for nest sites.

In the lowlands, as a result of drainage, arablisation and woodland clearance, semi-natural vegetation such as reedbeds, willow scrub and woodland may now be restricted to the river corridor. But an ornithologically rich lowland river corridor will have, perhaps despite management, a diversity of features such as oxbow lakes, backwaters, unreclaimed land within meanders and residual woodland. These features will attract a wide range of common and perhaps more rare species that otherwise would not be found locally.

6. CONCLUSIONS

The importance of habitat diversity in determining the ornithological value of the river corridor has been emphasised above and there is a very close link between this and the scenic value of rivers. Rivers which are visually interesting are also likely to be good for birds.

Management procedures which reduce the habitat diversity of the river corridor will inevitably damage the overall bird community (Figure 2). Equally, because birds are often opportunistic and highly mobile, sympathetic management may help to increase habitat diversity and enhance the bird community. Whilst the detailed habitat requirements of individual species may still be only poorly understood, their general interests can be well served by protecting and promoting the diversity of the habitat within the river corridor.

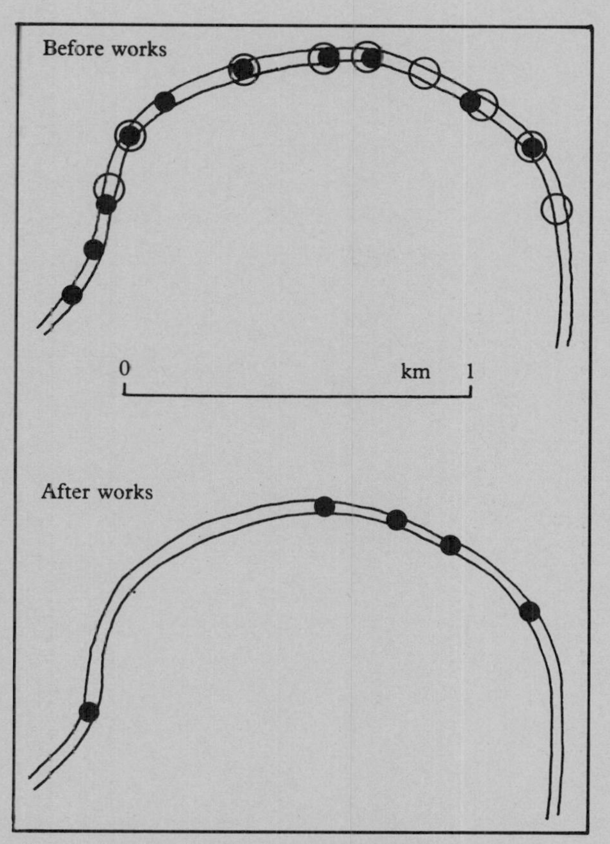

Figure 2: The impact of river engineering works on moorhen and coot, on the Great Ouse near Bedford. Dots indicate moorhen territories; open circles, coot territories.

7. SELECT BIBLIOGRAPHY

Identification

Peterson, R T, Mountfort, G, and Hollom, P, 1983. A field guide to the birds of Britain and Europe (4th edition). Collins, London.

Distribution

Marchant, J H and Hyde, P A, 1980. Aspects of the distribution of riparian birds on waterways in Britain and Ireland. Bird Study **27**: 183-202.

Sharrock, J T R, 1976. The atlas of breeding birds in Britain and Ireland. British Trust for Ornithology, Tring.

Habitat

Fuller, R J, 1982. Bird Habitats in Britain (especially Chapter 11). Poyser, Calton.

INTRODUCTION

This part describes techniques which have been adopted by drainage authorities – mainly in England and Wales – to retain or reinstate wildlife habitat features of rivers. The schemes we have chosen each illustrate a particular structure or change in practice which has permitted part of the river's plant and animal community to flourish. We hope that this body of experience will encourage others to do the same or, even better, to develop these ideas for their own particular rivers.

Each technique has been presented in isolation, even when a particular scheme has made use of a variety of retention and reinstatement practices: thus, some schemes are referred to several times. Techniques are arranged so as to present a variety of options for channel and bank management – a source of ideas to be incorporated into each scheme design. It is usually the use of a combination of retention and reinstatement techniques which creates a successful scheme for wildlife conservation.

It cannot be stressed too often that conservation measures need to be incorporated into scheme design from the outset, if they are to work. 'Conservation' cannot be an isolated item tacked on once a scheme has been completed.

Habitat retention is always preferable to reinstatement for the reasons discussed in 'Introduction 3: River Ecology and Wildlife Conservation'. In examining the options available for integrating wildlife conservation with river engineering operations, therefore, the first question to be posed is whether the river channel or river banks could, or should, be left entirely untouched. The possible answers – 'yes', 'partially' or 'no' then lead on to a variety of options. These are set out in tables 1 and 2, divided according to whether they are structural or biological engineering techniques. The latter have sometimes been termed 'biotechnical engineering' – that is, making use of the structural qualities of living plant (and even animal) materials for engineering ends. The numbers used in the tables key into the page numbers of this part.

When planning a scheme, all of the retention and reinstatement options will need to be considered, because a combination of several techniques will normally be required to conserve wildlife habitats from the impact of the scheme.

ARRANGEMENT OF THE TECHNICAL INFORMATION

Sections 1-3 refer to physical techniques (channel and bank conservation and the disposal of spoil); Sections 4-6 to vegetation management; and Sections 7-11 to conservation measures for specific groups of wildlife.

The techniques are arranged in a specific order within each section. Retention methods – techniques which avoid the disturbance or destruction of all or part of a particular habitat feature – appear first, and reinstatement methods – techniques which restore the physical variety of river habitats, or promote the recovery of wildlife communities once work has ceased – follow.

Each technique is described and its advantages and disadvantages discussed from both engineering and wildlife conservation viewpoints. In most cases, this introductory information is supported by one or more case examples of the use of the technique, presented according to a standard format:

1 Name of technique. Code Number.
Location.
OS 1:50,000 map number and national grid reference.
Name, address and telephone number of originating drainage authority or other organisation.

2 Site Summary. This provides outline details of the physical parameters of the site and whether the scheme was capital or revenue work. Where a name appears, this person has agreed to answer enquiries about the technique described. This is not to imply that this was the only person responsible for the success of the project – river works are always the result of team work, integrating the skills of design and operational engineers, biologists and others. Enquiries should normally be addressed to the Divisional Manager, for the attention of the person named, as appropriate.

3 Work Description. Provides a description of the technique, with an evaluation of any engineering difficulties that were encountered during operations.

4 Habitat Comments. Subjective observations based on ecological principles, made during brief site visits, intended to illustrate the main benefits (or costs) to wildlife habitat conservation of employed techniques. In those few cases where biological monitoring work was carried out, we are most grateful to the research workers involved for making their data available to us.

PRE-DESIGN HABITAT SURVEYS

Consideration of the options presented in tables 1 and 2 must be based on ecological survey data, against which the potential effects of the operations under study can be assessed. The Nature Conservancy Council, local Nature Conservation Trusts, Royal Society for the Protection of Birds and Otter Haven Project all have professional staff who can frequently help with the provision of such information.

Survey should involve the preparation of a 1:1250 map (and in some cases 1:500), annotated with

TABLE 1: 'Can, or should, the channel be left entirely untouched?'

YES – consider these options:

Structural
71 flood banks
76 flood storage areas
83 flood bypass channels
89 multi-stage channels

Biological
214 tree planting to shade out aquatic plant growth

PARTIALLY – consider these options:

Structural
98 partial dredging
101 conserving riffles and pools
103 meander conservation

Biological
204 weed cutting and dredging

– and all reinstatement options for disturbed reaches (see following column)

NO – consider these reinstatement options:

Structural
111 reinstatement of pools and riffles
118 low stone weirs
126 current deflectors (groynes)
131 shallow water berms
137 shallow bays
142 whole channel realignment

Biological
219 establishing aquatic plants

Other Considerations:
209 use of aquatic herbicides
214 influence of grazing on aquatic vegetation
218 channel enlargement for weed control

TABLE 2: 'Can, or should, the banks be left entirely untouched?'

YES – consider these options:

Structural
71 flood banks
76 flood storage areas
83 flood bypass channels
202 off-site dumping of spoil

Biological
149 fencing
154 banktop alder planting

Consider use of barge-mounted excavators

PARTIALLY – consider these options:

Structural
89 multi-stage channels
98 partial dredging
103 meander conservation
146 working from one bank
152 vertical earth bank protection
154 islands
197 spoil spreading
201 spoil disposal in banks
202 spoil disposal and trees

Biological
230 timing of mowing of bank vegetation
231 patch cutting of bank vegetation
243 working through scrub
244 hedges
246 marking trees to be treated
246 working between or around trees
249 coppicing trees and scrub
252 pollarding trees
256 retaining trees within floodbanks
278 minimal tree and scrub removal for otters
279 marking and retaining holt-trees for otters
– and all reinstatement options for disturbed reaches (see following column)

NO – consider these reinstatement options:

Structural
131 shallow water berms
137 shallow bays
135 stumps and logs
158 faggoting
165 spiling
166 wire mesh and willow
169 hurdles
175 natural stone
180 gabions
184 fabric and mesh revetment materials
191 cellular concrete revetment materials
272 fish shelters
281 artificial otter holts
284 bat roosting boxes
285 nesting banks for kingfisher and sand martin
289 wooden nestboxes
291 built-in nestboxes

Biological
171 reed planting for bank protection
234 natural recolonisation
235 seed mixtures
238 transplanting turf
258 tree and scrub planting

Other Considerations:
229 grazing of bank vegetation
233 burning of bank vegetation
233 burning and herbicides

information on existing physical and vegetative features and potential opportunities for habitat re-creation (areas suitable for tree and scrub planting, for example) (figure below). The following guidelines may help with survey work:

– It is not essential to identify all the animals and plants present, rather it is necessary to observe and record the physical and vegetative structure and variety of wildlife habitats present.
– Physical features which diversify river structure should be noted – pools, riffles, eroding cliffs, shoals, cattle drinking areas, old masonry.
– The structure, type and variety of river and bank vegetation should be noted – beds of submerged and emergent plants; trees, shrubs and hedges; flower-rich banks; wet meadows.
– Notes on animal life should be made, including sightings of birds, mammals, butterflies and other insects, and animal signs – nest holes, footprints and droppings.
– Remember that time of year and weather will influence observations. This should be taken into account. June to September is probably the optimum time for river habitat assessment, although an experienced observer should be able to assess the key features of a site at almost any time.
Data collected in this manner are a *minimum* requirement. They should provide a framework, however, to which further data can be added from other sources. They should also provide an indication of whether a particular river is so rich for wildlife that a detailed ecological survey should be carried out.

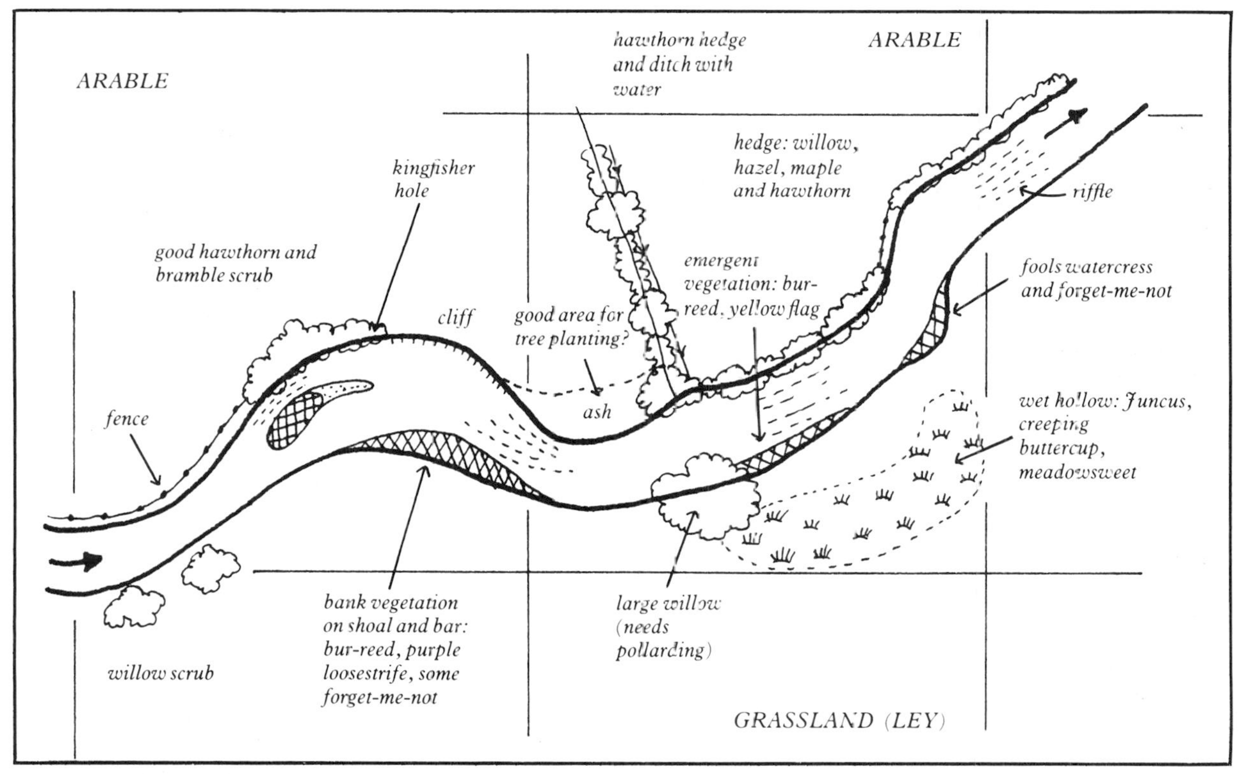

An example of habitat feature mapping using a large scale OS map.

TECHNICAL 1: CHANNEL FORM

The variety of substrate, water depth and water velocity in different parts of the channel cross-section provides the physical background for the plant and animal community of a river. For the reasons discussed in 'Introduction 3: River Ecology and Wildlife Conservation' it is essential that the structural diversity of the river channel be maintained when a scheme is being carried out. A structurally uniform reach is likely to support an impoverished, low density community of plants and animals.

As with any complex, established natural habitat, the retention of existing features is preferable to disturbance followed by reinstatement. Disruption to flora and fauna is less, since time is needed for natural processes to restore a community after engineering works – in the meantime productivity will fall and species be lost, possibly irreplaceably. Rivers, however, have one natural advantage over most other habitats, for their plant and animal communities are generally adapted to recover after catastrophic disturbances – especially from floods. The key to recovery, therefore, is to ensure that refuges are always located nearby, either within or adjacent to the reach being engineered, from which plants and animals can recolonise. This implies either leaving areas within the reach untouched, or scheduling works over short lengths of river. It follows that a degree of hydraulic inefficiency may result – an essential part of wildlife conservation – and allowance should be made for this in scheme design.

Channel design should aim to retain variation in depth, substrate and velocity: the key to providing this is in retaining variable bank slopes and a sinuous river planform. In this section, methods of retaining complete channel habitats are described between pages **71** and **89**; practices for partial channel habitat retention are illustrated between pages **89** and **111**.

If engineering operations disturb a river channel, a number of options are available to help reinstate the variety of physical habitats and so to aid the wildife community to recover. Whether capital or maintenance, all should be considered at the design stage, prior to the start of work.

Channel reinstatement has two interdependent aspects:

i *Structural* – the creation of varied water depths, bank slopes, substrate sizes and sediment deposition pattern; construction of a uniform trapezoidal channel should be the last resort. This is considered on pages **111** to **144** and in Technical **2** and **3**.

ii *Biological* – the introduction of a variety of plants to create shelter, cover and breeding sites for a range of animals. These are covered in the reinstatement sections for the individual wildlife groups: aquatic plants **219**, bankside plants **234**; trees and scrub **258**; fish **272**; otters **281**; bats **284**; and birds **285**.

Almost invariably, river channel operations will disturb bankside habitats as well. The interdependence of river bank and channel wildlife communities (such as the input of organic matter from bankside vegetation to the river channel) means that the aquatic wildlife communities will be reduced if bankside communities are impoverished. Channel reinstatement options, therefore, will usually have to be integrated with bankside habitat reinstatement options (see 'Technical 2: Bank Form').

FLOODBANKS

Embanking a river must provide one of the oldest and simplest methods of flood alleviation. The height of the floodbanks depends on the distance they are set from the banktop. In general, least damage to wildlife occurs if banks are set back from the river channel and they are constructed of spoil imported onto the site or won from borrow-pits, rather than material dredged from the river.

a High banks set close to the river – These require a relatively large quantity of material for construction and may require a longer length of bank to be built (figure over). Since importation of spoil is expensive, and borrow-pit excavation unacceptable to landowners, who have grown used to deriving benefit at minimal inconvenience and cost, material is frequently obtained through channel dredging.

The result is the construction of a deep, narrow flood channel, producing higher flood velocities; a great contrast to pre-scheme conditions and likely to be damaging to flora and fauna. The maintenance requirement of such channels is usually high: regular mowing (to maintain a tightly-knit sward for protection against scour; to provide for ease of bank inspection; and to prevent the growth of woody vegetation which may give burrowing animals cover) is usually required.

The river corridor is narrowed and intensive agriculture is more likely to be brought closer to the river – making contamination from herbicides and fertilisers of wildlife habitats within the river channel more likely.

b Low banks set at a distance from the river – A smaller mass of material is likely to be required for construction and a shorter length of bank may have to be built (figure over). Thus, obtaining spoil through means other than channel dredging is more likely.

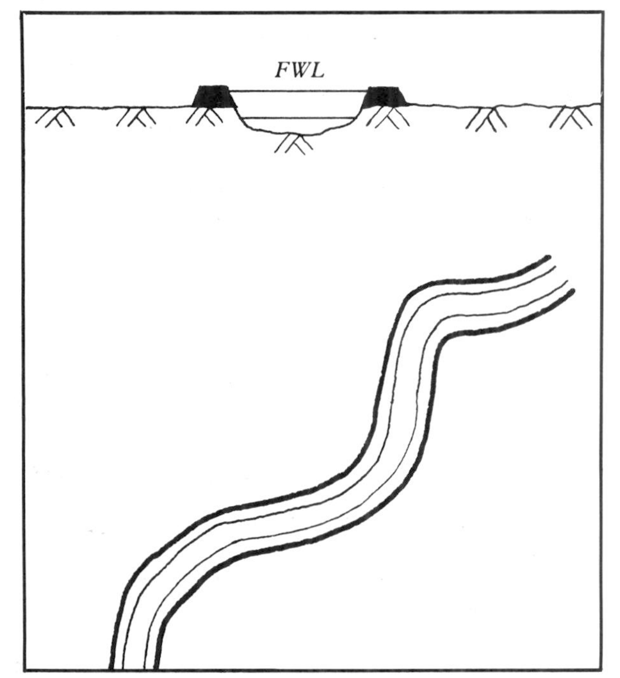

Diagrammatic cross-sectional and plan view of high floodbanks set close to the river.

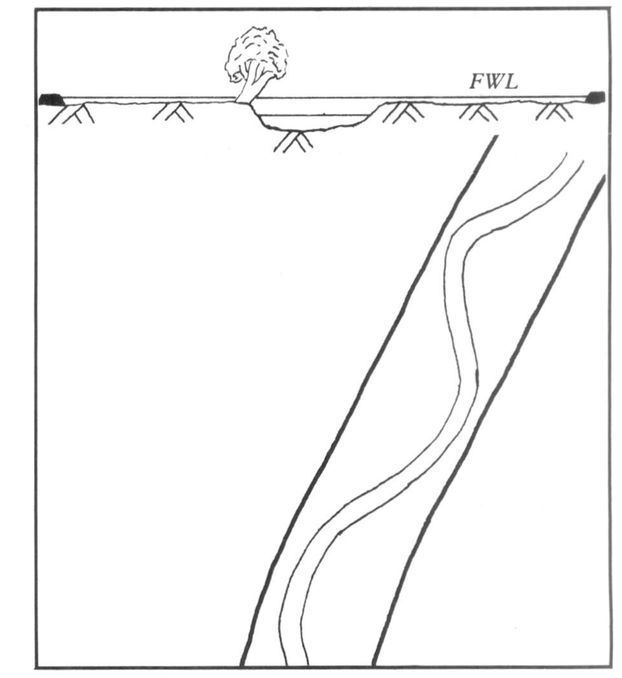

Diagrammatic cross-sectional and plan view of low floodbanks set back from the river.

A broad, shallow flood channel is created and flood velocities will be only slightly higher than before. Thus, the contrast with pre-scheme conditions is less than in (**a**) above and less detrimental to the existing plant and animal communities.
The broad river corridor retains a buffer zone for the river and helps to reduce external influences, although pastoral agriculture will usually be possible (and indeed desirable) within the floodbanks.
The drainage authority may benefit from this option, for long-term maintenance costs are likely to be lower. However, landowners may object to losing drainage benefits on land within the floodbanks despite gains in wildlife, game and angling. Although much can be achieved through negotiation, the cost of extra compensation for setting floodbanks back may have to be budgeted into initial scheme design.
Obviously, there are gradations between these two extremes. A point to be borne in mind is that however floodbanks are constructed, inundation of the floodplain outside them will be reduced and this may result in wetland areas drying out unacceptably.

RIVER ASKER, BRIDPORT, DORSET
OS Map: 193. NGR: SY 479938
Avon and Dorset Division,
Wessex Water Authority,
2 Nuffield Road, Poole, Dorset.
Telephone: Poole (0202) 671144.

Site Summary
Flood alleviation scheme, capital works, 1981.
Lowland, urban fringe location.
Channel: 5-8 metres wide, 1-2 metres deep.
Banks: 1-2.5 metres high.
Substrate: sand, silt, clay.
Engineer: C Bray, Assistant Senior Engineer.

Work Description
As part of the Bradpole flood alleviation scheme (detailed description on page **90**) a floodbank was constructed up to 75 metres from the river bank, to contain one in 100 year floods. High ground close to the opposite side of the river made a further bank unnecessary (figure opposite).
Spoil for the floodbank was brought from the excavation of flood berms in another part of the same scheme. Detailed soil testing was carried out as part of the pre-scheme studies to confirm that the material was suitable.
The floodbank was set back from the channel, not only to increase flood storage, but also to train flood

waters spilling from the multi-stage section upstream, and to develop a smooth approach to the downstream bridge and gauging station (photograph below).
See page **91** for a sketch map of scheme layout. The fields between the river and the floodbank are pasture, and remain so, since there was no disturbance during construction.

The second stage of the scheme (not shown on the map on **91**) also involved building a floodbank to contain high flows. In the narrower valley, with houses, gardens and orchards close to the river, the bank was built close to the river's edge. Care was taken to avoid wild and cultivated trees. Again, material for the bank was taken from the berm excavation and not won from the river.

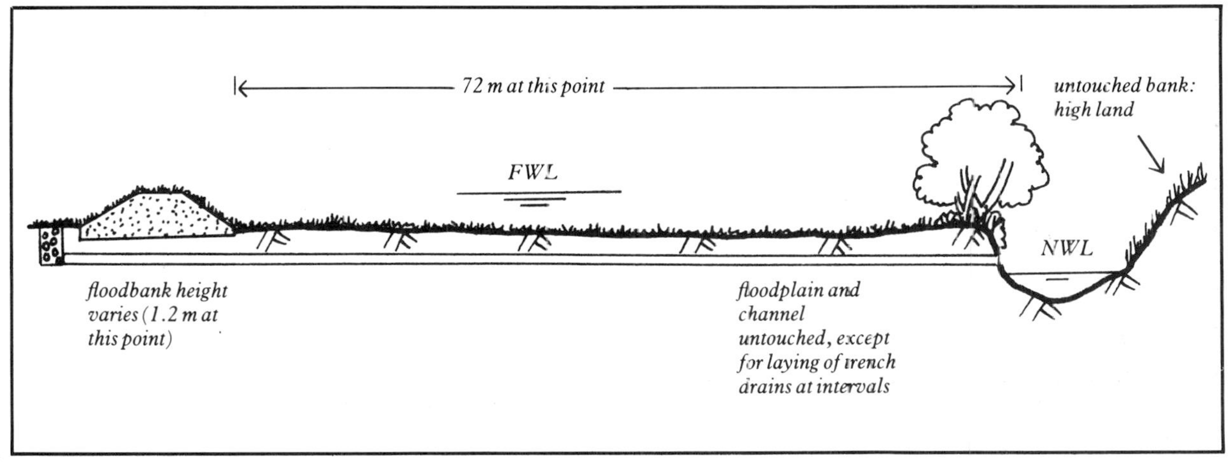

River Asker.

River Asker: Looking upstream from the new bridge with the recently constructed floodbank set back on the left.

Habitat Comments

1 At this point, the entire river corridor, including the channel, has been retained untouched.

2 The unharmed channel and banks provide a refuge from which animals and plant populations can spread out to recolonise adjacent disturbed areas.

3 The field beside the river is likely to remain as grassland, as it is still prone to flooding. Although it does not support any particularly rare form of wildlife, its retention in its present state will still benefit wildlife – by continuing as a habitat for grassland invertebrates and their predators, small mammals, seed-eating birds and, possibly, a breeding site for yellow wagtails.

RIVER WRIGGLE, YETMINSTER, DORSET
OS Map: 194, NGR: ST 597108
Somerset Division, Wessex Water Authority, Box 9, Kings Square, Bridgwater, Somerset. Telephone: Bridgwater (0278) 57333.

Site Summary
Flood alleviation scheme, maintenance works. Urban location.
Channel: 2-4 metres wide, 0.5-1.5 metres deep.
Banks: 1-2.5 metres high.
Substrate: clay, silt, gravel.

Work Description
The valley, constricted by a railway embankment and a road bridge, was liable to flooding more or less annually. Gardens, farmyards and a small industrial area were badly affected. The stream, however, with its cover of alders and scrubby bramble-thicket, was valued by the village residents, who may have resented drastic change to the landscape if the channel was enlarged.
A flood alleviation scheme was designed to cause as little disturbance as possible to the river's character within the narrow confines of the valley and village buildings.
Riverside trees were trimmed of overhanging branches, and some were coppiced. The majority of trees were alders, which have deep fibrous roots, binding the riverbank securely. If necessary, their growth can be checked by coppicing, but the mature trees, with few narrow stems and lowest branches at 1.5 to 2.5 metres above ground level, should withstand flood flows well for many years (photograph below).
Spoil was obtained free from local builders who wished to dispose of it. The floodbanks could not be set further back from the channel in this case because of the confines of village properties.

River Wriggle: The newly constructed floodbank curving away to the right, with the untouched channel and bankside trees on the left.

Habitat Comments
1 Channel habitats are undamaged, since no dredging was done (except for some shoal removal). There are likely to be changes, however, as high flows are now confined within a narrower flood channel. Increased scour *may* impoverish invertebrate and fish diversity.
2 The care taken over tree management within the floodbanks was admirable; a dense, heavily shading tree cover has been left, with some overhanging branches. The amount of material removed is probably insignificant to wildlife habitat on this densely tree-covered stretch. The structural complexity of the habitat, cover for birds and mammals, and food sources for all animal groups, remains much as it was before work started.
3 In this steep-sided valley, the river floodplain is very narrow. Building floodbanks so close to the river channel has not prevented adjacent wetland areas from flooding, and there is no significent habitat loss from this quarter.

UPPER LUGG, LEOMINSTER, HEREFORDSHIRE
OS Map: 149. NGR: SO 450620 to 480607.
Wye Division, Welsh Water Authority,
St Nicholas House, St Nicholas Street, Hereford.
Telephone: Hereford (0432) 57411.

Site Summary
Flood alleviation scheme, capital works, 1980-1.
Upland/lowland transition zone. Rural location.
Channel: 10-12 metres wide, 1-2 metres deep.
Banks: variable, up to 3 metres high.
Substrate: alluvial and glacial sands, clay and gravel.

Engineer: R Vivash.

Work Description
In this section, the Lugg is a fast-flowing, flashy river. Its gradient is falling, its course meandering, and it carries large quantities of coarse sediment. Floodbanks set well back from the river are a key feature of a major flood alleviation scheme carried out in 1980 and 1981 (figure and photograph below).
Spoil for the floodbanks was won from regrading the inner edge of meander bends (see **96** – multi-stage channels), so that part of the banks was excavated.

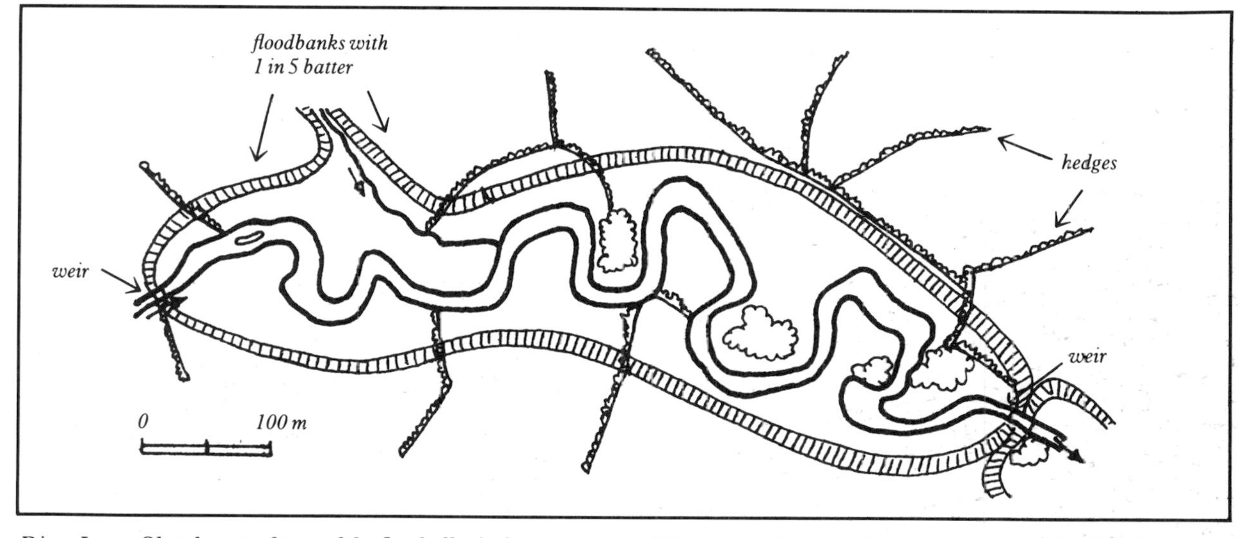

River Lugg: Sketch map of part of the flood alleviation scheme, showing floodbanks set back from the river keyed to the channel at weirs.

River Lugg: Low floodbank, grassed over, set 50 m back from the river channel (arrowed). The channel vegetation, including an ancient pollard oak, willow and ash scrub, and emergent aquatic vegetation has been retained intact.

The banks were graded to 1 in 5, with a crest width of 1 metre. The shallow slopes are more stable under cattle and sheep trampling than slopes of 1 in 1.5 or 1 in 2 (figure below), and the grass cover should resist erosion during flooding more easily. This is especially important in this case, where river gravels form the core of the banks.

The shallow gradient also allows farm machinery to cross the floodbanks at any point. Several lengths of bank were cut for hay in 1982, for example, two years after first seeding.

Habitat Comments

1 Setting back the floodbanks was part of the overall scheme design. It meant that less spoil was required and, since it was obtained by excavating the inner banks of meanders, the major part of the channel remained undisturbed.

2 The low gradient of the banks allows grazing or hay and silage cutting to maintain the necessary short grass cover. Hedges were re-established on field boundaries. This is preferable, for wildlife, to a uniformly gang-mown ryegrass sward.

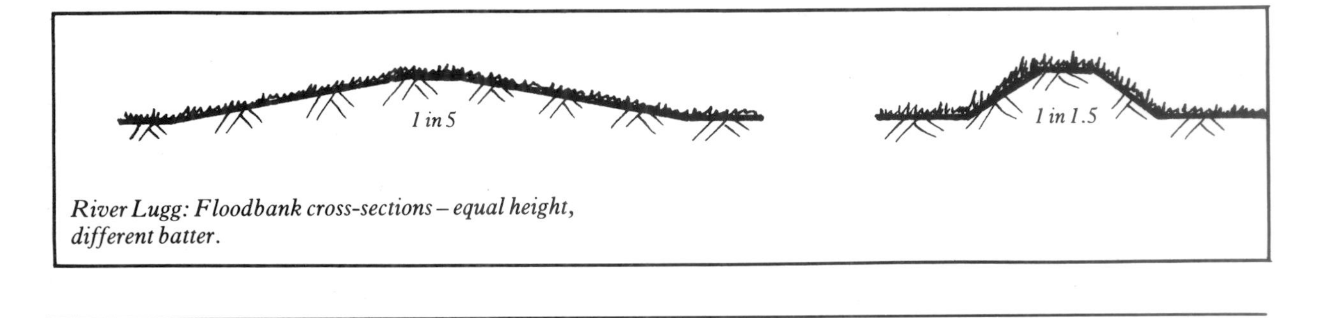

River Lugg: Floodbank cross-sections – equal height, different batter.

FLOOD STORAGE AREAS

Flood storage on – and off – river is becoming an increasingly popular technique for flood alleviation: 'It is the option everybody likes', one engineer optimistically commented. The range, in design and scale, of flood storage schemes is enormous, and only a few are described here.

Flood storage is generally viewed favourably by conservationists because the channel downstream need not be enlarged or maintained to as high a standard: thus disturbance of the plant and animal community is kept to a minimum. If wetland habitats or rough grasslands within the washland area are protected from drainage and agricultural improvement as well, then so much the better. Breeding and wintering areas for wildfowl and waders, wetland plant communities and rich insect populations might thus be protected – or created. Some of the more ambitious flood storage schemes have been used to create new lakes and wetlands, then used as country parks, aquasport centres and/or nature reserves. The Sandwell Valley scheme in Birmingham and the schemes around Milton Keynes in Buckinghamshire are prime examples of this sort of approach. *The creation of new, man-made lakes and wetlands, however, does not substitute for the loss of natural, established wetland habitats elsewhere.*

Flood retention reservoirs do not leave downstream river conditions entirely unchanged. The peak of the flood hydrograph will be reduced so that riverside wetlands are flooded less often. Because the same volume of water is discharged over a longer period, within the channel higher flows are produced for a longer period, often increasing annual erosion rates and sediment mobility. The physical environment will certainly be changed to some degree, and the wildlife communities of the river affected correspondingly. Positive changes might be new river cliffs, suitable for kingfishers and sand martins, and more extreme riffle and pool development; negative changes might be reduced shelter for fish from high water velocities (unless special provisions are made), and bank instability resulting in less tolerant management of bankside trees by landowners and drainage authorities. Changes in water temperature and chemistry may occur in schemes with large, long-term retention reservoirs, affecting fundamentally the stream invertebrate community and river productivity.

Whether a net benefit for wildlife will result from the construction of flood storage reservoirs will often depend on the location in which it is sited, the frequency of flooding, the height of normal water level within the washland area and the height of flood water level.

From the engineering viewpoint, the main difficulty can be the cost of purchasing the land required for the flood storage area. If the frequency, depth and duration of flooding is to change little, however, flood storage areas may be established through negotiation.

RIVER AIRE, SKIPTON BYPASS COMPENSATORY WASHLAND SCHEME, YORKSHIRE
OS Map: 103. NGR: SD 9552
Western District, Southern Area,
Rivers Division, Yorkshire Water Authority,
21 Park Square South, Leeds LS1 2QG.
Telephone: Leeds (0532) 440191

Site Summary
Flood alleviation scheme, capital works, 1975-83.
Rural location; upland/lowland transition zone
Channel: 10-15 metres wide.
Substrate: gravel, sands and silt.
Designer: YWA, Rivers Division.

Work Description
A road bypass scheme for Skipton resulted in a loss of washland storage: replacement flood storage had to be provided to compensate for the loss, and was funded by the Department of Transport.
In this section, the Aire is a gravelly river, 10-15 metres wide, straightened over a half mile when the railway was built in the 19th century. The embankment is now tree and scrub-covered. In contrast, the naturally meandering sections have treeless banks, some of which have been dry-stone pitched. Adjacent land use is permanent pasture.
The river was left entirely untouched, and is excluded from the washland by an embankment parallel with the river. The inlet spillway is designed to operate on average once every two years, and discharge to an excavated drainage channel which directs water to a manually operated concrete outfall structure. (Figures right and below; photograph over.)
Material for the floodbank was *imported* to the site, being overburden and waste (interbedded clay strata) from a local limestone quarry. Topsoil excavated from the washland drainage channel was used to cover the clay banks before seeding with a MAFF approved grazing seed mixture.
High discharges are held in the washland, spreading out over the old floodplain, which includes several poor marsh areas in old meander loops.

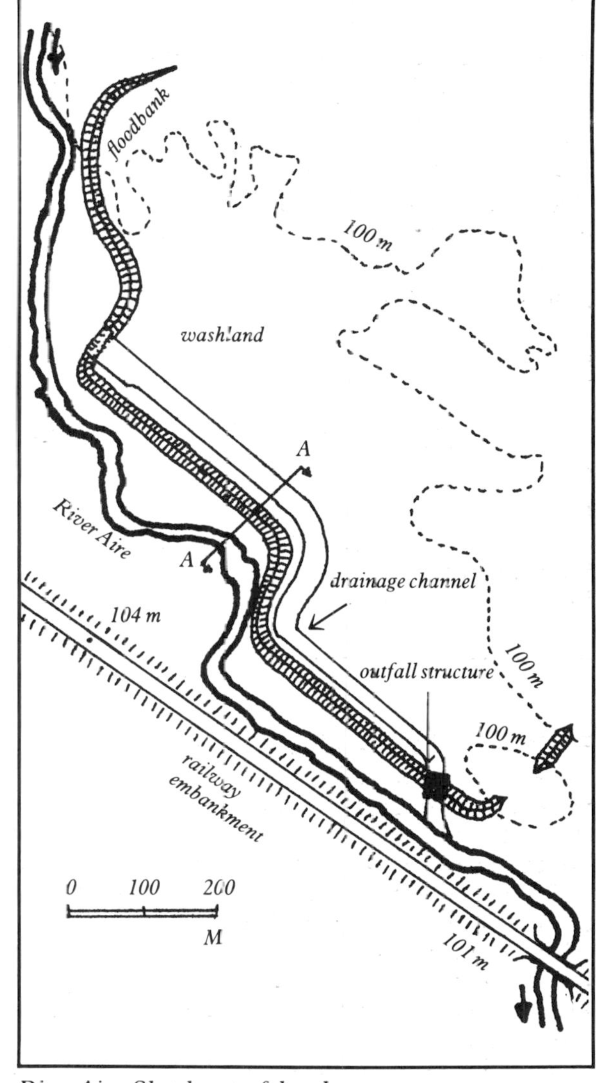

River Aire: Sketch map of the scheme.

River Aire: Typical cross-section (between A-A on Figure above).

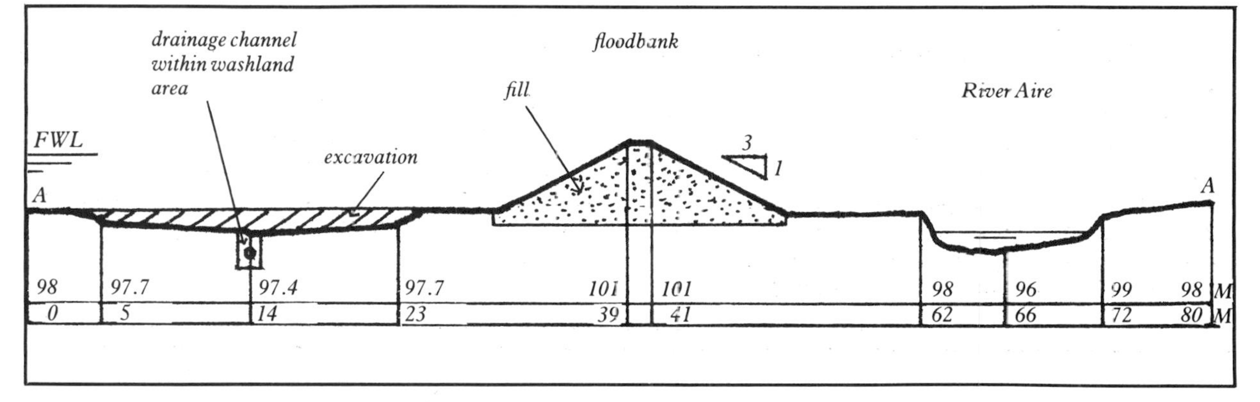

River Aire: High floodbanks, built of imported spoil, with the untouched channel of the River Aire on the left.

Habitat Comments

1 The channel and immediate banks were untouched by the scheme, leaving undisturbed habitats for waders and sand martins, aquatic organisms and the existing plant communities of the banks and temporary shoals.

2 Although a part of the washland area was excavated and underdrained in the scheme, the major part remains as low grade, intermittently flooded pasture, forming good breeding and feeding sites for waders such as curlews, snipe and lapwings.

3 The banks upstream of the railway embankment are bare of trees, dominated by rank grass and nettles. Patches of alder, willows and ash planted between the banktop and the floodbank would enrich the habitat, and could protect the bank should the river be shifting its course.

TUBBS BOTTOM WASHLAND, IRON ACTON, NEAR BRISTOL

OS Map: 172. NGR: ST 669828

Bristol Avon Division, Wessex Water Authority, PO Box 95, The Ambury, Bath BA1 2YP. Telephone: Bath (0225) 313500.

Site Summary

Flood alleviation scheme, capital works, 1981-82.
Rural location; lowland.
Engineer: A Hillyer.

Work Description

Urban development north of Bristol in the Bristol Frome catchment resulted in increased run-off and flood peaks in excess of the capacity of the culverts through which the River Frome flows in the older developed areas of the city. A study by Wessex Water Authority concluded that a large washland for storm water storage would be the most economic solution, compared to major channel and culvert works or diversion of flow by tunnel to another catchment or lower down the present one. (Figure right.)

Tubbs Bottom: Diagram of the scheme.

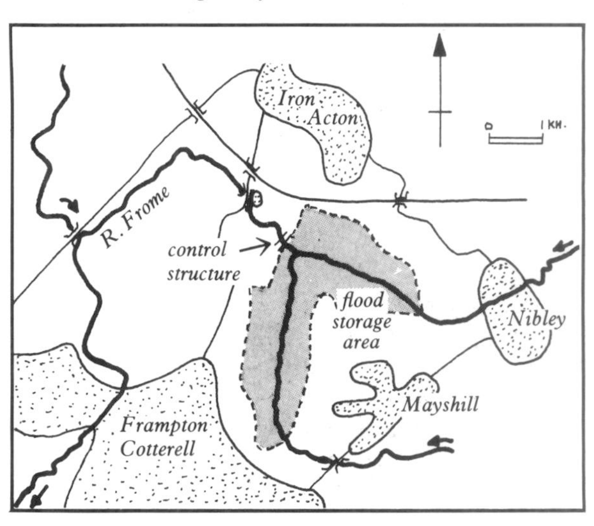

A small dam with two throttle culverts was built across the channel where it could be keyed into a rock outcrop on one side and high ground on the other. When river flows approach bank full condition (around 8 cumecs) the culverts serve to prevent higher flows from passing downstream by retaining excess flood water in the washland (photograph below).

Despite a long history of coal extraction and flooding, the land within the washland was successfully farmed. Farming will continue with the frequency of flooding essentially unchanged – although the depth and period of inundation will increase. The washland will be used approximately once every three years with 73 hectares (180 acres) of farmland being inundated to a maximum depth of three metres in the severest storm event.

Habitat Comments

1 The River Frome downstream of the impounding structure will not now need to be widened or deepened. Although trees have been removed and the channel has been dredged in the past, the river now has the opportunity to return to a more natural condition.

Tubbs Bottom: The flood-control barrier, keyed to a wooded outcrop on the far side. One of the half-round gates can be seen near the crest, prior to installation.

RIVER PAR FLOOD ALLEVIATION SCHEME, CORNWALL
OS Map: 200. NGR: SX 075543
Environmental Services (West Area),
South West Water Authority,
Victoria Square, Bodmin, Cornwall.
Telephone: Bodmin (0208) 3131.

Site Summary
Flood alleviation scheme, capital works, 1979.
Rural location.
Engineer: J Woods.

Work Description

Industrial and urban development, early piecemeal drainage projects and sedimentation (material produced from mining areas in the hinterland) have created high flood risks at Par. Most of this urban area is also tide-locked. Although the catchment area of the Par river is relatively small, the flood response is not flashy, due to storage in old mine workings and clay pits: rather the water builds up over a period of days and stays high for a similar time. The smaller watercourses respond much more quickly.

To provide Par with 1 in 50 flood protection, a major flood alleviation scheme was carried out and completed in 1979. A variety of options were used: the deepening and widening of existing channels; the construction of a new 3 kilometre flood relief channel; the installation of tidal flaps on a major tributary; and the construction of a new pumping station to take water from a small tributary into the embanked River Par. A major element of the design was the designation of flood storage areas, in two blocks, plus a secondary flood storage area at the confluence of the Par and Treesmill valleys (figure below).

The flood storage areas in the Par valley are poorly drained pasture. The areas in the Treesmill valley are wet willow woodland and permanently wet marshland. A low earth barrier closes off the storage area on Treesmill stream, with a hand operated sluice controlling flow. The embankment is grassed, and cattle-grazed with the rest of the adjacent, downstream pasture. Upstream the woodland – almost permanently wet, rich in mosses, lichens, ferns with gnarled and twisted trees – is virtually inaccessible to man for most of

River Par: Map of the scheme.

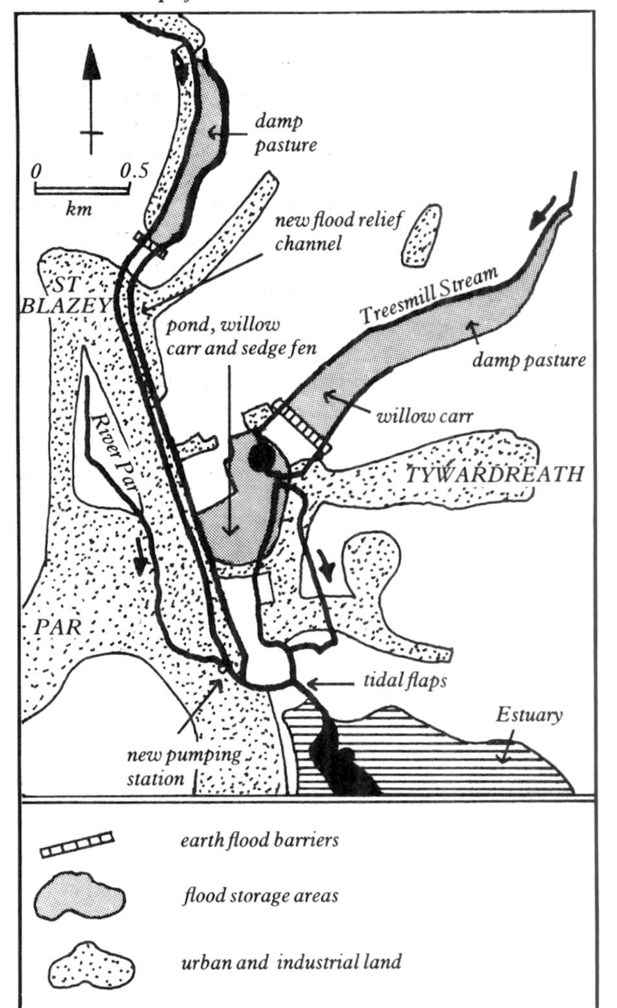

River Par: Willow carr and sedge fen in the secondary flood storage area at the confluence of the Par and Treesmill.

the year. It forms a rich, secluded habitat for birds, mammals and invertebrates. Part of the area is open sedge/reed swamp with occasional pools of water. It is a type of wetland not uncommon in Devon and Cornwall, but nationally rare.
Old field boundaries persist under the woodland cover; it was grazed within living memory, but abandoned early this century, probably as a result of failing underdrainage systems.
The secondary storage area in the confluence of the valleys also conserves wet willow and sedge fen. It has been partly developed as an amenity area. A pond has been excavated and planted up attractively with trees and aquatic plants. The spoil has been used to make causeway-footpaths around the pond and through the marshland. By designating the area for flood storage, a recreation area has been developed for local people, and part of a valuable wildlife habitat has been protected from destruction by the disposal of domestic refuse – its previous designated use (photograph on previous page).

Habitat Comments
1 Without designation as flood storage areas, the marshlands would probably be improved on a piecemeal basis and lost as wildlife habitat. The simple construction of barriers and sluices, without any excavation – except in the small amenity area – ensures that the special willow community is conserved, for the benefit of wildlife and local people – an elegant example of 'integration'.
2 Floodwater will remain standing in the willow fen for longer than previously, which may lead to some changes in the ground flora.
3 The conservation of valley wetlands is the important feature here, not the river channel.

SANDWELL VALLEY BALANCING LAKE, BIRMINGHAM
OS Map: 139. NGR: SP 0392.
Tame Division, Severn Trent Water Authority,
Tame House, 156/170 Newhall Street,
Birmingham B3 1SE.
Telephone: 021-233 1616.

Site Summary
Flood alleviation, capital works, 1982.
Lowland, urban-fringe location.
Design: Divisional Engineers' Department, Tame Division.

Work Description
A 12-hectare lake was excavated to take peak one in 50 year flood flows from the River Tame. The scheme has involved major channel works – and is *not* an example of undisturbed river environment. It does illustrate, however, an imaginative design which includes conservation of a wetland area as washland. In addition, the ends of the lake have been designed with a minimum depth of 0.5 metres, plus irregular islands, to encourage ornamental waterfowl in one area and wild birds in another to breed and overwinter.
An initial design would have required excavation of the existing wetland as part of the lake – thus destroying a valuable wild area within the City of Birmingham. The final design, with environmental factors taken into account, makes use of the wetland in its existing state as a temporary washland, and incidentally preserves more existing hedgerows (figure and photograph overleaf).

Habitat Comments
1 Unlike other schemes described here, the flood storage area has been excavated to form a permanent lake, with sufficient spare capacity to store temporary flood waters. The only 'habitat' conserved has been the wetland as a part of the flood storage capacity (compare to **79**, the Par Valley), and preservation of hedgerows in the spoil area.
2 In the narrow confines of the Sandwell Valley within Birmingham, the conservation and careful management of a natural wetland is admirable – even as part of a much larger scheme which has caused major environmental disturbance.
3 With careful reinstatement and long-term management the balancing lake should be a richer and more attractive habitat than the pre-scheme riverside conditions.

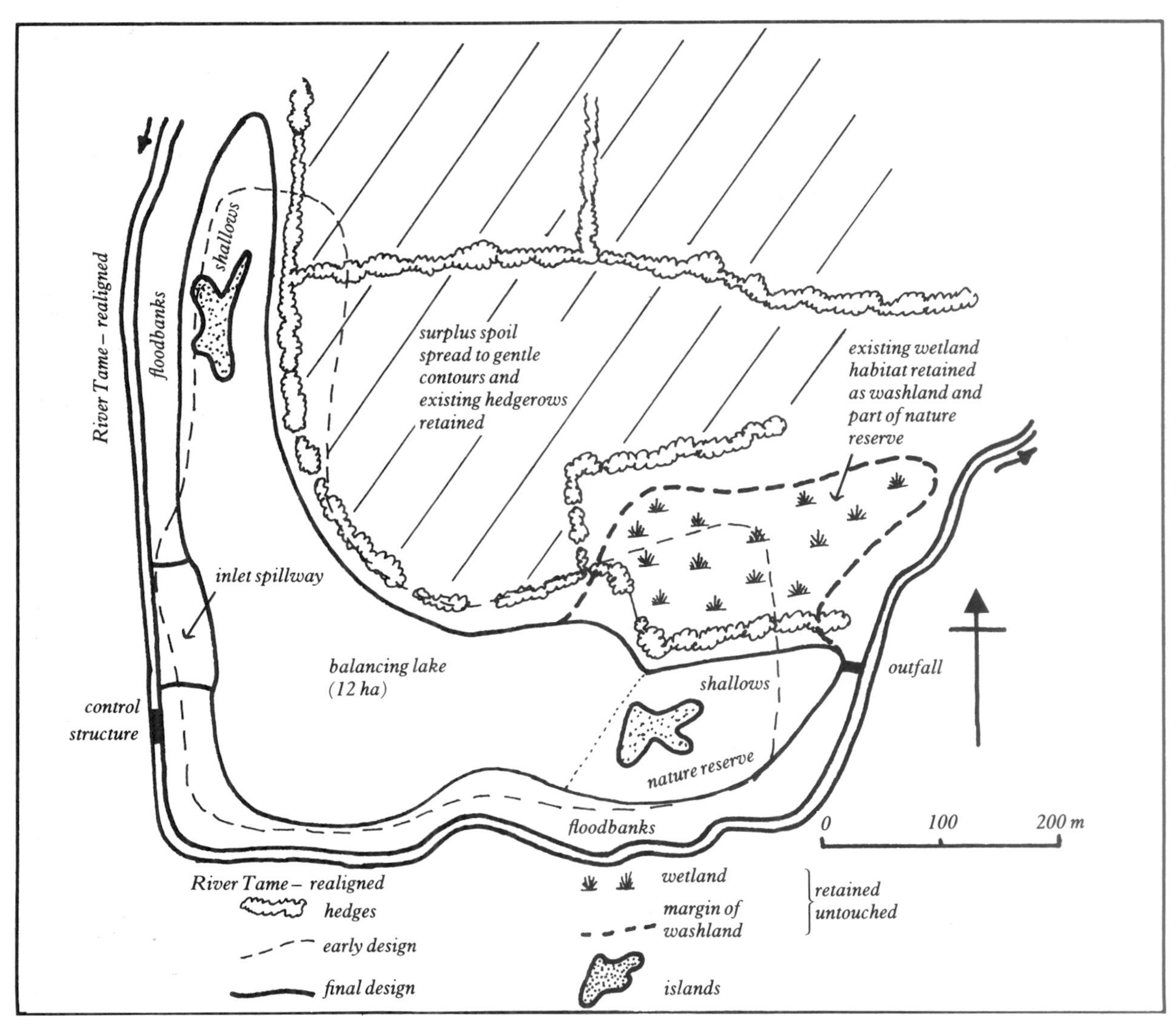

Sandwell Valley: Map of the balancing lake.

Sandwell Valley: View north-east across the eastern shallow arm of the balancing lake (not yet flooded to full depth) with the wetland in the distance. Both the shallow area and the marsh are to be established as a nature reserve.

FLOOD BY-PASS CHANNELS

The key factor in this technique – for habitat conservation as well as hydrologically – is that the original channel is retained untouched and continues to take normal flows and small flood discharges. The by-pass channel creams off the highest peak discharges and re-routes them. By-pass channels can be designed either to be dry for most of the year, or to carry only a small proportion of the main channel flow, until flood events occur.

By re-routing high discharges away from the main river, it can remain undisturbed, or be maintained at a very much lower standard, without risk of flooding. Either practice will benefit wildlife, by allowing habitats to remain undisturbed for long periods. In game fishing rivers, therefore, this can be an acceptable flood alleviation technique.

A newly cut channel provides an opportunity to develop new wildlife habitats.

Wet by-pass channels – In designing the channel, reinstatement practices should be considered, and weed problems anticipated. If traditional trapezoidal channel form is chosen, because of shallow low flow conditions, there are likely to be problems with excessive plant growth. Making use of existing hedges and tree lines, dense tree planting on the southern bank should shade the new channel and reduce weed growth. Future maintenance work should be programmed to work from one bank only (figure below).

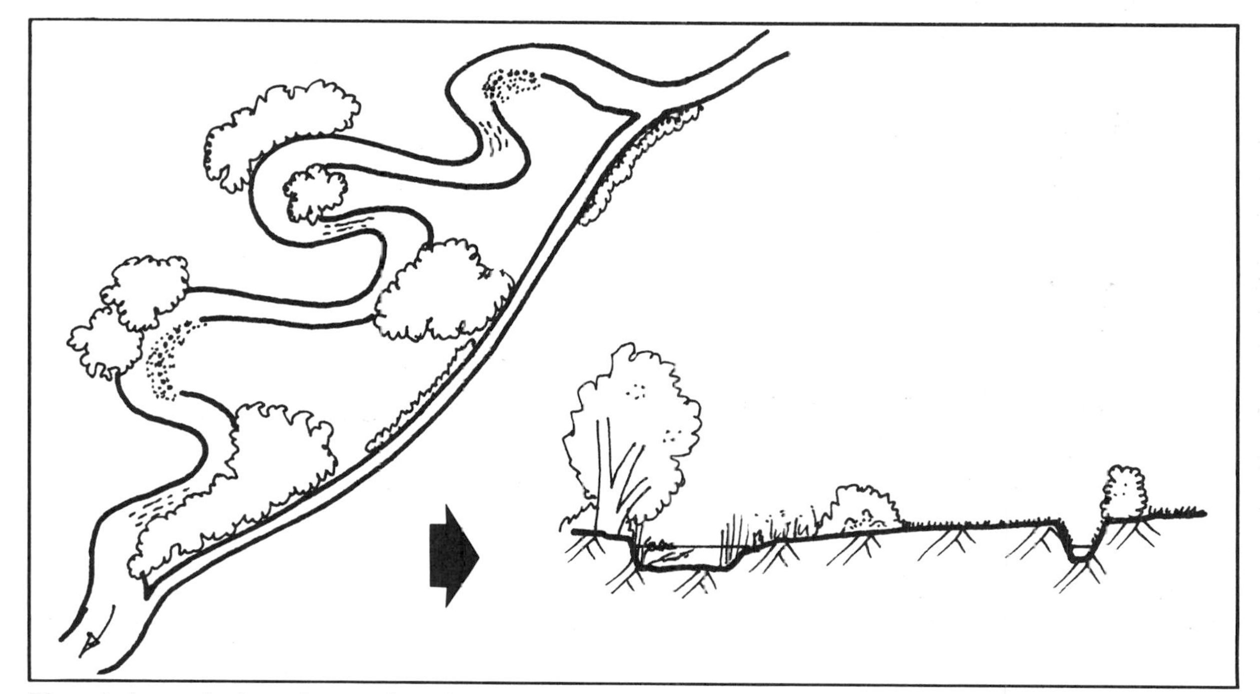

Theoretical example of a wet by-pass channel.

Dry by-pass channels – Dry flood by-pass channels may be grazed, or plant cover kept short and non-woody by mowing annually. Otherwise the conditions are likely to be ideal for the development of reedbed or willow and alder fen which, although

Theoretical example of a dry by-pass channel.

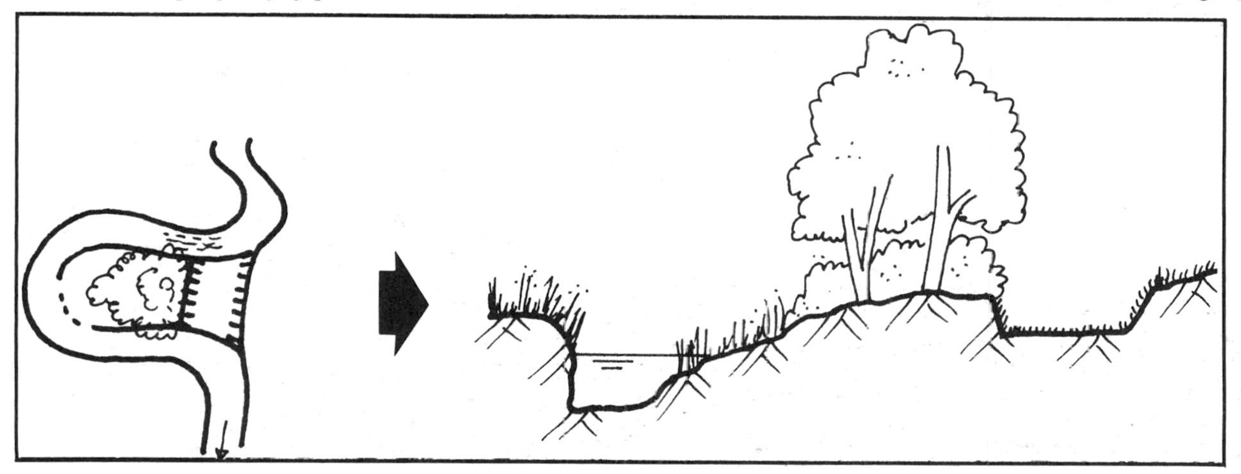

good for wildlife, would prevent the channel from serving its hydrological purpose.
The height of the threshold – that is, the flood stage at which water enters the channel – is critical. Unless it is carefully designed, scour or silt deposition will occur, depending on main river conditions and river plant form at the threshold (figure on page 83).

RIVER THRUSHEL, LIFTON, DEVON
OS Map: 201. NGR: SX 393853
Environmental Services (West Area), South West Water Authority, Victoria Square, Bodmin, Cornwall.
Telephone: Bodmin (0208) 3131.

Site Summary
Flood alleviation scheme, capital works, 1970.
Village/rural location.
Channel: 3-5 metres wide at NWL.
Banks: 1.5-3 metres above bed level.
Substrate: silt, gravel, bedrock.
Engineers: F L Oates and J Woods.

Work Description
A short flood by-pass was cut across the neck of a meander as part of a flood alleviation scheme for the village of Tinhay, carried out by the late Cornwall River Authority in 1971. New floodbanks and floodwalls were constructed and part of the channel edge excavated to train water flow on the approach to the by-pass channel and bridge (figures below and opposite).

River Thrushel: Plan diagram of the Tinhay flood alleviation scheme.

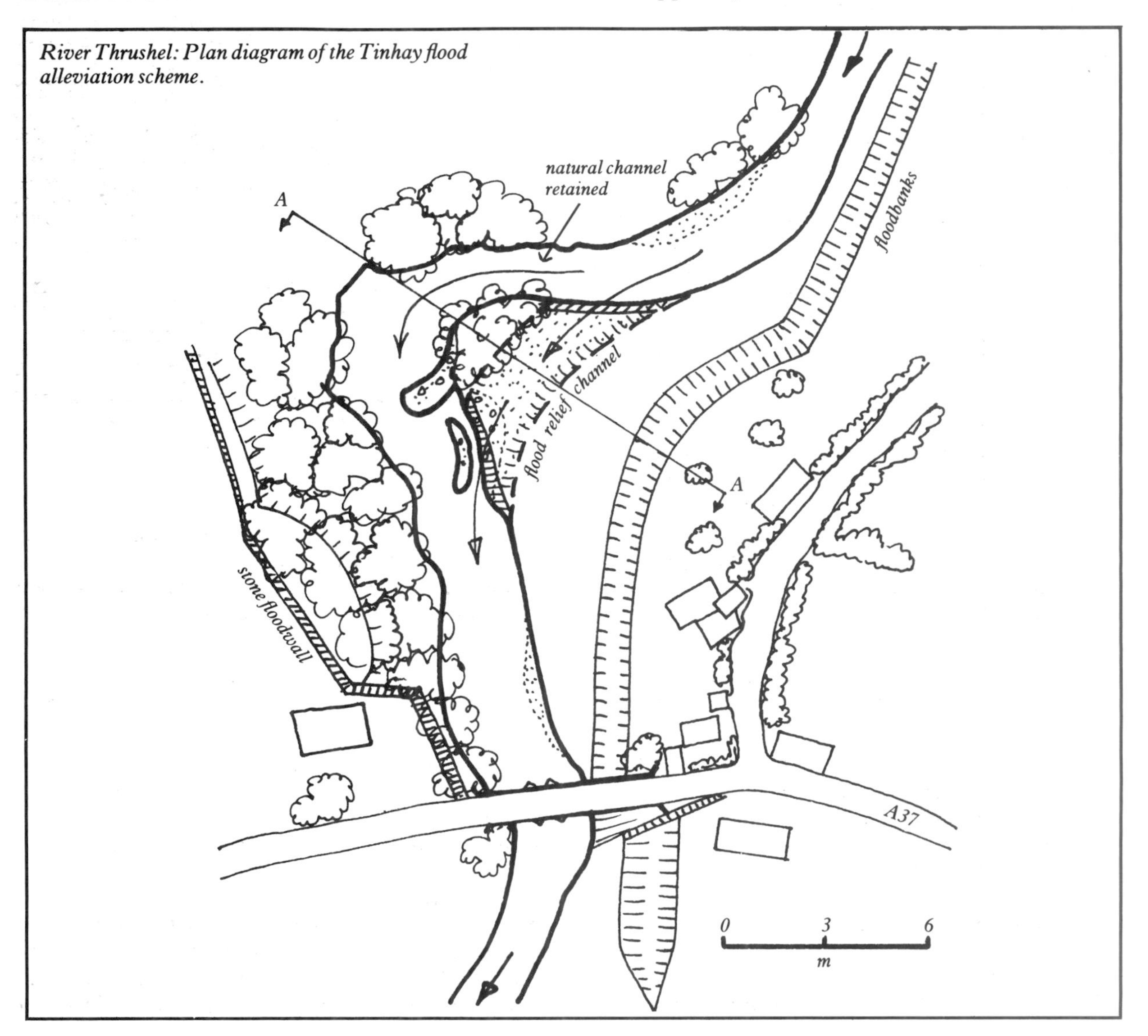

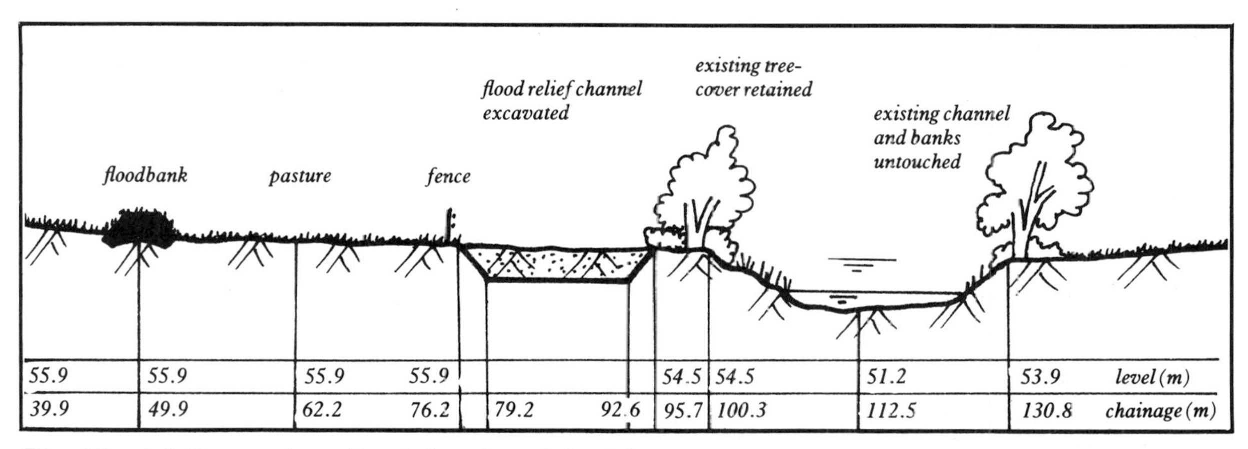

River Thrushel: Cross-section at line A-A on figure below left.

The by-pass channel was excavated to about 1 metre above the main channel bed. Both the threshold and the exit sills were stone pitched. The channel was seeded with an agricultural grass mix and it now has a well-established and stable plant cover of mixed wetland herbs and grasses. It was fenced off from the adjacent pasture, so that stock are excluded and the banks are not damaged by trampling. As a result, alders have colonised and they must be kept in check by slashing during annual or biannual maintenance.

After 12 years the by-pass channel is functioning as designed, without excessive siltation or scour. The main channel has recovered well, with good tree cover and small lateral beds of emergent plants where silt has accumulated. The trees between the bend of the meander and the by-pass channel form a refuge for wildlife in a small patch of mature vegetation. The by-pass channel has formed a new type of damp grassland habitat (photograph right).

River Thrushel: View across the flood by-pass channel, with the main river channel in the background.

Habitat Comments

1 Retaining all-year flow in existing channel is excellent – the aquatic habitat remains virtually unchanged for invertebrates and fish.

2 Retaining existing bank vegetation is excellent. Careful tree management during work ensured complete recovery. The small patch of trees now isolated by the by-pass channel provides an undisturbed 'island' refuge for wildlife – especially good as cover for birds and mammals.

3 The 'damp' by-pass channel provides a new habitat for wetland plants and animals.

RIVER FROME, PALLINGTON TO NINE HATCHES, DORSET

OS Map: 194. NGR: SY 770910

Avon and District Division,
Wessex Water Authority,
2 Nuffield Road, Poole, Dorset.
Telephone: Poole (0202) 671144.

Site Summary

Flood alleviation/land drainage improvement scheme, capital works 1977-79.
Rural location, chalk stream and former water meadows.
Land use: pasture, game fishing and shooting.

Work Description

The Frome valley suffered from both summer and winter flooding and the landowners and occupiers requested a land drainage improvement scheme. The game fishing, landscape and wildlife of natural

wetlands along the river, however, were also recognised as being of great value. A scheme was designed so as to achieve 'maximum drainage benefit without adversely affecting either the fishing or the ecology of the area'.

A biological appraisal for the scheme was carried out by the Regional Biology Unit of WWA who surveyed areas of conservation interest within the benefit area, and examined the general ecological effects of the proposal in respect to salmon and trout, otter, reed warbler, sedge warbler, Bewick's swan, sand martin, kingfisher and botanical interest. They concluded that, given attention to detail to retain trees, shrubs and hedges, and close liaison at field level between WWA biological and land drainage staffs, engineering operations should not damage existing habitats.

The scheme was carried out between 1977 and 1979. A former water meadow channel running approximately parallel to the main river was enlarged, so as to accommodate a one in five year flood and provide a freeboard of 1.10 metres for the two in one year floods. Manual control structures on the Frome allow one in ten year summer flows to be carried by maximising flows in the Frome itself, which acts as a carrier.

The by-pass channel takes 30 per cent of flows from the main river which, with other channel inputs, means that flows are about equal in the two channels during flood periods. During low periods the Frome carries the major flows.

An elegant part of the design is at the confluence of by-pass channels and the Frome. As the Frome is an important salmon and trout fishery there was concern that during high flows the greater volume of water at a higher velocity issuing from the by-pass channel would influence breeding fish to migrate into that rather than the Frome, their traditional spawning grounds. The by-pass channel therefore *divides downstream*, 50 per cent of its flow going direct to the Frome, the remainder joining with a smaller channel and thence the main river.

The main river was improved over part of its length, but pools, fish-lies and spawning beds were carefully reinstated as work proceeded (figure below).

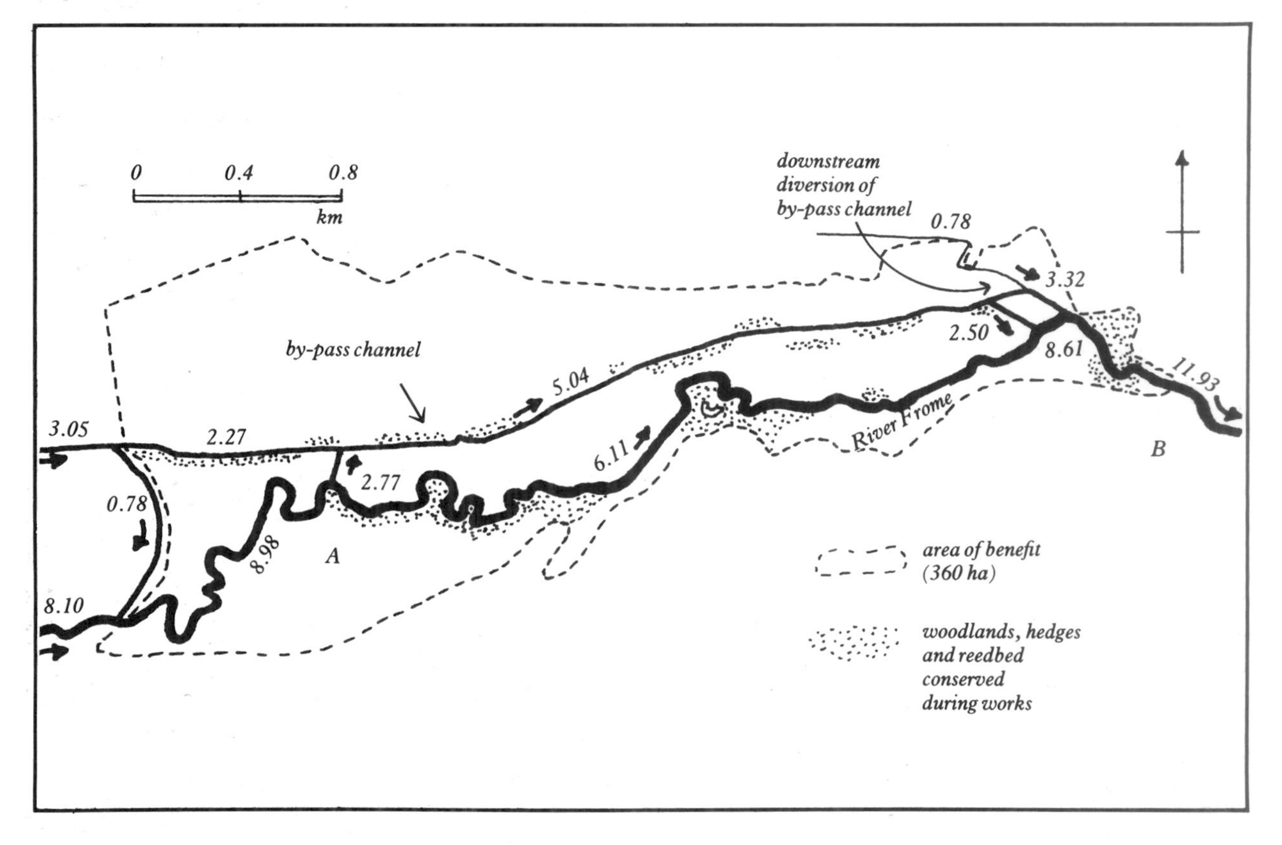

River Frome: Plan diagram of the Pallington to Nine Hatches flood alleviation scheme. The main river was widened and deepened from A-B, with careful reinstatement of pools, fish lies and spawning beds. The figures give the flow in cumecs during 2 in 1 year flows.

Habitat Comments

1 Although the main river was disturbed during this work, future maintenance standards can be lower than they would have been if it was carrying the entire flood discharge. Marginal emergent vegetation and wet woodland have been retained.

2 The new flood by-pass channel has replaced a shallow, plant-choked drain with a wider, deeper,

clean channel: the result has been a loss of habitat for wetland plants, invertebrates and young fish. Water levels in adjacent, untouched drains are now more stable, however, which compensates to some extent for the loss. Fish pools and broad shallows at cattle drinking points on the new channel have diversified its aquatic habitat so as to encourage spawning of those salmon which do ascend it from the Frome.

3 Lengths of hedges have been kept alongside the new channel, retaining cover and food sources while work was in progress. It also sets the pattern for future maintenance from one bank only.

RIVER ALNE, HENLEY-IN-ARDEN, WARWICKSHIRE
OS Map: 151. NGR: SP 153659 and 153663
Avon Division, Severn Trent Water Authority, Finham Reclamation Works, St Martins Road, Finham, Coventry CU3 6PR.
Telephone: Coventry (0203) 415115.
Regional Architects' Department, STWA, Abelson House, 2297 Coventry Road, Sheldon, Birmingham.
Telephone: 021-743 4222.

Site Summary
Flood alleviation scheme, capital works, 1979-80.
Lowland, urban location.
Channel: 4-5 metres wide, depth variable.
By-pass channels: 3 metres wide at water level.
Banks: variable slopes, 1 in 3 to 1 in 1.
Substrates: sandy clay, gravel.
Engineer: R Tinley.
Landscape architect: J Purseglove.

Work Description
Capital flood alleviation works through the town of Henley-in-Arden in 1979-80 deepened the channel by up to a metre. Capacity was also increased at two critical points by the excavation of flood by-pass channels. Throughout design and implementation attention was given to landscape, amenity and wildlife habitat conservation.

The by-pass channel upstream of Beaudesert Street (at 153663) was designed only to take high flows, but it is damp all year. After it was excavated a few common wetland plants were transplanted into it by volunteers, but it is now grazed by horses (as is the rest of the field) and grasses now dominate (photograph below). A concrete sill protects the upstream lip of the by-pass channel, but flood-waters have scoured a pool in the channel and deposited silt.

The by-pass channel downstream of Beaudesert bridge (at 153659) is designed to take a flow of water all year, the upstream end being controlled by a low weir. The area had a marshy area close to the new channel, so the opportunty was taken to increase habitat diversity. Soil and associated plant material (mainly meadowsweet) was dredged from

River Alne: The by-pass channel above Beaudesert Bridge, which only takes flood flows.

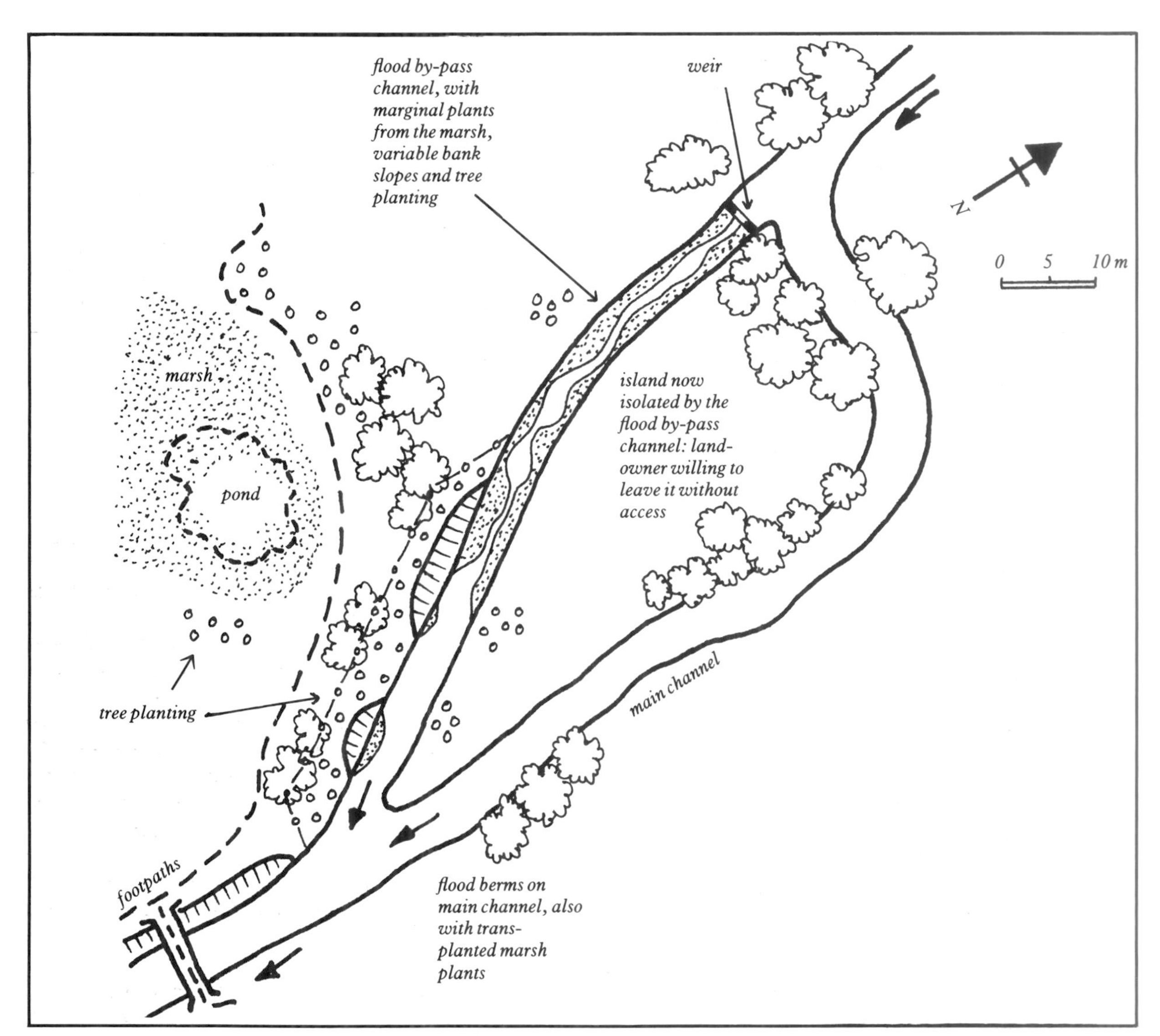

River Alne: Plan diagram of the bypass channel below Beaudesert Bridge.

River Alne: The by-pass channel below Beaudesert Bridge, with all year flow, two seasons after construction.

the marsh, which was being excavated for a small riverside pond and dumped into the channel to form low irregular berms on each side (see **224** for further details). In addition, the banks were graded to variable slopes and the top edge 'eased' to give a less abrupt change of slope. Trees were planted on the southern bank for half the channel's length, as shade, and to separate the channel from a public footpath (figure left).
The island cut off by the new by-pass channel has been left isolated, without a bridge. Without grazing it has developed a dense tall grass cover; the existing willows were left untouched. The original channel was deepened in this stretch as elsewhere, but disturbance was confined to the main bank, not the new island.

Habitat Comments
1 In this case, flood by-pass channels were cut at the same time as the main channel was deepened so that, unlike example **84**, this does not illustrate complete channel conservation. However, because the new channels have increased the flood carrying capacity, maintenance of the main channel can be to a lower standard, or at longer intervals. In the long term there should be less disturbance to instream habitats, plants and wildlife.

MULTI-STAGE CHANNELS

The principle of multi-stage channels has been well established in river engineering for many years. In their simplest and crudest form, multi-stage designs can be little more than complex trapezoidal channels, with all the same problems from the habitat and landscape point of view. The development of computer modelling to calculate backwater effects and roughness for different channel parameters and different flood stages has, however, made much more subtle, complex and 'natural' designs possible. The FLOUT and FLUCOMP programmes, developed by the Institute of Hydrology, are the best known in Britain.
For flood alleviation (so that lowering the river bed level should be unnecessary) high flows can be contained within wide berms cut above normal water level, so increasing the capacity of the immediate floodplain instead of the channel. With care, this can be achieved with no disturbance to the existing river channel at all. The width of berms, the height of the berms above normal water level, whether berms are cut on one bank or both, and whether more than one level of berm is cut, are all variables in design which will be dependent on site factors such as valley width, adjacent land use, soil types, geology and height of water table, as well as the standards of flood alleviation required.
The advantages to wildlife conservation and fisheries of leaving the channel untouched may be lost if the banks are 100 per cent disturbed. Trees and bankside plants provide shade and organic input to the channel, benefiting invertebrates and fish in particular. If possible, berms should be cut on one bank only, or on alternate banks, so that only 30-50 per cent of the bank community is disturbed at any point.
When a berm is cut, the banks are more stable and resist scour more effectively if the existing waterside plants are left intact. Even if the bank tops are scraped off, roots and rhizomes in the soil help to bind the bank, and growth quickly regenerates. In addition, bands of undisturbed plants are a source of recolonising material (seeds, roots, rhizomes, fragments) for disturbed areas downstream.

The advantages of multi-stage channels will vary according to design needs and situation, but may include:

- The regime of the river channel is unaltered, self-scouring, and may need less maintenance than previously.
- Banks are more stable, because they are overtopped early in rising floods, and also any slumping resulting from undercutting will be less because of reduced bank height.

Advantages to wildlife include retention of existing channel habitats and recreation of low-lying river margins, which will compensate to a limited extent for the drastic loss of damp meadow floodplain habitat which has taken place along many rivers in the last few decades.
For notes on the re-instatement and management of grasslands on berms, see Sections **234**, **235** and **238**.

RIVER ASKER, BRADPOLE FLOOD ALLEVIATION SCHEME STAGE I, DORSET

OS Map: 193. NGR: SY 479938
Avon & Dorset Division,
Wessex Water Authority
2 Nuffield Road, Poole, Dorset.
Telephone: Poole (0202) 671144.

Site Summary

Flood alleviation, capital works, 1981.
Lowland, urban fringe location.
Channel: 5-8 metres wide, 1-2 metres deep.
Banks: 1-2.5 metres high.
Substrate: sand, silt, clay.
Designer: C Bray. Assistant Senior Engineer.

Work Description

Serious urban flooding in 1970 led to the design of a multi-stage flood alleviation scheme, to one in 100 year standard. With summer flows as low as 0.3 cumec, and flood flows up to 49 cumec to be contained, a 'conventional' deepening, widening and embanking scheme would have been unworkable. In addition, the riverside was a popular recreation area for local people and has attractive old bridges which, for landscape and historical reasons, were worth preserving.

Pre-scheme studies included monitoring of groundwater levels, studies of soils and geology and extensive computer modelling. Flood routing and flood-wave storage were projected using the 'FLOUT' model; backwater and roughness were calculated with 'FLUCOMP'; and flood studies and predicted conditions were modelled using the Institute of Hydrology's 'Flood Studies' methodology. The final scheme design was prepared after detailed consultations with landowners and occupiers, and other interested parties.

The river runs against high ground throughout this stretch, so a berm on one bank only was used. The channel was regraded in a short section, and slightly widened at the lower end of the scheme where a land developer, responsible for building a causeway and bridge across the floodplain, straightened a section to improve the approach to the bridge.

By excavating a broad upper and narrower lower berm at the upstream end of the reach, and using the spoil to build a flood bank downstream, both flood storage and flood routing were achieved. Heights of floods and velocities should be reduced at the downstream bridge, and more than 90 per cent of the channel and channel edge remained undisturbed. The lower berm is designed to be overtopped on average five times a year, taking up to a one in two year flood. The upper berm will then flood on average once in three years, and (with high ground and embankments) contain up to a predicted one in 100 year flood of 49 cumec, with 0.3 metre freeboard. Shallow flooding at an early stage in rising floods will reduce velocity, and hence bank erosion (figures below and right; photograph overleaf).

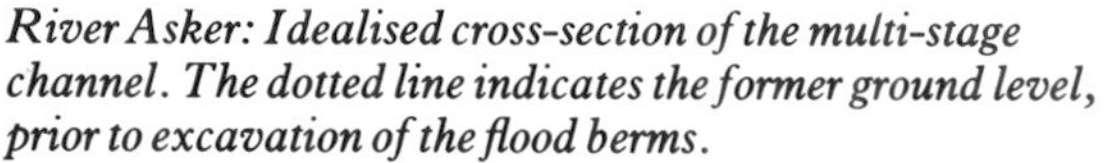

River Asker: Idealised cross-section of the multi-stage channel. The dotted line indicates the former ground level, prior to excavation of the flood berms.

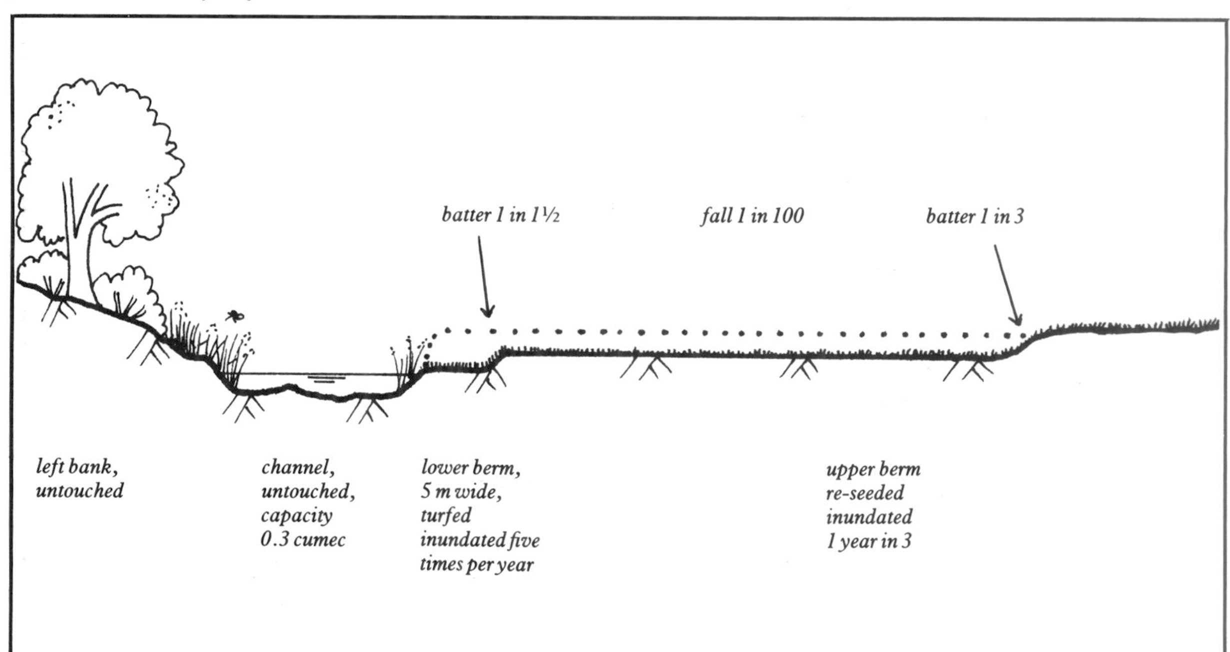

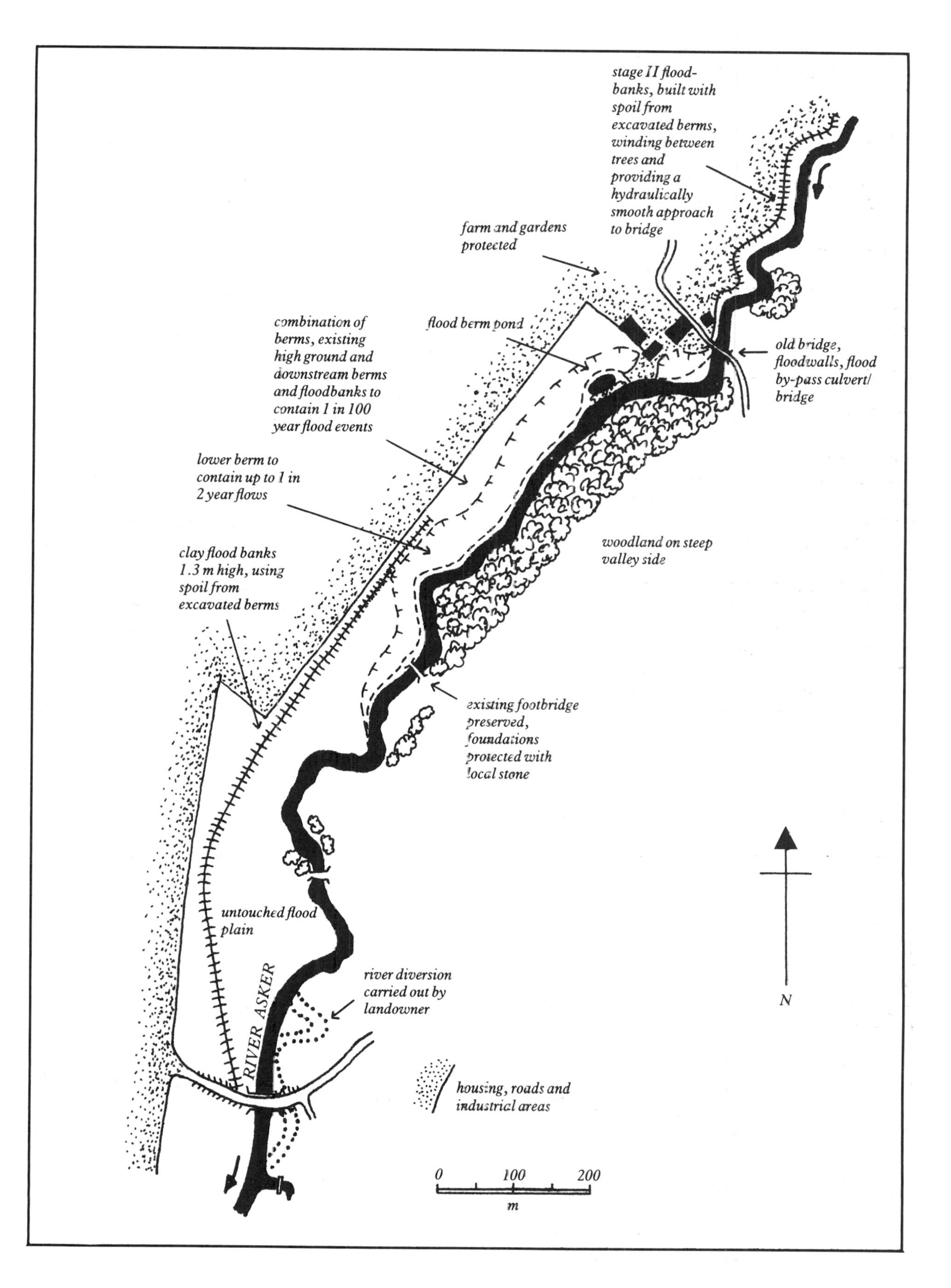

River Asker: Plan diagram of the Bradpole flood alleviation scheme.

River Asker: Looking downstream from the pond area, two months after completion of work. Note the untouched left bank, mature fringe of emergent plants on the right bank, good grass cover on the lower berm, and standard tree planted on the slope between lower and upper berm levels.

River Asker: Looking upstream towards the old footbridge. The lower berm, on the far bank, acts as a flood by-pass channel around the bridge, its foundations protected with local blockstone.

Turf was laid on the lower berm, to ensure that scour did not occur in the first floods after construction. Nylon mesh with topsoiling and seeding was considered, but rejected as it was considered to be less suitable than turf on the footpaths; the original specification was to use local turf skimmed from the upper berm area. The upper berm was topsoiled and seeded with an agricultural grass mix. Both areas were mown in the first year, before they were well enough established for grazing.

Habitat Comments

1 Retention of more than 90 per cent of the channel and channel edge undisturbed is excellent. The river habitat for aquatic plants, invertebrates and fish, as well as cover for waterside birds, insects and mammals, has been conserved.

2 Broad, shallow berms allow regular shallow flooding of a narrow strip which is ideal for winter feeding for wildfowl and waders, and which in time may develop an interesting 'marsh' flora of sedges, mints and even orchids.

3 A major habitat loss was the floodplain grassland, in this case not a valuable community and easily reinstated. In some valleys, however, especially where old watermeadow systems used to operate, riverside grasslands can be very rich in flower and insect life and should not be damaged if at all possible.

4 Disturbance caused by people walking the riverside footpaths will probably limit the use made of this stretch of river by birds and mammals, at least in summer.

5 The new pond creates a new still-water habitat in the area, adding diversity to the river corridor for wildlife.

RIVER RODING, ABRIDGE, ESSEX
OS Map: 177. NGR: TQ 466970
Eastern Division, Thames Water Authority,
The Grange, Crossbrook Street, Waltham Cross, Hertfordshire.
Telephone: Waltham Cross (0992) 23611.

Site Summary

Flood alleviation scheme, capital works, 1979-80
Village-edge, rural, lowland location.
Banks: before scheme 1.5-2 metres; after 0.5-2 metres.
Channel: 2-3 metres wide.
Substrate: clay, sandy and silt
Designer: D Wojcik

Work Description

The Roding flows in a clay catchment, with a deep steep-sided channel cut 1.5-2 metres into the floodplain. It has a characteristic meandering pattern of alternate shallow riffles and deep pools, providing ideal conditions for coarse fish – especially chub.

To alleviate flooding of the village of Abridge, the B172 road (which connects Abridge with Theydon Bois) and of agricultural land (mainly improved pasture) between Abridge and Loughton, a scheme was designed to provide one in 70 year flood protection at and above Abridge village and one in 10 year protection for the agricultural land downstream.

The scheme was prepared so as to conserve the fishing interest and the landscape and to improve both where feasible. The design was based on maintaining the lower third of the natural river (ie, below the mean summer flow level) to act as a low flow channel. The extra flow capacity was created by excavating a flood channel at times of high flow (figure overleaf). The scheme was carried out over 3.5 kilometres of the Roding, for a 10 month period and cost about £200,000 (at 1980 prices).

The low flow channel carries 2 cumec; the berms are designed to carry up to 50 cumec, being partially flooded up to six days in summer and a total of 70 days a year.

55,000 cubic metres of spoil were excavated, and disposed of in four main fill areas closeby. Filling low-lying patches was included in compensation calculations with adjacent landowners. Excavation of the flood channel required the removal of only five trees (in a 3,600 metre stretch) and infilling of three meanders, shortening the channel by 120 metres. Monitoring before and after the scheme was carried out showed that the number of pools and riffles had returned to normal 12 months after completion. While the berms were being excavated run-off carried much sediment into the river, causing temporary partial silting in about 40 per cent of the pools.

Where the channel was straightened 'Reno' mattresses were used to prevent scouring of the channel, and the new bank protected with larch pole piling or gabions. Indeed, the most serious habitat loss was of vertical earth bank, the length of which was reduced by 75 per cent (from 6.5 per cent of bank length to 1.5 per cent). Prior to the scheme there had been kingfishers nesting in the banks within the reach and this species has now been lost as a breeding bird – although it is still seen feeding. In contrast, the water vole, which burrows low down in the bank, lost less than 25 per cent of its habitat. Observations since completion of the scheme indicate that much of this bank protection work may have been unnecessary for the reasons shown in the figures overleaf.

The next section under construction, about 1.7 kilometres between Abridge and Brookhouse, in-

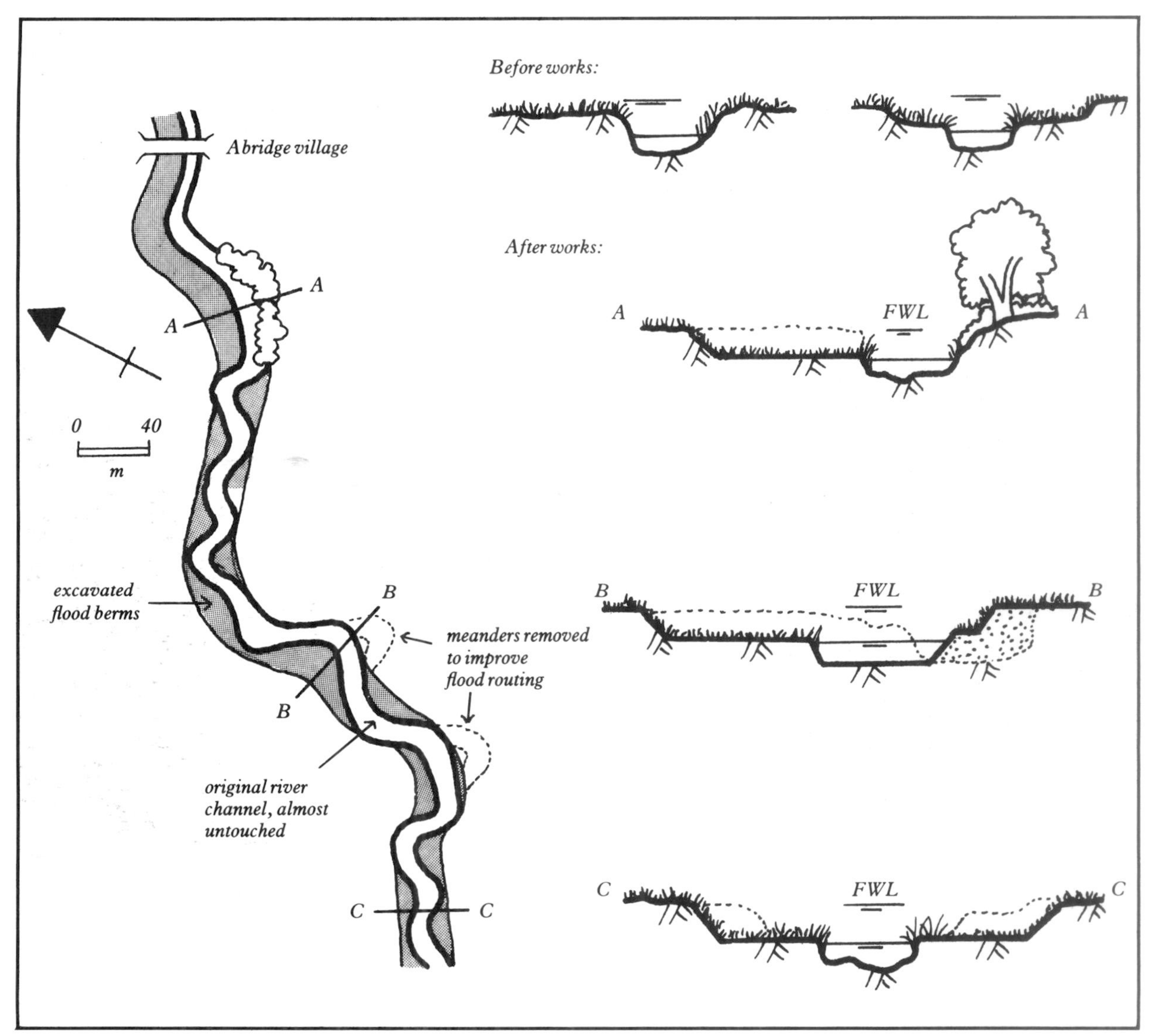

River Roding: Plan and cross-sectional diagrams of the two-stage channel below Abridge.

River Roding: Original channel during spate flows.

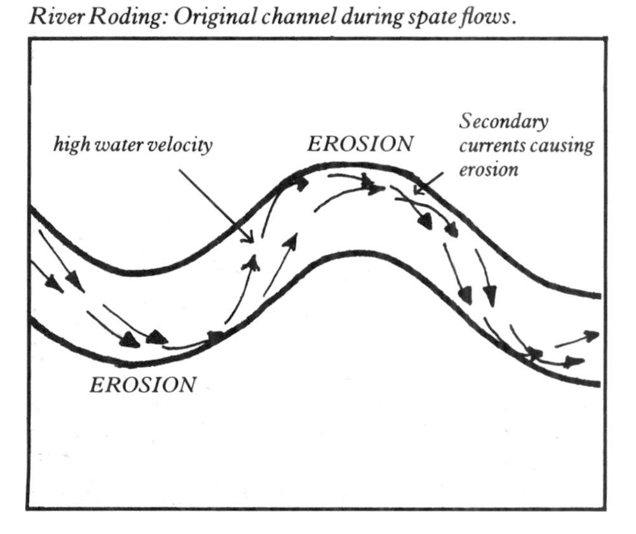

River Roding: Modified channel during spate flows.

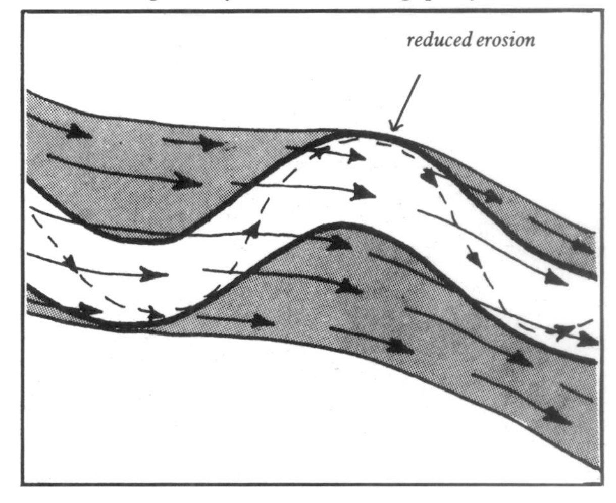

cludes no bank protection, permitting retention of more vertical earth cliffs.

Fish habitat was improved within a variety of structures (see **273**). Reseeding on the berms was most successful using hydraseeding techniques, and some bankside vegetation was re-established, where necessary, by hand transplanting clumps of plants from adjacent stretches.

Management of the berms has caused problems in one part of the scheme where the landowner changed his adjacent land-use from grazing to arable, allowing grasses on the berm to grow up into a reedbed type of community. Downstream, where the berms are grazed along with adjacent fields, no problems have developed. Silt trapped by plants on the berm has caused no appreciable loss of flood capacity, and as long as the grasses are kept grazed no problems are anticipated (photographs below).

River Roding: In August 1982, two years after the completion of work. The flood-berms on both sides have been grazed by cattle.

River Roding: Just below Abridge in May 1981, with water spilling out of the low flow channel onto the flood berm.

Habitat Comments

1 Retention of more than 95 per cent of the channel untouched is excellent, conserving the aquatic habitat for fish, invertebrates, and in this case, water voles.

2 Although the bank habitat was much disturbed (less than 50 per cent intact) the net effect has been beneficial. Before the scheme the upper bank was dominated by nettles and the lower bank by a mixture of tall plants including common reed, purple loosestrife, bur-reed, willowherbs and comfrey. In excavating the berms it was the upper bank that was lost, while the lower bank species remained largely undisturbed. Bur-reed has increased since the scheme, and canary grass and creeping bent grass have spread out into wetter parts of the flood berm. In many areas the waterside plant community is richer than before the scheme – though this may be only a temporary feature.

3 Cover for invertebrates, birds and small mammals remains good. Although the number of breeding water bird species has fallen from eight to six, the number of territories was slightly greater in 1981 than before work started in 1979.

4 The dragonfly population has apparently increased.

5 The broad berm, with frequent shallow winter flooding, provides a valuable new habitat, in a catchment where damp riverside grasslands are now rare. As such it will principally be of value to small numbers of waders.

6 A comparative ecological study designed to evaluate the impact of the scheme was undertaken as a CASE studentship between TWA and University College, London, under the auspices of the Natural Environment Research Council. This has provided much valuable data with which to assess the success of the scheme, of practical value in designing further stages of flood alleviation work on the Roding.

UPPER LUGG, LEOMINSTER, HEREFORDSHIRE
OS Map: 149. NGR: SO 450620 to SO 480607
Wye Division, Welsh Water Authority,
St Nicholas House, St Nicholas Street,
Hereford.
Telephone: Hereford (0432) 57411.

Site Summary
Flood alleviation scheme, capital works, 1980-81.
Rural location.
Upland/lowland transition zone, wide floodplain.
Channel: 10-12 metres, 1-2 metres deep.
Banks: variable, up to 3 metres high.
Substrate: alluvial and glacial sands, clay and gravel.
Engineer: R Vivash.

Work Description

As part of a major flood alleviation scheme (described in detail in **118** Low Stone Weirs), a broad shallow berm was cut on the inside of the meander loops, so creating a multi-stage channel. The spoil was used to build low floodbanks at a distance from the channel. The meander shaping was combined with protection of the outer bank with willow, using a variety of methods (see Sections **168** and **247**) (figures below and right; photograph right).

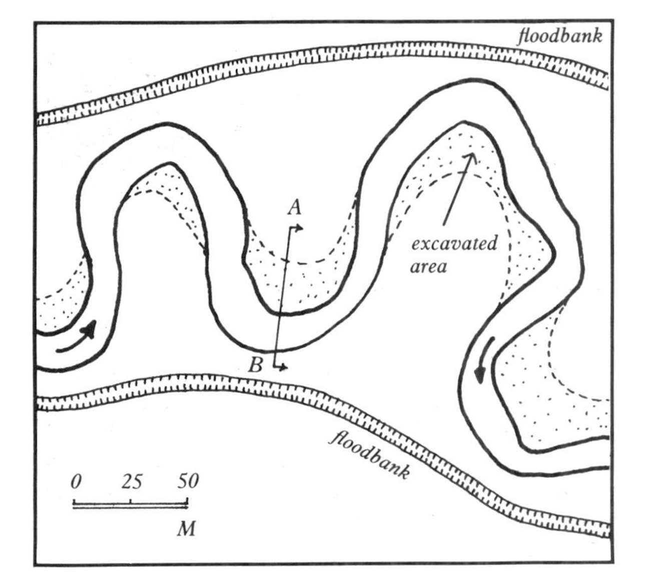

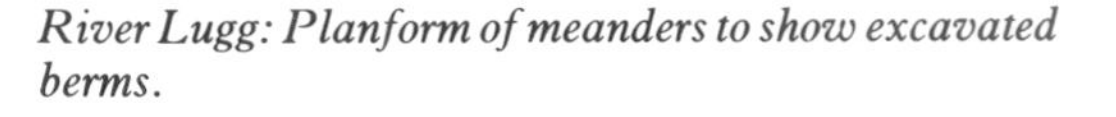
River Lugg: Planform of meanders to show excavated berms.

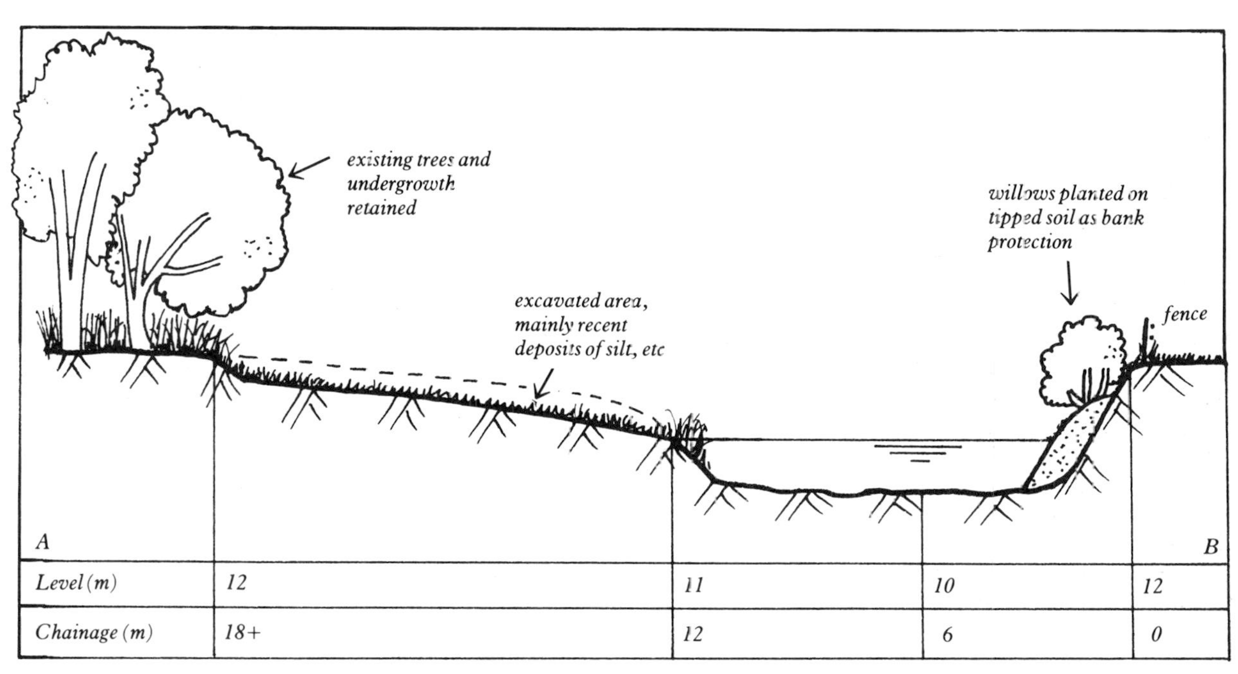

Level (m)	12	11	10	12
Chainage (m)	18+	12	6	0

River Lugg: Typical cross-section of meanders at A-B in figure below left.

River Lugg: The inside of a meander bend, shaped to a very shallow gradient and re-seeded, shown a year after work. Now sheep and cattle grazed.

Habitat Comments
Although channel disturbance was great at the time of work being done, the design simulates natural meander cross-sections, and will require little maintenance and, therefore, reduced disturbance in the future.

Note
A similar technique has been used in executing the River Lugg Improvement Scheme, located downstream of Leominster, where several miles of multi-stage channel/flood embankment have been created as shown in figure overleaf. The advantage to wildlife has again been retention of the river channel, untouched.

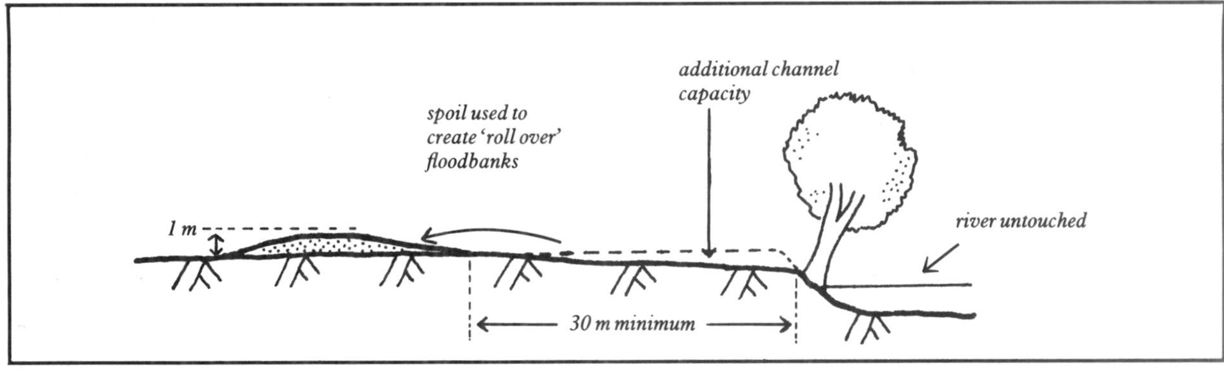

River Lugg: Idealised cross-section of the improvement scheme.

PARTIAL DREDGING

If a channel has to be dredged and deepened, it may still be possible to conserve a significant proportion of its aquatic plant and animal community, by dredging only two-thirds of its width or less.

By this means the *variety* of conditions and their associated species can be maintained. A part of both 'edge' and 'middle' communities remains undisturbed, and so survives to aid the recolonisation of dredged, disturbed areas. Leaving a narrow fringe alone is not the same, for the 'middle' community is lost (figures below).

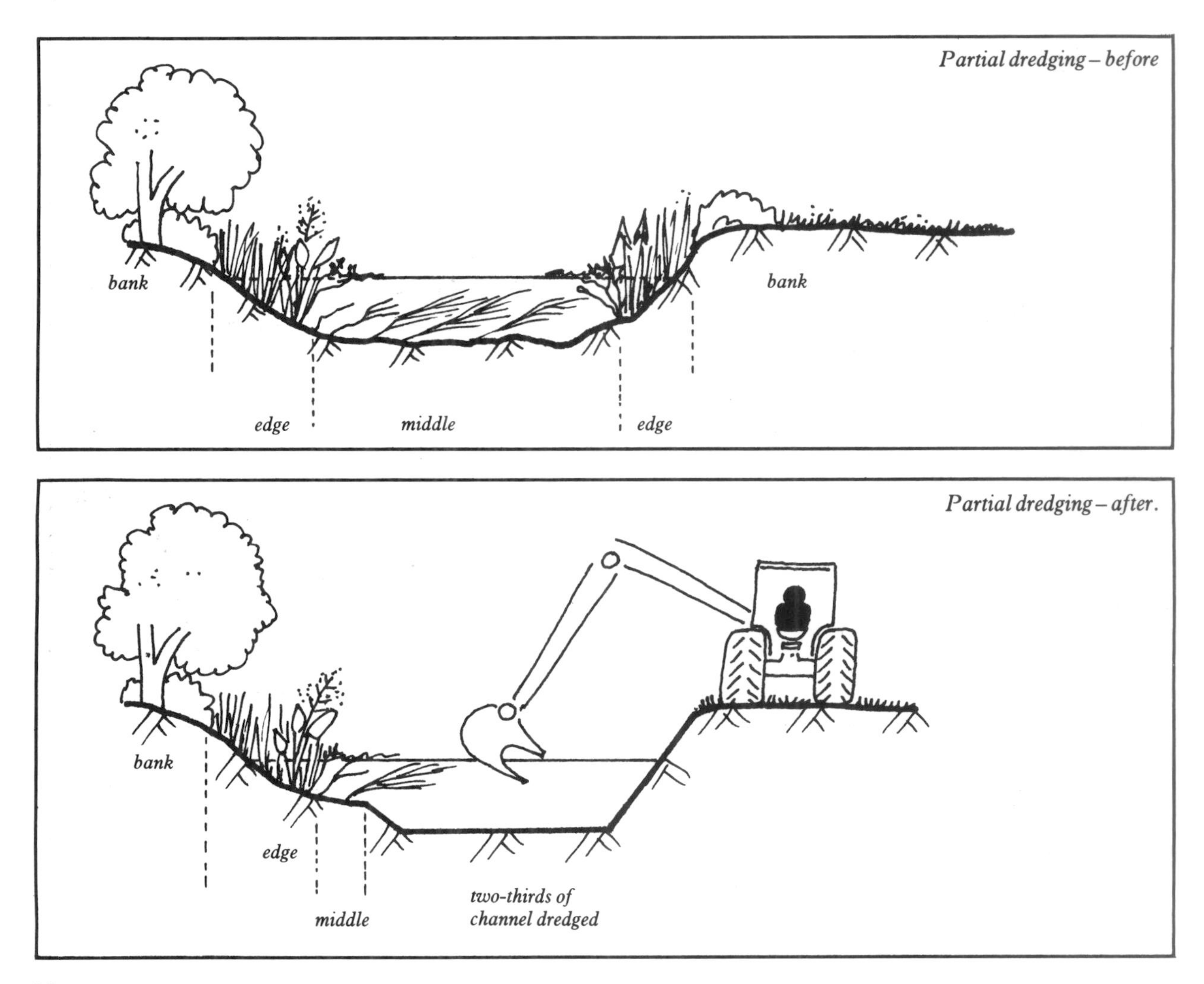

To compensate for loss of capacity, if this is likely to impair required flows, the area dredged can be slightly overdeepened. Care must be taken, however, to ensure the channel is not deepened excessively, or the aquatic plant community on the untouched side will be left stranded and will die. In narrow channels, a large drop in water level may encourage bank plants to grow unacceptably, causing them to shade out submerged and floating species.

As a rule of thumb, shallow water emergent plants are less tolerant of water level changes than deep water species, whether floating, submerged or emergent. The figure below indicates 'acceptable' and 'unacceptable' water level changes in different types of channel.

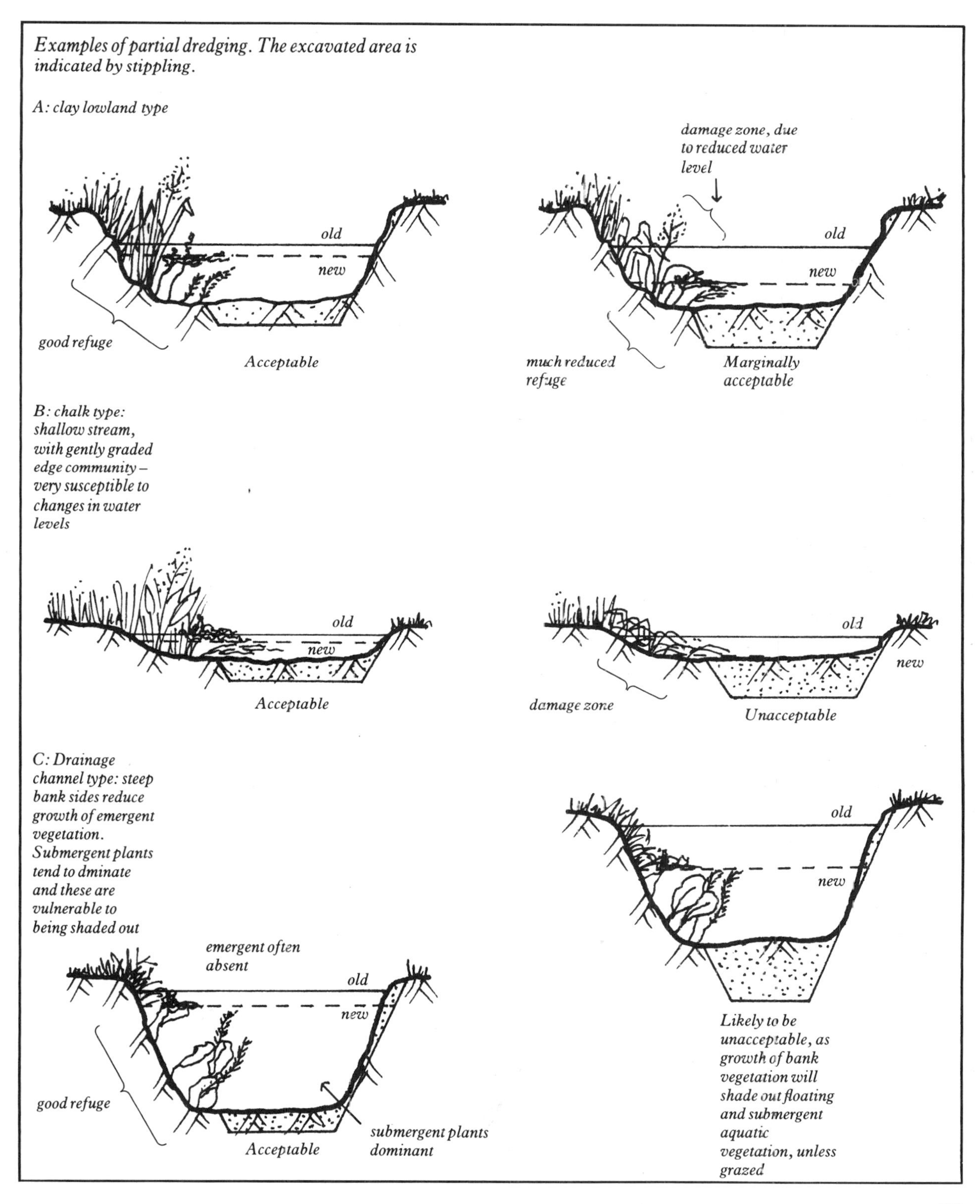

In leaving 30 per cent or so of the channel untouched, it is logical to leave the adjacent bank community untouched as well, and to work from one bank only, changing the working bank as necessary. Thus, the whole riverine community benefits from this approach to channel management (figure below).

See also sections on patch cutting of aquatic vegetation on **204**, patch mowing of bank vegetation on **231** and working from one bank only on **146**.

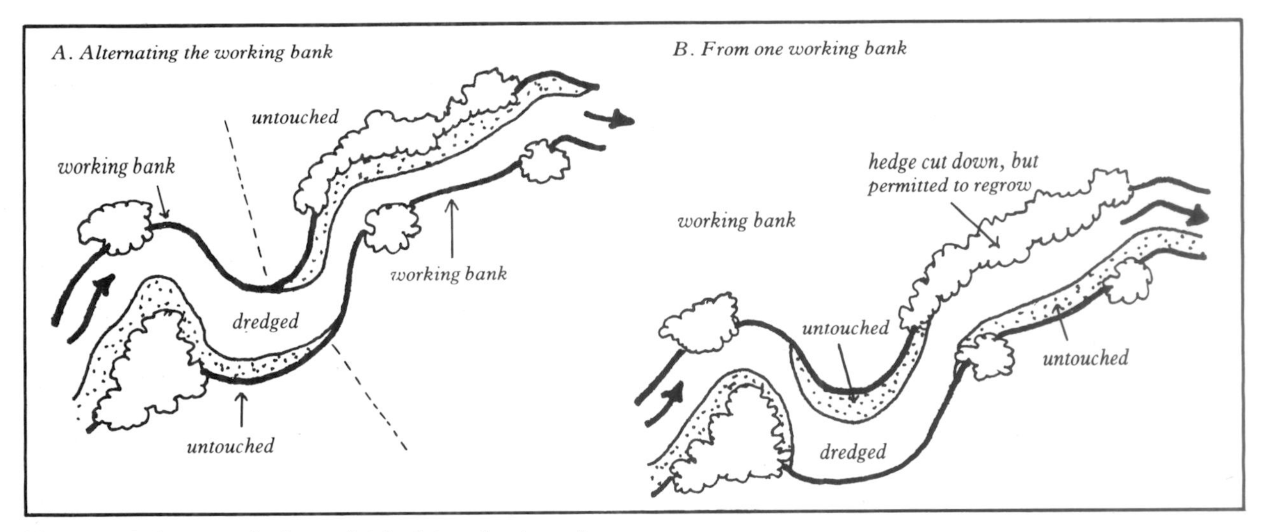

Two approaches towards the partial dredging of a channel: A – alternating the working bank; B – from one working bank.

RIVER TOVE, COSGROVE, MILTON KEYNES
OS Map: 152. NGR: SP 792439
Bedford Area Office, Cambridge Division, Anglian Water Authority, Cambridge Road, Bedford MK42 0LL.
Telephone: Bedford (0234) 63111.

Site Summary
Maintenance works, 1982.
Lowland, rural location.
Channel: 3-5 metres wide, depth variable.
Banks: 1-2.5 metres high, slopes vertical to 1 in 4.
Substrate: mud, soft silt, cemented gravel in riffles.

Work Description
With the help of the Nature Conservancy Council's Assistant Regional Officer for Northamptonshire, the AWA Great Ouse Division carried out a maintenance dredging operation over 11 kilometres of the River Tove, in mid-summer 1982 (note: this is part of an ongoing programme). Parts of the river have a very rich aquatic plant community. It also holds two rare animal species: the Spined Loach, and a water bug, *Aphelochaeris*, which inhabits deep pools.

Dredging was carried out with a dragline excavator. The operator showed great skill in working between trees, leaving riffles and deep pools untouched and dredging out only two-thirds of the rest of the channel.

Habitat Comments
1 Clearly far less damage has been done to the channel habitat than in a normal maintenance dredging operation; this is excellent.
2 The channel was lowered by only 0.5 to 1.0 metre. The fall in water level in an already steep-sided clay river has not been damaging.
3 This maintenance scheme incorporated several other options for conserving channel and bank habitat, including: working from one bank; retaining almost all riffles and pools untouched; cutting a shallow notch just below normal water level; transplanting clumps of emergent plants; and protecting eroding cliffs at the toe, but not grading them. (See also Sections **101** and **206**.)

CONSERVING RIFFLES AND POOLS

A smooth, uniform bed-profile is reflected by low species diversity: to encourage a wide variety of wildlife it is essential to have a variety of physical habitats. If a channel has to be regraded, therefore, every effort should be made to leave riffles and deep pools untouched – or more particularly, the hydraulic mechanisms that created them.

Turbulent, shallow water in riffles increases oxygenation of the water (if it is less than saturated). The channel bed is usually gravel or coarse sediment which provides the right conditions for spawning for many fish species, and the right habitat for a variety of insect larvae, which may later provide fish with food. Deep, quiet water in pools provides the opposite: less rich in oxygen, but more stable, rich in organic matter and sheltered – the right conditions for the decomposer organisms vital for the rapid recycling of nutrients and the right conditions for holding resting adult fish. The two extremes of bed conditions, therefore, in part support different communities of flora and fauna, and in part provide for the different requirements of fish at different stages of their life cycles.

When dredging is carried out, whether capital or revenue, only a *proportion* of pools and riffles should be disturbed, if at all possible, leaving the remainder as *refuges* from which the disturbed areas can be recolonised.

Reinstatement of riffles and pools is described in Section **111**, but unless machine operators are already very skilled in such work and great care is taken to match sediments to the previous conditions, success may be shortlived and the results disheartening. Riffles or pools put in the 'wrong' place tend to shift and be filled in with sediment. Studies of natural channels show that riffles recur at predictable intervals of five to seven river widths, suggesting that they are a natural expression of the channel's regime and sediment load. This can be used as a guide in planning reinstatement.

If lowering the river bed level would result in an unacceptable loss of deep pools, excavation of new pools immediately downstream of the existing ones may compensate for the change in conditions, provided some form of scouring mechanism is introduced to deter siltation.

A varied bank profile should also be created to help sustain the varied river-bed profile.

Riffles and pools have been retained at a number of locations, particularly when the river has been of importance for angling. It is almost impossible to illustrate the underwater conservation of habitat with black and white photographs, however, and the schemes involved (usually maintenance dredging) have not had drawings of the long profile, either before or after work, to judge them by. Despite the importance of this management practice for the conservation of a rich channel community, it is therefore perhaps the least well documented in this manual.

RIVER TOVE, COSGROVE,
MILTON KEYNES
OS Map: 152. NGR: SP 792439
Bedford Area Office, Cambridge Division,
Anglian Water Authority, Cambridge Road,
Bedford MK42 0LL.
Telephone: Bedford (0234) 63111.

Site Summary
Maintenance work, 1982.
Lowland, rural location.
Channel: 3-5 metres wide, depth variable.
Banks: 1-2.5 metres high, slopes vertical to 1 in 4.
Substrate: mud, silt, cemented gravel in riffles.

Work Description

Maintenance dredging of the Tove, a typical clay lowland stream, was modified to conserve key physical and biological features of a reach of Site of Special Scientific Interest quality (although not yet notified under Section 28 of the Wildlife and Countryside Act 1981). The rich aquatic vegetation, a locally rare fish (the spined loach), an unusual invertebrate inhabiting deep river pools (*Aphelochaeris*) as well as its 'typicality' as an example of clay stream are amongst the reasons for its importance.

Water depths and substrates are very variable. Pools are up to 2 metres deep, and riffles 20-50 centimetres deep at low summer levels. Substrates range from mud and silt to cemented gravels. Dredging was very selective, avoiding nearly all of the riffles and all pools – 50-60 centimetres of silt being removed from elsewhere (photograph overleaf).

Habitat Comments

1 Retaining riffle-pool structure maintains the diverse physical habitat for invertebrates and fish. Dredging to uniform depth would have impoverished the wildlife interest of the river for many years.

2 Combined with other practices which ensured that refuges for aquatic plants and animals were retained throughout, this provides an excellent example of a sympathetic scheme. (See also Sections **100** and **206**).

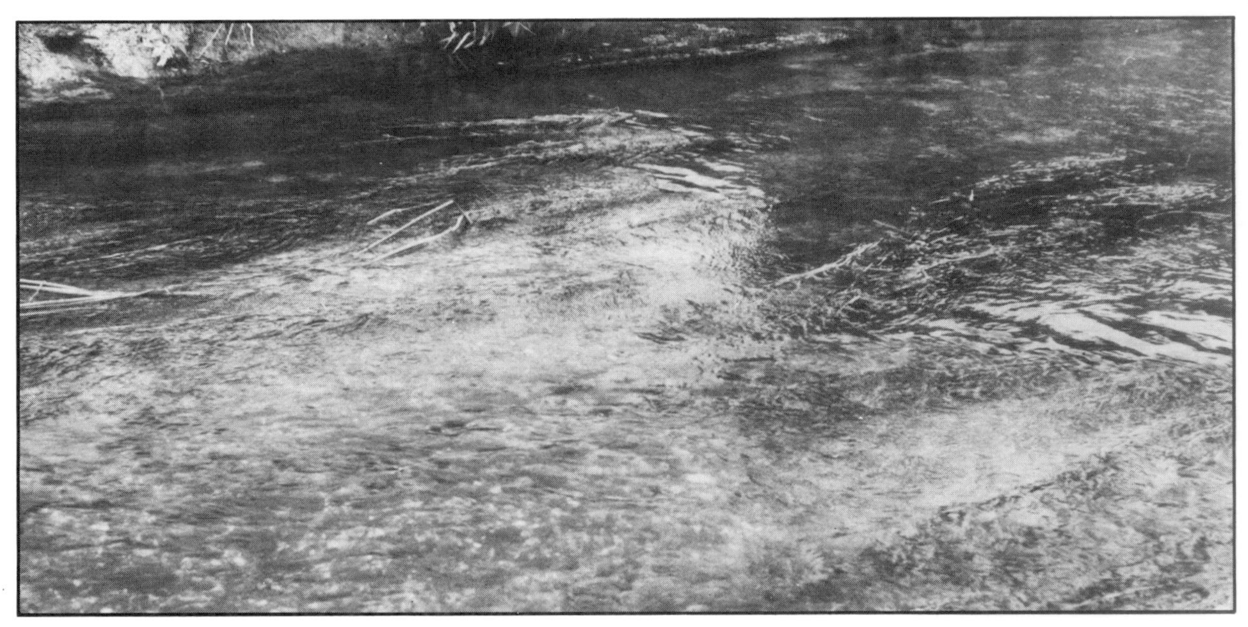

River Tove: A gravel riffle, retained during maintenance dredging.

RIVER STOUR, TREDDINGTON-ON-STOUR, WORCESTERSHIRE
OS Map: 151. NGR: SP 260434
Avon Division, Severn Trent Water Authority, Finham Reclamation Works, St Martin's Road, Finham, Coventry.
Telephone: Coventry (0203) 415115.
Regional Architects' Department, STWA, Abelson House, 2297 Coventry Road, Sheldon, Birmingham.
Telephone: 021-743 4222.

Site Summary
Maintenance dredging, 1981.
Rural village-edge location.
Channel: 3-5 metres wide, depth about 1 metre.
Banks: 2-3 metres high, now with a 1 in 2 batter.
Substrate: clay and gravel.
Engineers: D Alcott and W Garrad.
Landscape architects: J Purseglove, M Ericcson.

Work Description
Maintenance dredging of the Stour in 1981 reduced bed levels by up to 1 metre. Throughout the work

River Stour: The mill pool at Treddington-on-Stour, 12 months after dredging. The riffle remains, and emergent plants are recolonising areas of shallow water.

care was taken to maintain the wildlife habitats and landscape features of the river corridor (see Sections **139**, **253** and **262**). At the site of an old mill sluice, the riffle at the exit of the millpool and the pool itself were carefully treated.
The mill pool – a man-made feature – had become choked with debris and organic detritus from overhanging trees. The trees also deeply shaded the pool so inhibiting decomposition, and reduced flow velocities in the pool prevented the material from being washed downstream. The pool was partially cleared out, leaving clumps of aquatic plants around the edge, and some of the trees were cut back to allow more light in. The riffle was left untouched for a distance of approximately 20 metres downstream of the pool (photograph left).

Habitat Comments
1 The care taken in maintaining the sluice has retained a variety of habitat features as well as the riffle and pool – including a vertical bank, and a marshy area where the bank had slumped, which are absent elsewhere in the locality.
2 The uniformity of most of the dredging downstream is relieved by the retained pool and riffle. Animals and plants from these areas should be able rapidly to recolonise the disturbed areas as soon as the physical habitat becomes suitable again (which might take several years).

MEANDER CONSERVATION

From the engineering viewpoint, meanders have been difficult to accommodate in calculations of channel behaviour. Straight channels were easier to understand and construct. Yet meanders are of key importance to wildlife conservation for they exhibit all the variations in channel habitat that have been discussed elsewhere in this section – eroding cliff; pools and riffles; turbulent and still water; sun and shade; sheltered and exposed sites. Meander removal immediately reduces the structural diversity of a river, and as a consequence its biological richness as well. Less drastic work to 'ease meanders' is equally devastating as the complexity of bank slopes, channel depths and sediment distribution are lost under a uniform trapezoidal channel section.
The major meander no longer required for hydrological reasons is often lost because it provides a convenient and cheap site for the disposal of spoil. If meanders are to be retained in this situation, it is essential that the cost of disposing of spoil in an alternative, ecologically acceptable manner is budgeted into the scheme from the outset (see Technical 3: Spoil Disposal **197**).
Straightening a watercourse is also shortening it – a direct loss of wetland habitat. Straightening increases slope, and unless coupled with extensive bank stabilisation, the channel will almost invariably erode its banks, becoming wider. Without regular maintenance, a less efficient channel for discharging flood water will result. The regular maintenance and bank stabilisation works mean that river habitats will be more frequently disturbed and artificial materials may be introduced, to the detriment of wildlife and plant communities.
Meander conservation may have administrative advantages. Often the river is the boundary between two ownerships, so that retaining an old meander may prevent the exchange of land ownerships – expensive in time and money to the estates department of a drainage authority, whose administrative costs are usually charged to the scheme.
It is also important to make the distinction – not always made by engineers – that their function is to carry out drainage works alone, and not to rationalise field patterns by infilling meanders and straightening river channels. This is frequently done to please landowners, especially when they are not receiving a lot of direct benefit, such as when a scheme is done to alleviate flooding in a nearby village, rather than to improve land drainage.
Fortunately, drainage engineers are now learning from past experiences, and the wildlife conservation and river engineering case for meander retention is being recognised. The schemes described in **71** Floodbanks, **83** By-pass Channels and **89** Multi-stage Channels, all provide excellent examples of this. Other designs, however, which may require channel deepening or widening, make use of meanders to provide refuge areas for wildlife, while the main channel by-passing them is severely disturbed.

Some of the options are:

A A flood by-pass channel is cut across the meander, only taking flood flows. This option causes least disturbance to river habitats.
B A new channel is cut; at least 50 per cent of pre-scheme flows are maintained through the meander by a small controlling weir on the main channel.
C A new channel is cut; flow and water levels in the meander are maintained by a small weir at the downstream end.

D A new channel is cut; the meander remains as a backwater, emptying and filling as a flood peak passes. A wetland, marshy habitat will gradually develop as the 'backwater' silts up.
E A new channel is cut; the meander is cut off entirely and changes to a pond-type habitat.

Of these options, the latter two cause greatest change. Since many cut-off meanders become tip-sites and are infilled, these should not be used unless the landowner is sympathetic to wildlife or game conservation.
A final option (example **111**) of leaving an old meander loop partially infilled on the edge of a new channel, to form a low crescent-shaped berm, has been occasionally used. It is included here for the sake of completeness, for it cannot be described as retaining existing natural habitats!

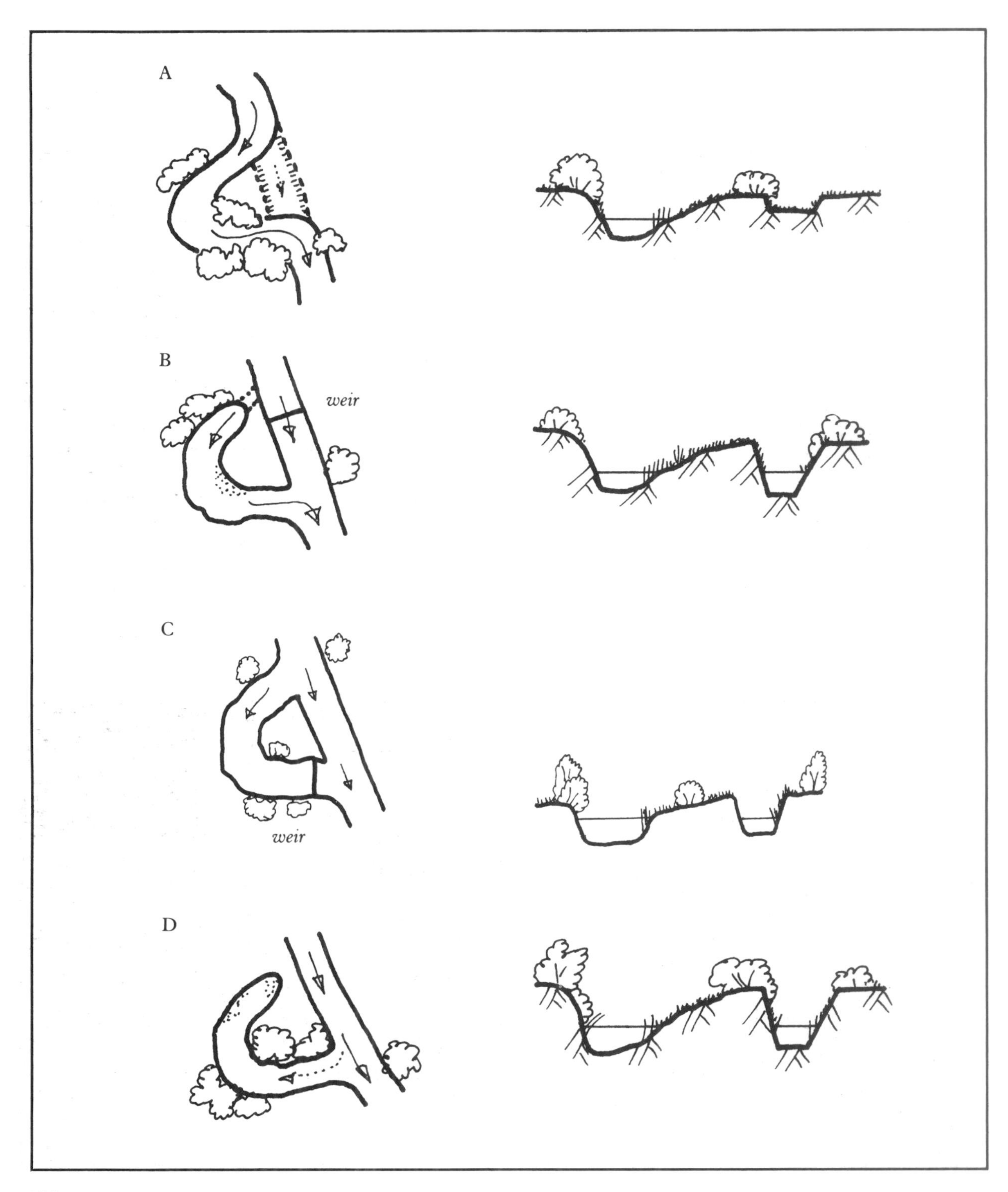

RIVER WITHAM, WESTBOROUGH, LINCOLNSHIRE
OS Map: 130. NGR: SK 855445
Lincoln Division, Anglian Water Authority, 50 Wide Bargate, Boston, Lincolnshire.
Telephone: Boston (0205) 65661.

Site Summary
Maintenance works, 1974.
Rural location.
Channel: 6 metres wide.
Banks: 3-4 metres high.
Substrate: clay, gravel.
Designer: H G Lunt.

Work Description
An agricultural land drainage scheme was carried out in 1974 on the River Witham. At Westborough a landowner strongly objected to the loss of his meandering stretch of the river and insisted that a reasonable flow be maintained through it.
The Witham is a moderate-sized, clay, lowland stream, here about 40 kilometres from its source. There is wide variation in water flow between normal and flood conditions. Prior to the scheme, the channel had been heavily maintained, so the cross-section was already trapezoidal and relatively uniform. The flood alleviation work involved straightening tight meanders, deepening and slightly widening the main channel and using the spoil to build up floodbanks close to the banktop. A uniform trapezoidal channel was left with banks 3-4 metres above normal water level, shaped to a batter of 1 to 1½, and seeded with grass. Subsequent channel management includes occasional work to prevent tree and scrub growth; maintenance dredging as required (probably on a five to ten year cycle); and annual aquatic weed control.
To maintain flow through the meander loop, a 45-centimetre diameter pipe was laid at normal summer water level through the earth bank closing the upstream end (photograph below). A small, sheet-piling weir was put in the new cut to ensure a

River Witham: View of the meander, downstream from the inlet pipe.

River Witham: The main channel on the right, showing the weir, which ensures that a flow is maintained through the pipe and helps reduce scour in the new cut.

flow through the pipe, and to control scour in the newly straightened course (photograph above). The downstream end of the meander has been left open, graded to the bed level of the new cut (figure right).

The cut-off section of bank in the meander loop was planted with small trees, but all have failed. Except for limited dredging at the downstream end of the inlet pipe to maintain flow, the banks and channel of the old course have not been touched since the work was done. The existing hedges and trees shade the channel. A natural pool and riffle structure has developed, with beds of submerged aquatic weeds.

Habitat Comments

1 It is unfortunate that the rest of the river has been left as uniform as it is, with no allowance for natural vegetation to develop in the water or on the banks, but the meander does at least provide a refuge for wildlife and so makes the reach more diverse.

2 The meander channel had three species of aquatic plants not seen in the main channel. Fish fry were shoaling around the inflow pipe under the fallen tree.

3 Bank vegetation was far more varied on the meander than in the main channel, including a small patch of woodland plants under an old hedge, and three old black poplar pollards which might have been removed if they were growing on the main channel. A fallen dead elm is more tolerable on a 'backwater' like this than on the main channel – it is a site for many insects which in turn may be fed on by birds and mammals.

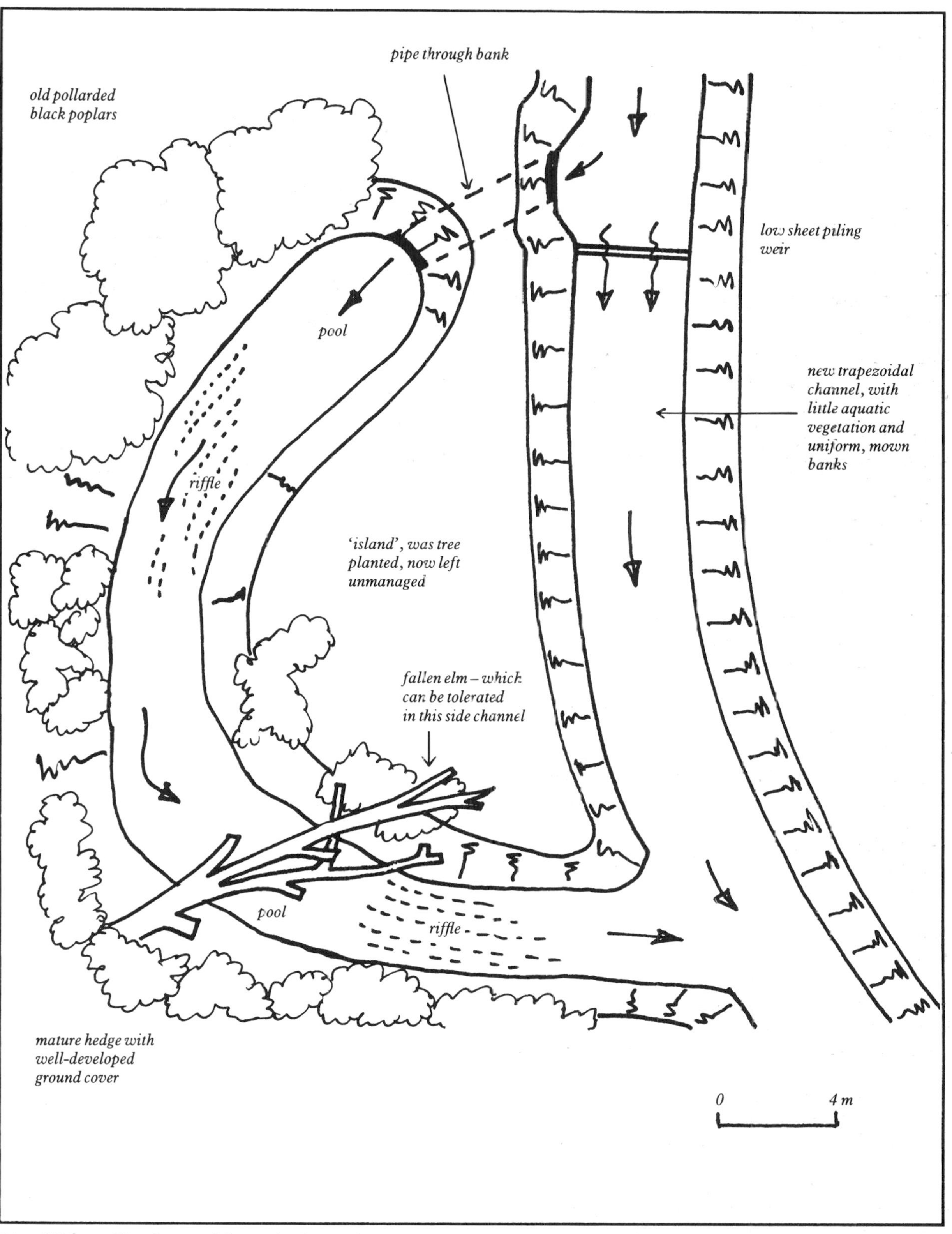

River Witham: Sketch map of the retained meander.

RIVER RIBBLE, SETTLE, NORTH YORKSHIRE

OS Map: 98. NGR: SD 809609

Rivers Division, North West Water Authority,
PO Box 12, New Town House,
Buttermarket Street, Warrington WA1 2QG.
Telephone: Warrington (0925) 53999.

Site Summary

Maintenance works, 1958.
Rural location, upland/lowland transition zone.
Channel: 10-12 metres wide; depth variable, over 1 metre deep in places.
Banks: variable, from vertical earth banks 2 metres high to shallow, low grazed/gravel shoals.
Substrate: gravel.

Work Description

Within a distance of about 300 metres the River Ribble, south of Settle, flows through two tight meanders – presenting a danger to the floodbanks enclosing it. In order to prevent this, a new channel was cut in July 1958. The northern loop was left open to the new channel at its downstream end, to act as a backwater. The southern loop was linked to the new channel by a pipe.

After 25 years, the northern meander loop remains as open water, between high eroded banks. Silting has occurred, permitting rushes to colonise the shallow areas of water. Sallow bushes have grown at the toe of the banks at several places (photograph above).

The southern loop is now a small area of shallow flooding. The outlet pipe has silted up. It has been bisected by a fence. The northern, steep-graded side has a fringe of floating sweetgrass, buttercups and rushes, and a firm clear-cut edge to the water. The southern, cattle-grazed side is severely poached: no open water is present. The vegetation includes well-grazed yellow flag and rushes (photograph below).

River Ribble: The northern meander loop, open to the main river channel (in the foreground).

Habitat Comments

1 The OS maps (figures on right) show that prior to the scheme, the Ribble was highly mobile. Shoals, pools and cliffs were transient. The scheme has temporarily stabilised the system and increased the variety of wildlife habitats present.

River Ribble: The southern meander loop, with open water on the left-hand, sheep-grazed, side of the fence.

2 The southern loop has infilled: at present the intensive grazing means it provides little cover – but is a potential feeding site for waterfowl.
3 The northern loop provides sheltered conditions with good cover for breeding duck. It provides a habitat for those species of aquatic plants and associated fish fry and invertebrates which cannot tolerate the main river conditions (which are turbulent, with gravel shoals and no emergent aquatic plants).

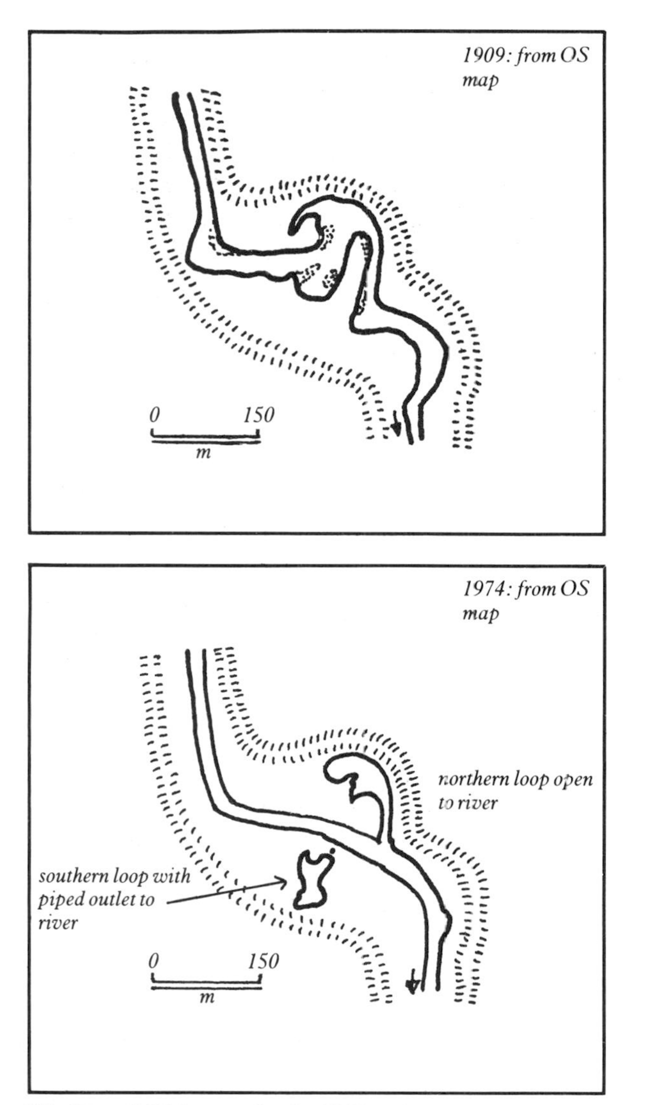

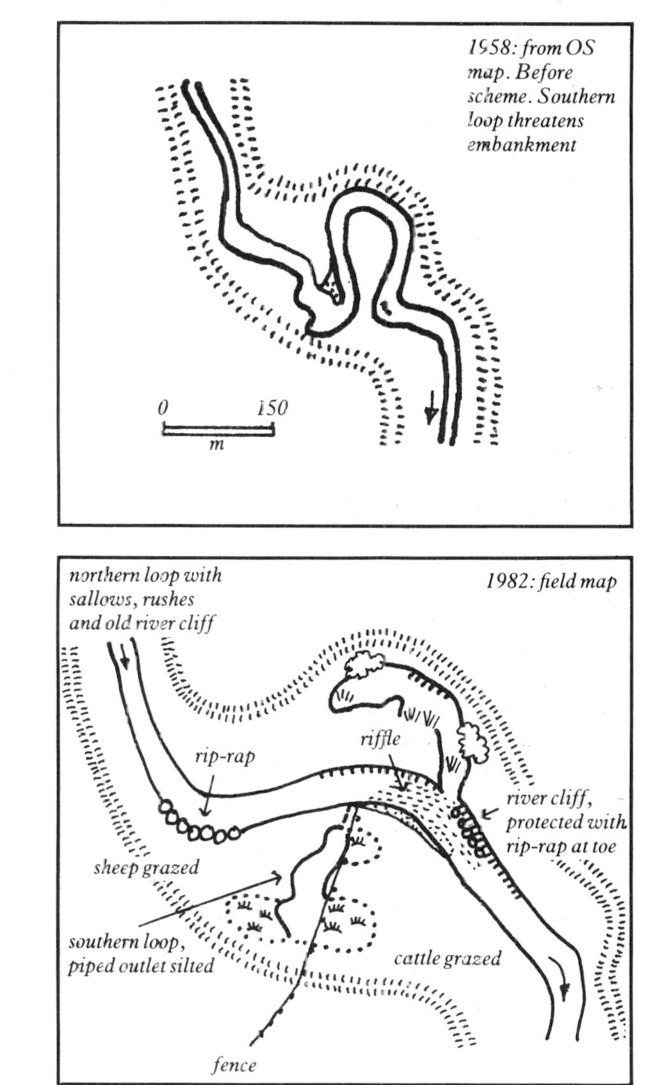

The River Ribble, near Settle, 1909 to date.

RIVER TEME, LEINTWARDINE, HEREFORDSHIRE
OS Map: 137. NGR: SO 415728
Lower Severn Division, Severn-Trent Water Authority, 64 Albert Road North, Great Malvern, Worcestershire.
Telephone: Malvern (06845) 61511.

Site Summary
Flood alleviation scheme, maintenance work, 1981
Rural location.
Upland/lowland transition zone.
Channel: up to 15 metres wide, depth variable.
Bank: 0.5-2.5 metres high.
Substrate: cobbles, gravel, sand, alluvial and boulder clays.
Adjacent land-use: pasture.
Supervisor: B Draper.

Work Description
In this area, the Teme is a swift, gravelly, fairly large river, meandering actively within a wide gravelly floodplain. River training was initiated in 1956 as a maintenance operation, primarily to reduce flooding of the road network, but also to reduce the risk of stock being marooned during winter floods. The works described here were initiated during 1980-81.
As a result of the work, two meanders were isolated, but retained for flood storage as well as wildlife habitat. High embankments cut off the upstream end of each meander; at the downstream end, low sections of bank were left to act as spillways in high flows.
The two meanders are quite different in character. One has a high outer cliff and the inner side is marshy with a flower-rich plant community. The second is on gravel, open to sheep-grazing and in consequence is poorer in plant cover and species.
A withy bed, formerly in the bend of the river, was cut through during the construction of the new channel, but retained to help stabilise the banks. Those trees nearest to the channel were pollarded for safety. The lateral erosion of banks in the new channel still needs watching carefully. Downstream, current deflectors and tipped stone were used to protect the new outer bank from scour. Bankside alders were also coppiced (figure below).

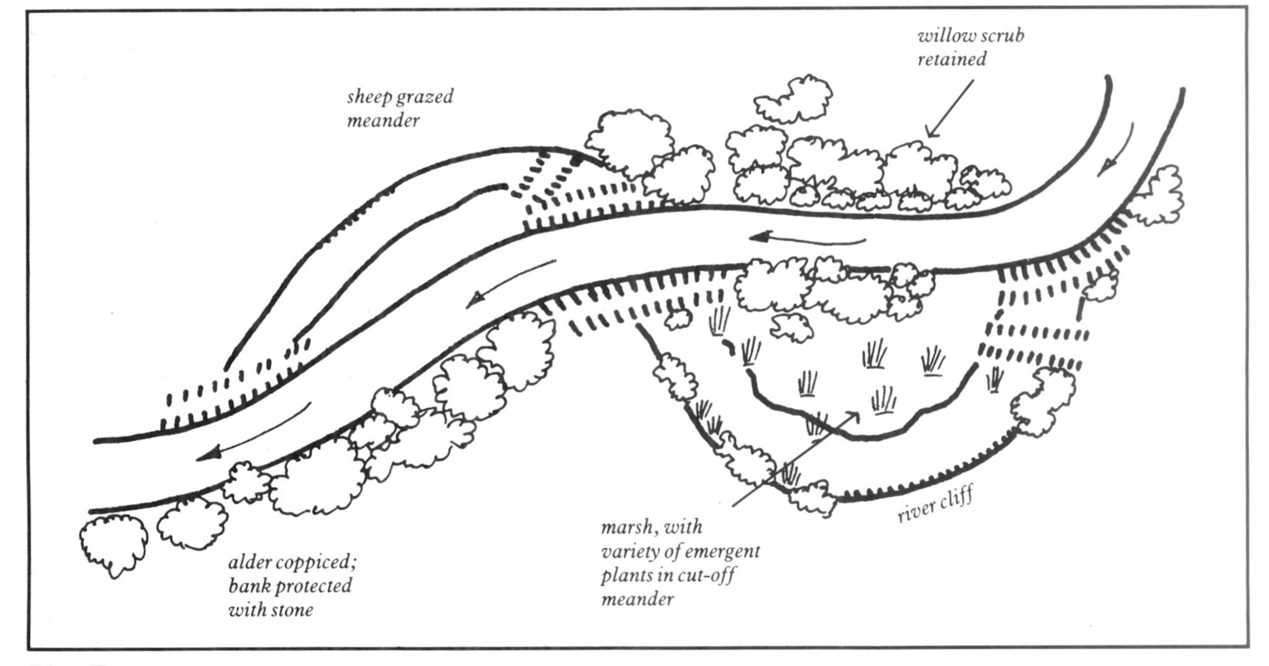

River Teme

Habitat Comments
1 The meander loops have been retained as wetlands, but do not conserve the existing river habitat. As the main river habitat is itself well maintained in a natural state, this increase in habitat diversity is to be welcomed.
2 The cutoff which is not grazed contributes more to wildlife habitats than does the sheep-grazed pool. Willows, emergent plants and marsh plants give cover to birds and mammals, and varied food sources for invertebrates.
3 On this reach of the River Teme, due to the high water velocities during times of flood, planting at the river edge is often unsuccessful. Experience has shown that natural regeneration amongst protective stone is more effective. Planting of trees and scrub is usually carried out, at levels higher up the riverbank.

RIVER STOUR, THROOP, NEAR BOURNEMOUTH
OS Map: 195. NGR: SZ 114959
Avon & Dorset Division, Wessex Water Authority, 2 Nuffield Road, Poole, Dorset.
Telephone: Poole (0202) 671144.

Site Summary
Flood alleviation scheme, capital works, 1972
Rural location.
Channel: 15 metres wide.
Substrate: alluvial sand and clay.
Contact: M West.

Work Description
The Stour at Throop was straightened both to alleviate flooding and to permit construction of a gauging weir by the late Avon and Dorset River Authority. The scheme was completed in 1972. Downstream of the gauging weir a meander loop was partially infilled, but it remained wet and has developed a wetland plant community; a sparse bed of common reed is present; willow is now invading (figure below).

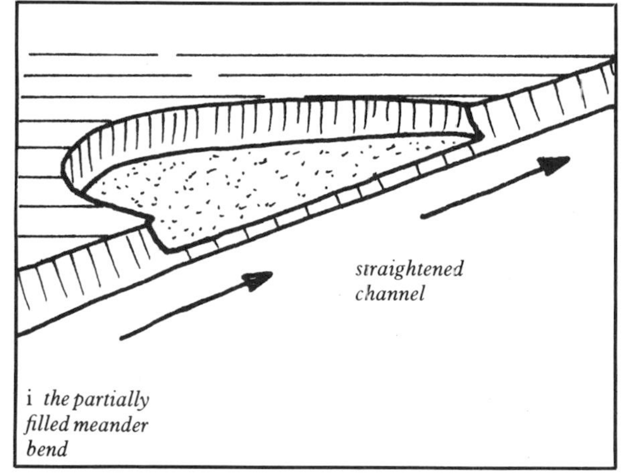

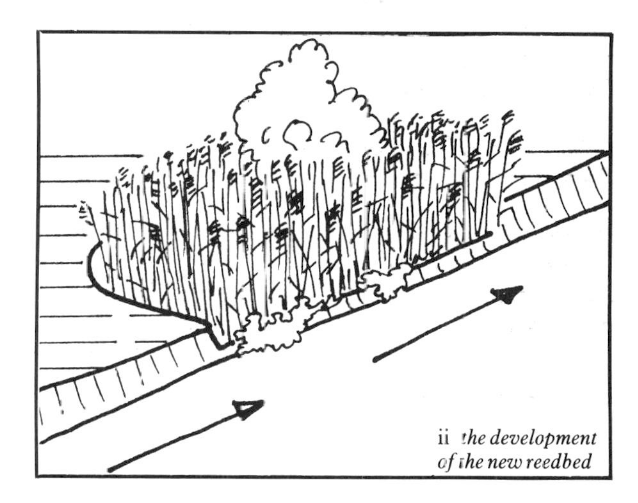

River Stour.

Habitat Comments
1 Although most of the meander loop has been lost as wildlife habitat, part has been retained, providing a useful feature.
2 The developing reedbed and willow provides breeding sites for reed and sedge warbler. Reed and willow are rich in insect life, so making food available for insectivorous birds.
3 The damp conditions may suit amphibians, for part of the year at least.
4 Reedbeds are a limited riparian wildlife habitat and any measure which encourages their growth is to be welcomed. Planting reed would speed the colonisation process (see Section **222**) and aid bank stability.

THE REINSTATEMENT OF POOLS AND RIFFLES

The structural variety of pools and riffles is one of the most important aspects of the channel environment, in particular for invertebrates and fish. Variation in sediment size, organic matter accumulation, current velocity – both above the river bed and filtering through the sediments of it – and associated variation in oxygen concentrations and water chemistry, is greater where there is a riffle-pool structure in a reach. Uniform stretches provide uniform conditions, with little or no shelter in high flows, so that only an impoverished animal community will be able to inhabit them.
Riffle-pool construction is usually carried out to help protect fisheries' interests. While almost any attempt to vary water depths and sediments will benefit invertebrates and therefore provide food for fish, not all options provide suitable conditions for fish breeding.

The re-creation of pools and riffles can be achieved by:

A Modelling the bed during dredging.
B Replacing existing gravel shoals on the new bed, after dredging.
C Importing gravels and boulders to form riffles.
D Excavating variable cross-sections of the bed and banks, so that deposition and scour result from

divergent and convergent flows.
E Building a low weir, to initiate a downstream pool with a riffle at its exit.

One, or a combination, of these methods may be employed at a given location – although their success is variable.
Excavating the bed to different levels or replacing gravel shoals on a dredged channel, has been most often attempted in Britain. Both practices require a high degree of experience and skilled judgement on the part of a machine operator and his supervisors, and too often results are disappointing; the substrate shifts in the next high flows and the pools are lost. Importing gravel to form artificial riffles and spawning beds has been apparently successful in the few cases where it has been tried – possibly the expense of the operation means that more care is taken in design and execution. There are few British examples of designing and constructing variable cross-sections to deliberately encourage natural pool and riffle formation – but the technique has been employed successfully in the USA.
Pool and riffle creation is an important aspect of channel reinstatement. Because of the expense and uncertainty of the techniques involved, however, conservation of the existing channel profile is by far the best option if at all possible.

RIVER PIDDLE, WOODLANDS, DORSET

OS Map: 194. NGR: SY 863910
Dorchester Area, Avon and Dorset Division, Wessex Water Authority, Wessex Road, Dorchester.
Telephone: Dorchester (0305) 66811.

Site Summary
Maintenance works, 1982.
Lowland, rural location.
Channel: 2.5-4 metres wide, depth variable 0.3-1 metre.
Banks: up to 0.5 metre, ungraded.
Substrate: alluvial clay and gravel.
Engineer: L Miles.

Work Description
Maintenance dredging works on the Piddle in 1982 lowered bed levels by about 30 centimetres. Being a chalk stream, the additional freeboard was sufficient to extend grazing in riverside pastures by up to two months a year.
The river is a valuable game fishery, and the valley provides a rich habitat for a wide variety of plants and animals, including otters. Local landowners were anxious to maintain the fishing and wildlife interest of the area, while improving land drainage. In dredging the Piddle, care was taken to regrade the river bed only where necessary. Any regrading followed the profile of the original bed. Gravel riffles were lowered, but were retained as riffles; pools and fish lies were deepened. Additional pools and fish lies were excavated where judged useful in straight reaches. The operation was carried out working upstream so that the dragline operator could always see down to the bed through clear water (figure below).
Dredging was carried out by direct labour. Over the years, the Area's team has gained much experience of the type of work, essential to its success.

River Piddle: Detail of part of the dredging work, redrawn from Wessex WA plans.

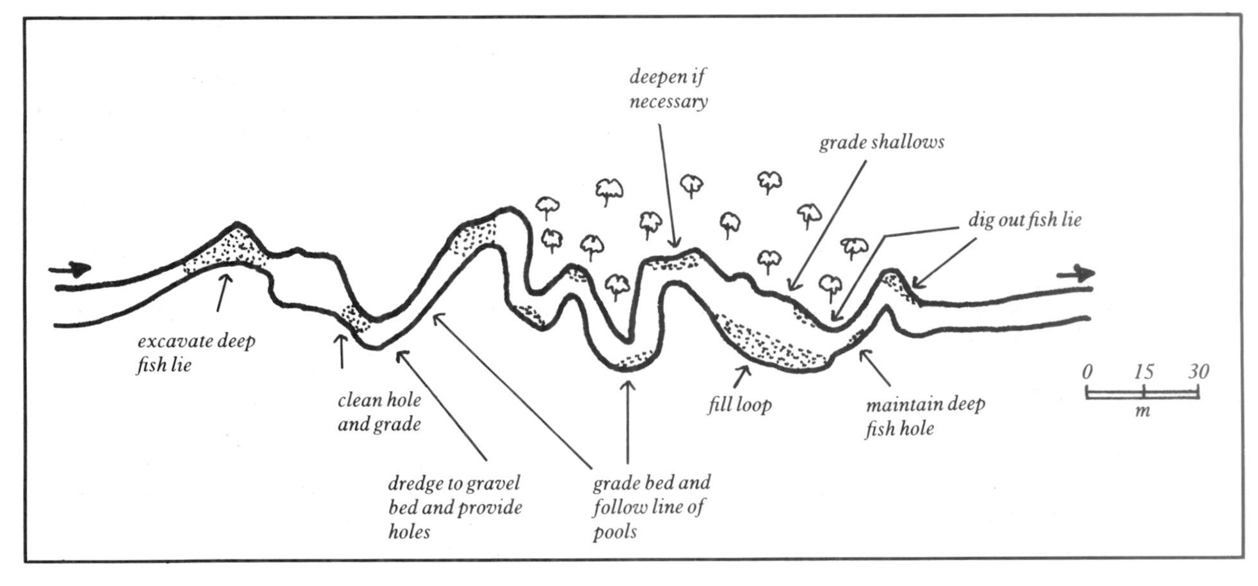

River Piddle: The bed of the river was dredged in this reach in 1979. Pools and riffles were recreated in the pattern of the original river bed. Mats of water crowfoot indicate shoals.

Habitat Comments

1 Insufficient time had elapsed since the work on this stretch of the Piddle had been carried out to judge the degree to which fishing and wildlife habitats were affected by dredging operations. Elsewhere on the Piddle, however, dredged similarly in 1979, the channel had maintained its varied pattern of pools, riffles and plant-covered shoals.

2 Recreating riffles and pools in the pattern of the original river bed is probably the most exacting work that hydraulic excavator or dragline operators can be asked to do. Success depends entirely on awareness and skill, and this in turn on training. Dredging is so widely used, and so profoundly affects channel wildlife communities, that perhaps more attention needs to be given to training.

AFON GWYRFAI, NEAR CAERNARFON, GWYNEDD

OS Map: 115. NGR: SH 552556 to 547564

Gwynedd Division, Welsh Water Authority, Penrhosgarnedd, Bangor, Gwynedd.

Telephone: Bangor (0248) 51144.

Site Summary

Water resource scheme, capital works, 1978-81.

Upland location, within a National Park.

Channel: 7-8 metres, 0.3 to 1.5 metres deep (after reinstatement).

Substrate: fine gravel and bedrock.

Discharge: 0.01 cumec compensation flow, plus 0.016 cumec for abstraction.

Designers: P Parkinson, Fisheries, Recreation and Amenity Officer and N Milner, Senior Fisheries Scientist.

Monitoring: N Milner.

Work Description

The Afon Gwyrfai is a relatively steep, short river in Snowdonia, rising at 480 metres, and flowing through two glacial lakes on its 24 kilometre course. Llyn Cwellyn, the lower of the two, is one of three remaining lakes in North Wales with a natural population of arctic char and for this reason it has ben notified by the Nature Conservancy Council as a Site of Special Scientific Interest.

In 1978/79 a small dam was constructed on the outlet of Llyn Cwellyn and, downstream, 1.5 kilometres of the Afon Gwyrfai lowered by up to 2 metres and its course smoothed as part of a water resource scheme. Channel works left a relatively uniform trapezoidal channel with a fine gravel substrate. Prior to the scheme the reach had been a salmonid spawning and rearing area.

In spring 1981, a year after dredging operations had been completed, reinstatement works were carried out. In order to diversify the channel habitat, two artificial gravel spawning beds and two deep pools were constructed; small rocks were scattered to provide instream cover and flow patterns were diversified by the strategic positioning of boulders and groynes (see **119** and **127**). In spring 1982, blockstone revetment was interplanted with alder and sallows, and other trees planted along both banks.

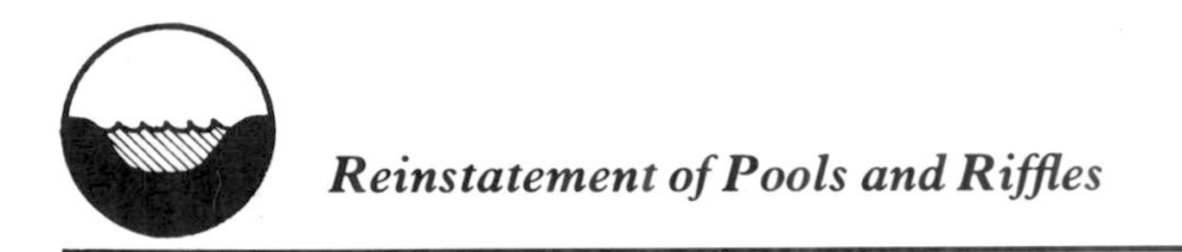

The scheme has been monitored from its inception by Water Authority fishery scientists and biologists to record the rates of recolonisation by fish, invertebrates and aquatic plants, and the utilisation of the new holding pools and spawning riffles.

To construct the spawning riffles, two sections (30 and 40 metres long) of stream bed were excavated to a depth of about 0.3 metres below bed level and appropriate gravel was substituted. This was shaped to give a longitudinally convex bed profile forming shallow riffles at the upper ends of each section. Downstream displacement of gravel was prevented by placing stabilising boulders across the stream bed at the lower end of each section (figure and photograph below). Different types of gravel were used on the two beds:

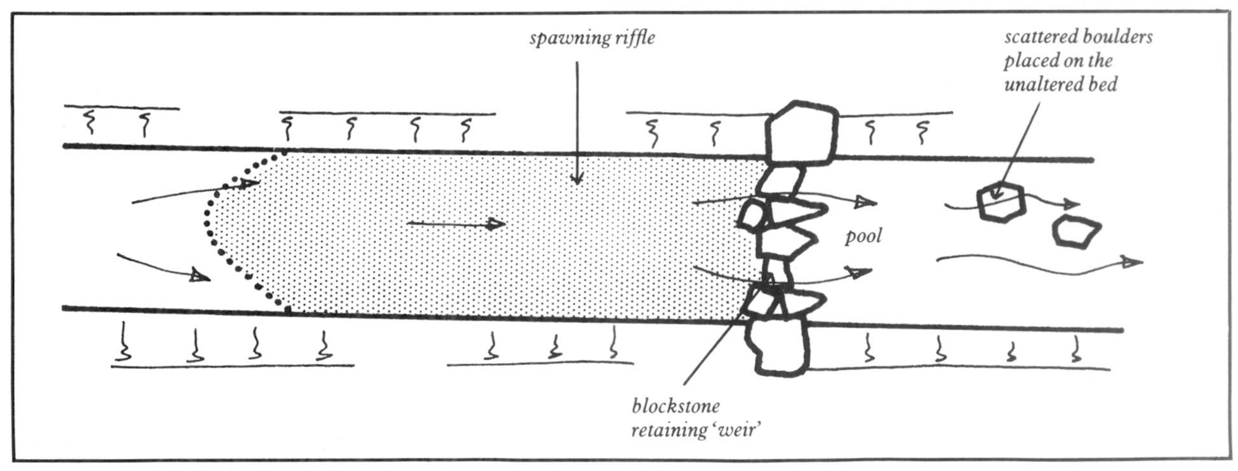

Afon Gwyrfai: An idealised plan of a spawning riffle.

Afon Gwyrfai: A spawning riffle.

1 Simulated spawning gravel (geometric mean diameter 16.6 millimetres, standard deviation 3.6 millimetres). A mixture of graded crushed quarry gravels designed to simulate the measured particle size composition of natural spawning areas in the Gwyrfai.
2 Local lakeshore gravel (geometric mean diameter 25.7 millimetres, standard deviation 3.6 millimetres), of a size composition within the range known to be used by salmon and sea trout.

In the first post-reinstatement spawning season (81/82) some (two to four) small redds (the holes where fish bury their eggs) were seen on spawning bed one. By December of the second season, at least 12 redds were seen on bed one and four on bed two and adults were seen holding up in the artificial pools. Recruitment of resident fish, namely one- to three-year-old trout, has continued during the two years following reinstatement. Present numbers are similar to those recorded before the abstraction scheme.

Habitat Comments
1 The effectiveness of the spawning riffles has demonstrated the value of carefully simulating conditions of profile and size compositions found in natural redds.
2 The shelter afforded by the deep pools and the instream artificial cover has allowed the reinstated zone to be used by adult and juvenile salmonids at levels similar to those before the scheme.

GUM BRANCH, CHARLOTTE, NORTH CAROLINA, USA

(After Keller E A, 1977. Pools, riffles and channelization. Environmental Geology **2**, 119-127.)

In a paper which examines the hypothesis that fluvial processes can be partially controlled by changing channel morphology, Keller describes a 130-metre experimental section of the Gum Branch stream in which pool and riffle formations were induced by varying channel cross-sections.
Gum Branch, a small, alluvial stream, had been first channelised 25 years previously. By 1974, it was sediment-choked, scrub-lined and rubbish-strewn – increasing the urban flood hazard. The intention of the design was to renovate the stream so that a more functional and aesthetically pleasing riverine environment developed.
No structures were used, but the design called for two types of channel cross-section – asymmetrical and symmetrical. The batter varied from 2:1 to 3:1 (ie 1 in 2, to 1 in 3, in British terminology). The asymmetric cross-section converges fast flows, causing scour near the steeper bank, and deposition near the shallower bank; the symmetric profile diverges flow. By alternately merging symmetric and asymmetric cross-sections, a series of point bars emerged, adjacent to the 3:1 slopes, as planned, following the first above normal flows (figures on right).
The cross-sections, pools and riffles remained stable from summer 1974 to autumn 1975. During that period there were four overbank flows, and the bars always emerged after the floods in the same relative positions. The pattern was lost in October 1975, however, under an influx of sediment from an upstream road construction site. By 1977 the channel looked much as it did prior to the scheme.

Keller concluded that sediment control and storm water management is needed in conjunction with channel work, and without it a channel morphology programme is probably doomed to failure.

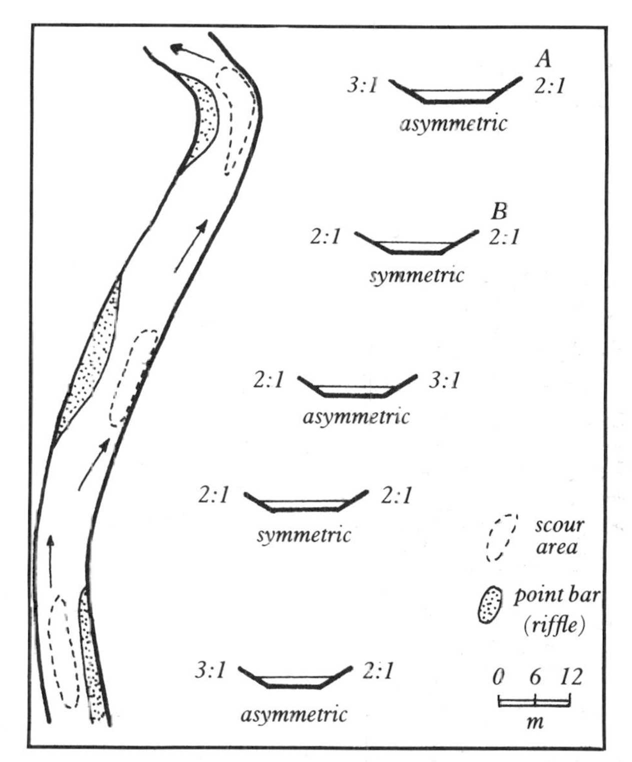

Gum Branch: Idealised map, showing desired channel morphology and designed cross-sections (after Keller, 1977).

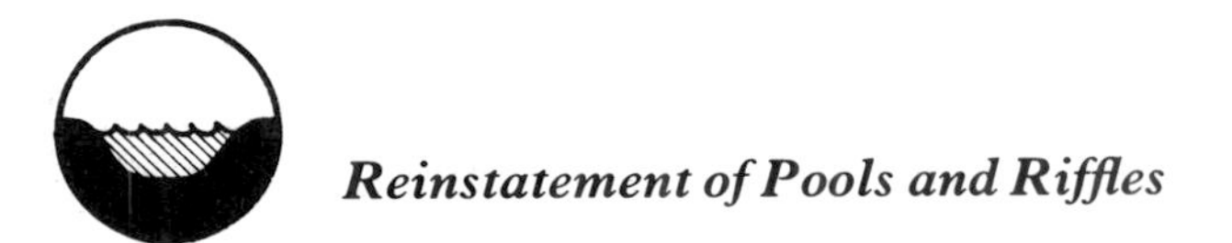

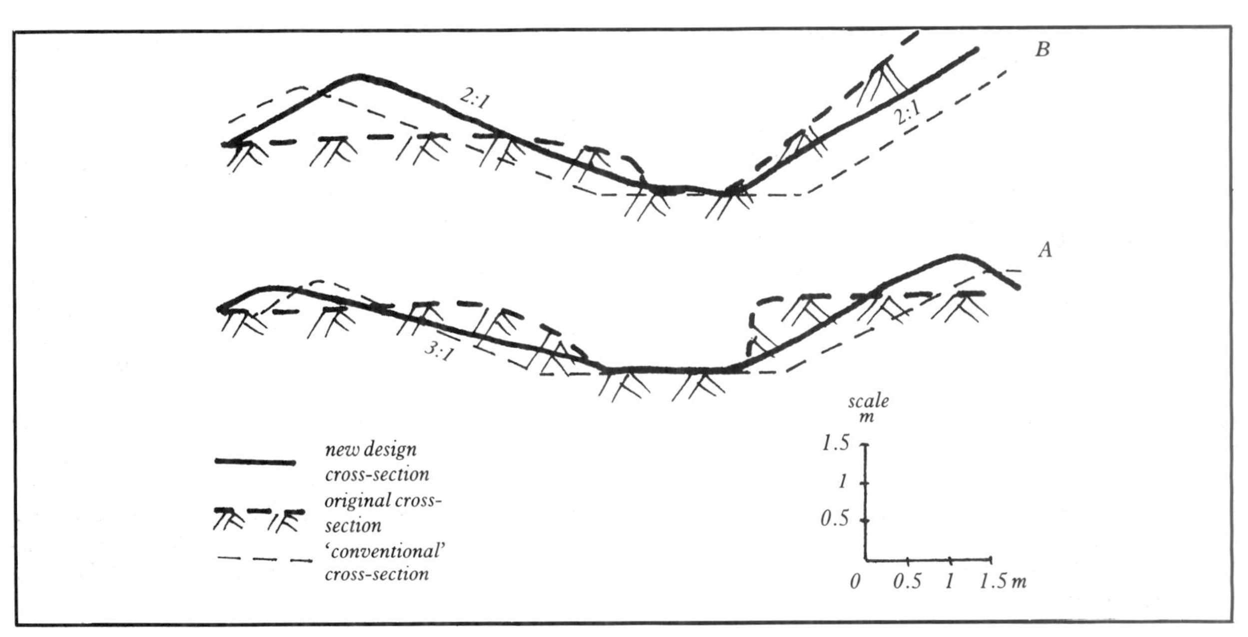

Gum Branch: Comparison of cross-sections before and after modification and a 'conventional' design (after Keller, 1977).

Gum Branch: Riffle and pool reinstatement (after Keller, 1977).

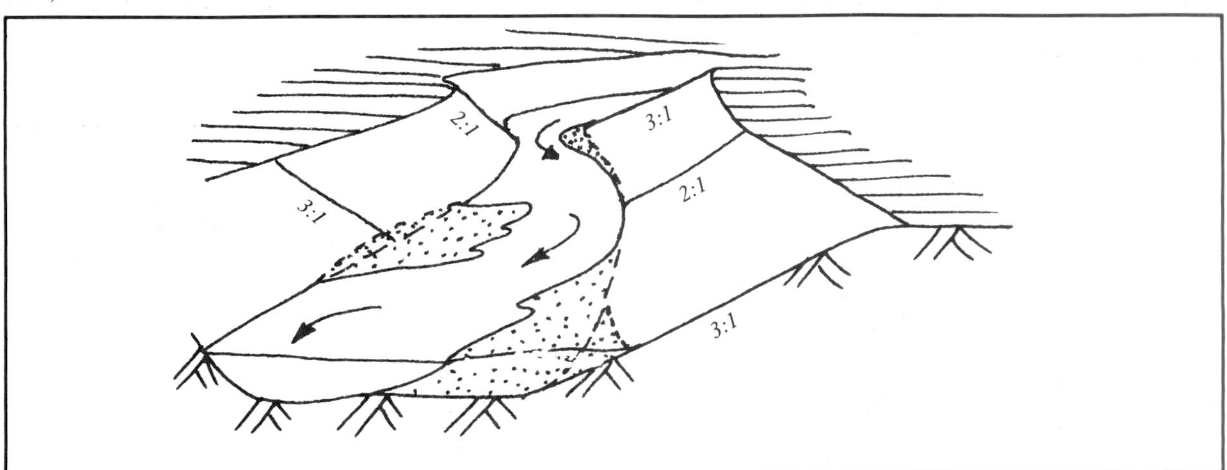

Habitat Comments

1 This approach is very promising for the re-instatement of managed channels. If integrated designs, such as Keller advocates, are implemented (with stormwater management and sediment control) then the frequency of maintenance might be reduced, and the channel allowed to reach its own equilibrium.

2 The cross-sections show that even with this 'novel' design, which aimed to produce a variable channel, natural variation in bank slopes was lost (eg the steep cliff in cross-section B). Possibly slopes steeper than 1 in 2 could have been incorporated to compensate for this, perhaps in a compound channel section.

3 The design illustrated here still leaves a very uniform bank habitat (in this case grassed and mown short, with all tree and scrub cover removed). Imaginative patch-planting of bankside and banktop would be needed to alleviate this. Possibly willow instead of stone revetment could be used on the steepest bank sections, providing shelter and cover for wildlife, both aquatic and terrestrial.

RIVER ISBOURNE, SEDGEBERROW, WORCESTERSHIRE
OS Map: 150. NGR: SP 028384
Avon Division, Severn Trent Water Authority, Finham Reclamation Works, St Martins Road, Finham, Coventry CU3 6PR.
Telephone: Coventry (0203) 415115.
Regional Architects' Department, STWA, Abelson House, 2297 Coventry Road, Sheldon, Birmingham.
Telephone: 021-743 4222.

Site Summary
Flood alleviation scheme, capital works, 1982.
Lowland, rural location.
Channel: about 3 metres wide, depth 1-1.5 metres.
Banks: 2.5 metres, variously graded, steep.
Substrate: glacial clay, sandy clay.
Engineers: M Bagraith and A Redhead.
Landscape Architect: J Purseglove.

Work Description
The Isbourne is a small lowland river running in a narrow channel, deep cut into sandy clay soils. Severe flooding in the village of Sedgeberrow was alleviated by re-routing the channel and dredging the bed by a metre. The scheme has cost about £200,000 at 1982 prices, of which £7,000 was allocated for landscaping.
To relieve the uniformity of the channel, and to create a landscape feature, a pool of approximately 600 square metres was excavated on the outside of a meander bend near to where a small tributary joins the river.
The outer bank remains untouched, with the tributary now cascading into the pool (since bed levels were dropped). The inner bank is graded to about 1 in 3 and the top eased to give a rounded profile – it has been left without topsoil or seeding to regenerate naturally. The bank top and a large adjacent area will be planted with pine, larch and beech and fenced off (figure and photograph overleaf). A cattle drinking bay has also been excavated on the outer bank of the next meander bend downstream so that stock will not trample and foul the edge of the pool.
Since the landowner concerned was not willing to provide land for a pool or tree planting, the water authority bought 2,260 square metres of land lying in the meander bend. The cost of purchase fell within the landscape budget.

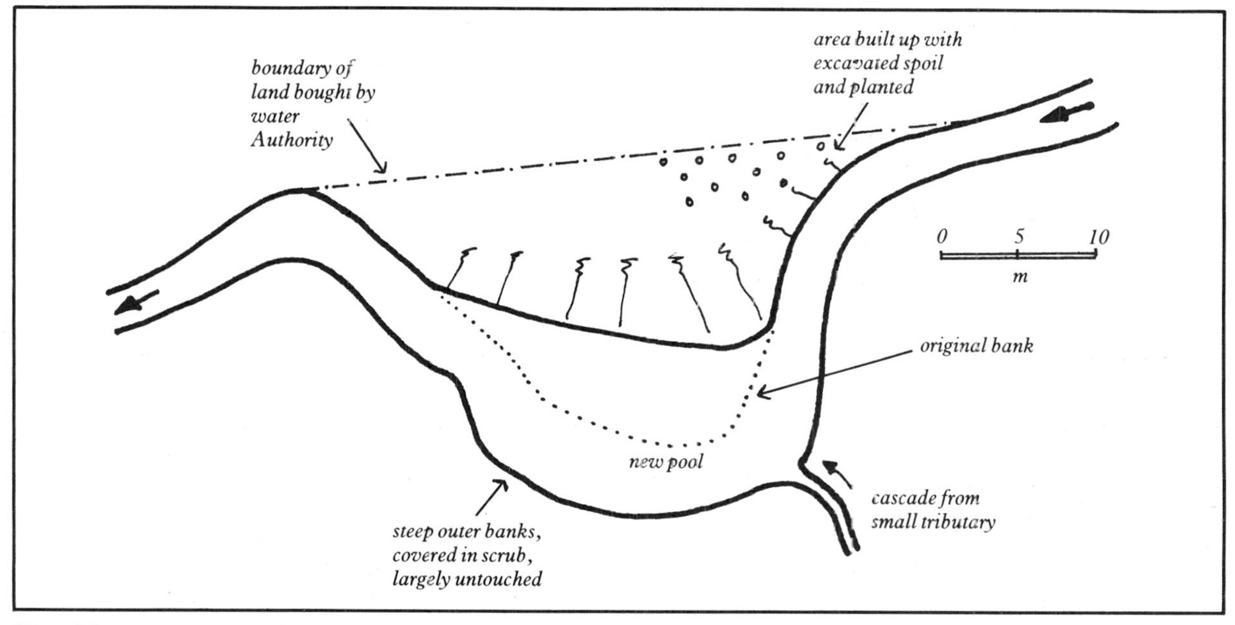

River Isbourne.

Habitat Comments
1 The pool has increased the variety of flow conditions and depth within the channel. It can be expected that this will benefit invertebrates and fish. As the site matures, emergent plants are likely to colonise the shallow edge, further diversifying the habitat and possibly providing nesting sites for ducks and moorhens.

River Isbourne: The pool looking upstream from the inside of the meander bend. Note the scrub and trees retained on the far bank.

LOW STONE WEIRS

Small weirs, either submerged during all flows or only during high flows, are useful devices for improving channel habitat. They can be constructed to suit a variety of design purposes. Often very simple structures, and cheap to construct, weirs can make a distinct improvement to both river wildlife habitats and scenery. By breaking the pattern of water flow, and creating turbulent conditions, the water is better oxygenated than in quieter reaches. Particles of organic matter are constantly swept over the substrate, and can be filtered out for food by web-spinning caddis larvae and black-fly larvae. The hard, stable substrate may be colonised by mosses, lichens and encrusting algae which provide food and shelter for stream invertebrates. These in turn provide food for fish and some riverine birds – especially dippers and pied and grey wagtails which are typically associated with the turbulent water of weirs and rapids.

Natural blockstone, preferably of local origin, is the most appropriate material for weir construction, both from the aesthetic and wildlife point of view. The crevices, cracks and rough surface of blockstone provide more sheltered space for invertebrates than the smooth surface of concrete or sheet-piling. Tipped concrete, bricks or broken breeze blocks look unsightly, and may alter water chemistry as lime leaches out, only permitting lime-loving flora and fauna to colonise them.

Stone-filled gabion baskets or 'reno' mattresses may be the only feasible material in many lowland districts, and they provide a reasonable alternative. Particularly in clay or silty rivers, the gabions quickly silt up and are colonised by higher plants, which mask the unattractive wire mesh, and are an additional wildlife resource.

In swift, spatey gravel rivers, however, the use of gabions in midstream seems dangerously short-sighted. Twenty-year-old gabion weirs in such sites have been observed broken and torn open, leaving a mass of rusty wire which is as unattractive as it is potentially dangerous to livestock and humans. In any case, under such conditions the movements of stones within the gabions often prevent mosses from colonising them and much of their value as rich invertebrate sites is lost.

The following examples illustrate a range of weir designs appropriate for a variety of river conditions.

AFON GWYRFAI, NEAR CAERNARFON, GWYNEDD
OS Map: 115. NGR: SH 547564
Gwynedd Division, Welsh Water Authority, Penrhosgarnedd, Bangor, Gwynedd.
Telephone: Bangor (0248) 51144.

Site Summary
Water resource scheme, capital works, 1978-81.
Upland location.
Channel: 7-8 metres, 0.3-1.5 metres deep.
Substrate: fine gravel and bedrock.
Designers: P Parkinson, Fisheries, Recreation and Amenity Officer and N Milner, Senior Fisheries Scientist.

Work Description
See Section **113** for a fuller description of channel works and reinstatement, at this site.
In a fine-gravel river, downstream of a large lake, the dredged and uniformly graded channel was diversified by constructing a blockstone weir, current deflectors, artificial riffles, excavating two pools, and installing additional instream fish cover. The stone weir was sited on a bend, with a pool (about 1.5 metres deep) excavated downstream. The outer bank was protected with blockstone revetment. Locally quarried blockstone, 1-1.5 metres across (here flat-bedded slate and shale), were laid across the channel, held in place by old railway track driven vertically into the bed. The stones were unevenly placed so that water passes through as well as over the weir. Water depth, about 20 centimetres during low summer flows, is slightly greater in the middle of the weir than at its edges (figure below; photograph overleaf).

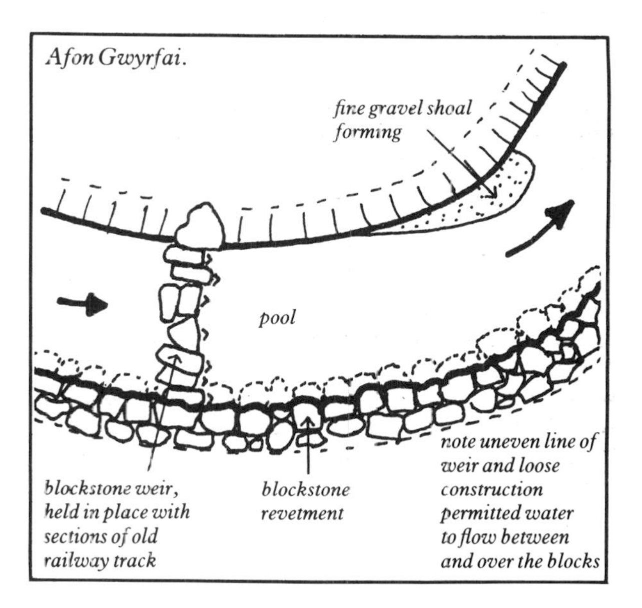

Habitat Comments

1 Dipper and pied wagtail were seen feeding at the weir during a brief visit, and trout were holding position in the downstream pool.
2 Mosses had started to colonise the downstream face of the weir within 14 months of placement.
3 An excellent example of sympathetic channel reinstatement, without which the dredged channel would probably have held only impoverished wildlife communities for many years.

Afon Gwyrfai: Detail of the low blockstone weir. Note the rails holding the individual stones in position.

RIVER KENT, KENDAL
OS Map: 72. NGR: SD 5192
Rivers Division, North West Water Authority,
PO Box 12, New Town House,
Buttermarket Street, Warrington WA1 2QG.
Telephone: Warrington (0925) 53999.

Site Summary
Flood alleviation, capital works, 1971-79.
Urban location.
Upland/lowland transition.
Channel: c30 metres wide, less than 1 metre deep.
Substrate: coarse gravel.

Work Description
To alleviate flooding in the town of Kendal, works were carried out between 1971 and 1979 to widen the Kent and to drop its bed level. The Kent is an unstable, gravel-laden river with great variation between low and high flows. As part of the work, low weirs were built across the bed at intervals to:

A Keep sufficient depth of water for fisheries.
B Concentrate low flows in the centre of the channel.
C Improve the visual impact of the scheme by avoiding the creation of unsightly shoals.

Local blockstone, 0.3-0.5 metre diameter, was set in concrete, so as to form a rough, 'natural looking', but stable surface. A lower midstream section was smoothed over entirely with concrete. Bridge piers were underpinned, constructed so as to appear similarly rough and 'natural'. Elsewhere, uncemented blockstones were laid as submerged weirs, similar to those shown above.
The low, mid-stream lip of each weir was designed to concentrate low flows, when the river tends to meander and braid through its gravelly channel (photograph right).

Habitat Comments

1 Initially, the concrete around the blockstones looked very ugly, but after one winter it was colonised by mosses and algae, as were the stones, and thus 'blended in'.

2 Although the concrete setting provides fewer crevices in which invertebrates can shelter than a 'dry' blockstone weir, this loss of potential habitat is probably unimportant in such a naturally rocky river as the Kent.

3 In an urban setting the rather formal design of this weir is fitting; it would not be so in a rural scheme.

River Kent: Low stone and concrete weir, Kendal.

UPPER RIVER LUGG, NEAR LEOMINSTER
OS Map: 149. NGR: SO 450620 to 480607
Wye Division, Welsh Water Authority, St Nicholas House, St Nicholas Street, Hereford. Telephone: Hereford (0432) 57411.

Site Summary

Flood alleviation scheme, capital works, 1980-1.
Upland/lowland transition zone, rural location.
Channel: 10-12 metres wide, 1-2 metres deep.
Substrate: alluvial and glacial sands, clay and gravel.
Engineer: R Vivash.

Work Description

The Upper Lugg Scheme II, carried out in 1980 and 1981, was designed to reduce flooding on adjacent land by increasing the river's flood carrying capacity, and at the same time controlling meander erosion within the reach to safeguard the integrity of the scheme.

Conservation needs were included from the inception of the scheme: the completed channel follows the original river course; it retains large stretches of the original riverside vegetation and trees; and it has a varied sequence of pools and riffles, still and fast water. The four stone weirs are an essential and integral part of the design, keying the pairs of floodbanks to the channel. They are designed to reduce flood velocities by creating still water reaches upstream to dissipate energy in the river. Secondly, they are attractive landscape features and provide a new, stable 'rocky' habitat in a stretch which otherwise is composed of unstable sediments.

Each weir was separately designed, varying according to both the location and the size of available materials. A 'typical' plan and section is shown here, illustrating the upstream 'apron' of blocks, shallow crest and long downstream 'glacis', with an endsill and several stones raised above the general level as 'breakwaters', the whole contained within blockstone wing-walls. The weirs are uncemented, armouring stones being carefully laid on layers of graded stones and gravels over either permeable or impermeable membranes (figures below and over; photographs overleaf).

Materials used: Locally quarried blockstones, up to 1 metre across in the floor of the weir, larger in walls.

Bedding stones, 0.15 metre diameter, laid on 0.25 metre layer beneath armouring stones.

Quarry gravel, 5-20 millimetres diameter to overlay 'Terram' filter membrane, in 0.05 metre layer.

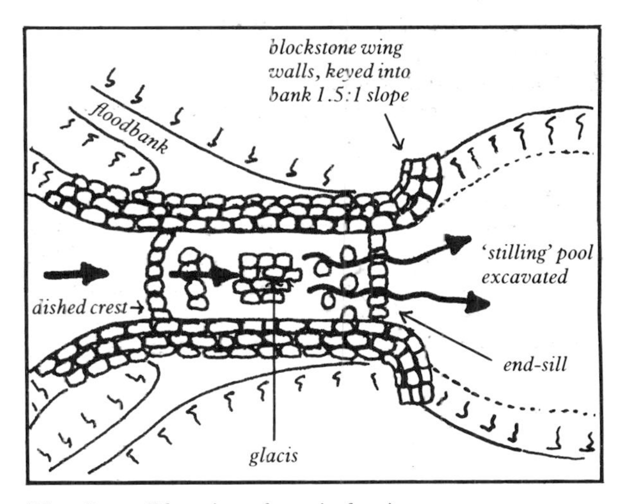

River Lugg: Plan view of a typical weir.

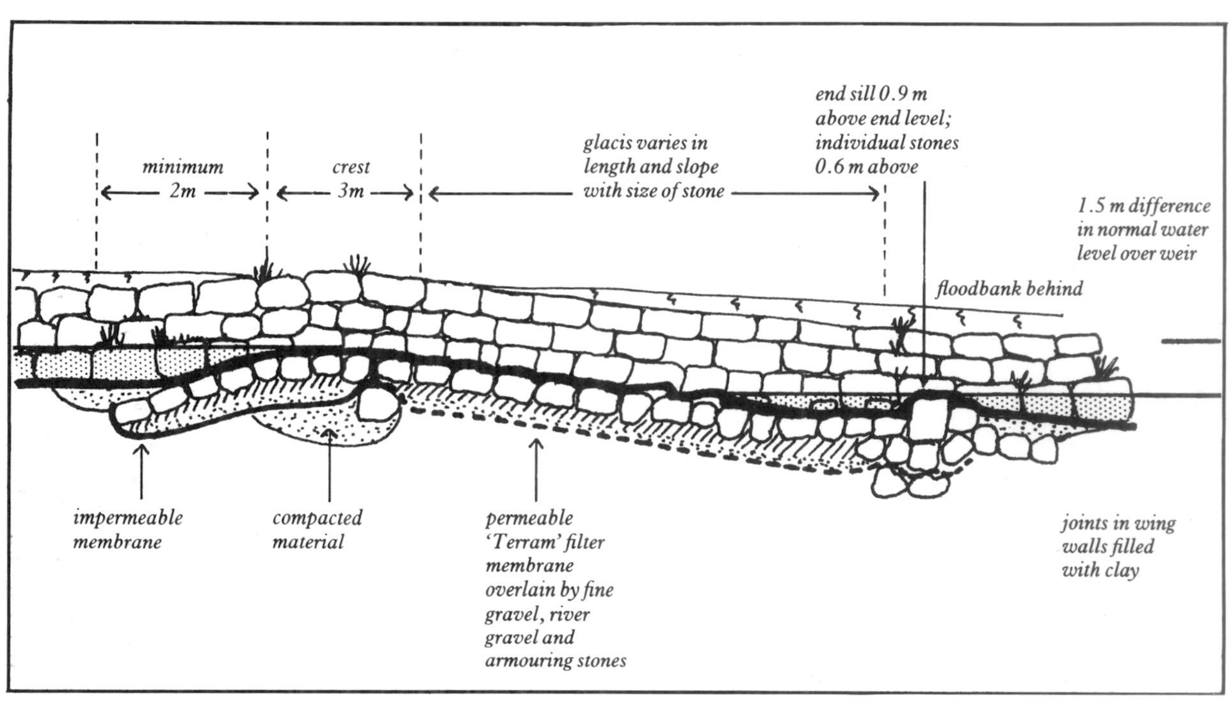

River Lugg: Sectional view of a typical weir.

River Lugg: A typical weir.

River Lugg: A downstream view of a typical weir.

Terram filter membrane, underlying the glacis, and wing-walls, restrained between stones on all edges.
Impermeable sheet, underlying the upstream apron, crest and walls.
Clay and selected river gravels for compacting, filling and layering between and below the membranes as required.

Habitat Comments
1 The weirs improve the aquatic habitat of this stretch of the Lugg, by providing both substrate and flow conditions that are otherwise absent.
2 Similarly, the bank habitat is made more varied by these natural rock structures and provides, amongst other things, shelter for small mammals and invertebrates, and potential nest sites for dippers and grey wagtails.
3 Despite the disturbance to the river over two summers, otter spraints were found on one of the weirs within a year – a sign of how quickly the river habitat returned to normal after the scheme was completed.
4 A weir of this capacity might well have been constructed in concrete and steel but the use of natural local stone, uncemented, has positively improved the wildlife habitat and landscape, in a way that concrete and steel never can.
5 The weirs each have large pools downstream, excavated to act as a stilling pool, and to supplement the stilling basin. The lip of each pool has formed gravelly riffles and shoals, diversifying the channel habitat further.

RIVER COLY, COLYTON, DEVON
OS Map: 192. NGR: SY 249943
Environmental Services (East Area),
South West Water Authority, Manley House,
Sowton, Exeter.
Telephone: Exeter (0392) 76201.

Work Description
To stabilise the sandy-clay riverbed of the Coly, after it was lowered by up to 1 metre as part of a two-stage flood alleviation scheme, a series of low stone weirs was constructed. 1,250-1,525 kilogram blocks were placed on their edge, in a single line, loose on the edge of the channel (photographs overleaf).
The low flow channel is 2-3 metres wide. It takes low flows of 2 cumecs, and bankful flows of 30 cumecs. Design flood discharge is 80 cumecs. The cost of materials, transport and labour for the weirs was 15 per cent of total scheme cost of £100,000 (1980 prices). See also **178**.

River Coly: The series of low stone weirs.

River Coly: Detail of one of the weirs.

RIVER RODING, ABRIDGE, ESSEX
OS Map: 177. NGR: TQ 466970
Eastern Division, Thames Water Authority, The Grange, Crossbrook Street, Waltham Cross, Herts.
Telephone: Waltham Cross (0992) 23611.

Site Summary
Flood alleviation scheme, capital works, 1980.
Rural, lowland location.
Channel: 8 metres wide, 0.2-6 metres deep (low water).
Substrate: clay, alluvial silts, concrete bank revetment.

Designers: D Wojcik, Project Engineer (New Works) and A Dearsley (Biologist).

Work Description
Natural blockstone is often prohibitively expensive in lowland areas of Britain. Gabion baskets filled with rubble or small quarry stone, however, provide a reasonably cheap alternative and have many of the same biological advantages.
The River Roding, in Essex, lies in a clay catchment, and blockstone could not be considered for constructing weirs, large or small. As part of the Abridge flood alleviation scheme (see Section **93**) the opportunity was taken to improve fish habitat

River Roding: The sheet piling and gabion weir.

over a 400 metre length of straightened, trapezoidal channel beside the M11, by deliberately interrupting the smooth flow of the channel with groynes and a small weir. (See page **129** for details of groynes and page **273** fish shelters.)

The weir was constructed with rock-filled gabion mattresses, each 4 metres×1 metre×300 millimetres, set immediately downstream of the low sheet-steel weir (figure below, photograph above).

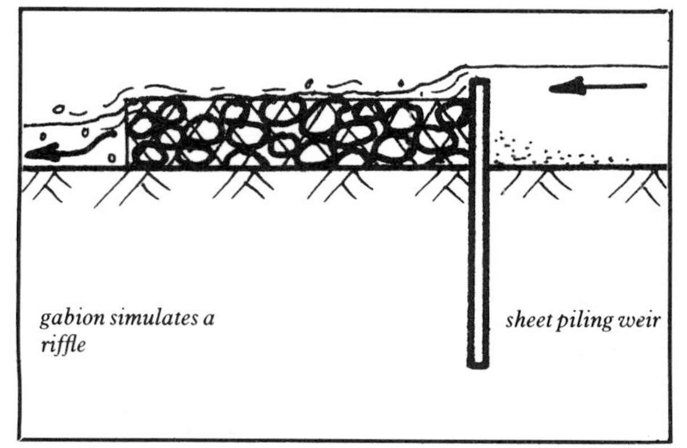

River Roding: The sheet piling and gabion weir.

An alternative weir/pool design for clay rivers.

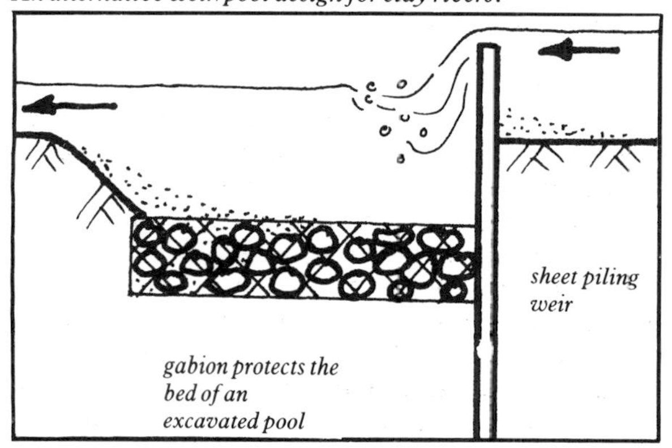

Habitat Comments

1 The sheet piling makes the weir effective and stabilises the gabion, but on its own it contributes little to diversifying the channel habitat.

2 The important part of the structure, as far as the stream community is concerned, is the rock-filled gabion which provides many crevices and niches for invertebrates to occupy, increases the surface area for algae to grow on and during low flows increases turbulence and aeration of the water flowing over and through it, so simulating a riffle.

3 A variation of this design, excavating the bed downstream of the sheet piling and laying the gabion on the bed to protect against scour, would create a fish-holding pool, but would probably not be as effective in increasing invertebrate populations as the design illustrated above (figure below left).

4 A sheet piling weir can similarly be 'naturalised' by piling boulders against its up and downstream faces. This avoids introducing wire which in future may become a hazard, and provides the weir with a natural appearance (figure below).

A sheet piling and stone weir (design used by Thames WA on the River Beam).

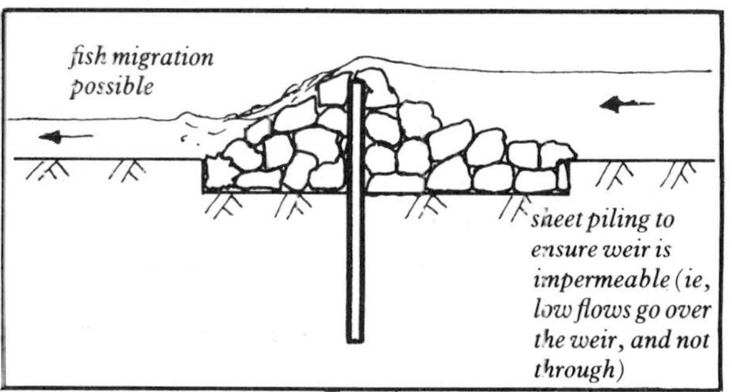

RIVER STOUR, ENSBURY, BOURNEMOUTH
OS Map: 195. NGR: SZ 081973
Avon and Dorset Division, Wessex Water Authority, 2 Nuffield Road, Poole, Dorset. Telephone: Poole (0202) 671144.

Work Description
As part of a comprehensive scheme to improve land drainage between Throop and Longham, a series of low flow weirs was constructed to protect fisheries interests. The Stour at Ensbury holds good stocks of coarse fish and occasional salmon and migratory trout.
Large blocks of quarry stone were positioned loose on the riverbed to create a sinuous weir. The far bank was protected with similar stone rip-rap (photograph below).

River Stour: The low flow weir at Ensbury.

CURRENT DEFLECTORS (GROYNES)

Although similar in many respects to low weirs, current deflectors (or groynes) only have a marginal impact on main water flows and water levels, and so can be used more freely.
Current deflectors are often installed for bank protection – to deflect the main force of the current away from the outer eroding bank. As with low flow weirs, however, the effectiveness of a groyne varies with the water flow: often they are less effective during bankful flows, when they are most needed. In such cases they should be combined with permanent bank protection, such as willow stakes or tipped stone. Deflectors can also be constructed to cause scour in the centre of the channel or deposition at the edges.
Biologically, current deflectors are of value in improving fish habitat. Groynes provide fish with shelter from fast water flow velocities, as well as increasing flow velocities in other sectors of the river channel – in sluggish streams, this may improve spawning conditions. In addition, groynes provide hard, stable substrates for colonisation by algae, mosses and their associated invertebrate communities. During low flows, if a groyne appears above water level, it may simulate temporary shoal habitats – suitable for colonisation by flowering plants.

The introduction of groynes may increase the biological productivity of a reach, since they increase the length of the bank channel boundary, and most biological activity occurs along the river margin. The example of the Roding illustrates how even a concrete-lined, trapezoidal channel can be improved biologically by the introduction of groynes and a small weir.
Current deflectors can be constructed from a variety of materials and designs. Natural blockstone is often most acceptable visually. Tree trunks, staked and wired securely, or lines of larch-stakes with or without a gravel infill are similarly 'natural' looking, and may be cheaper than blockstone. Stakes can be used to secure and mask stone-filled gabions in lowland rivers where blockstone is prohibitively expensive. Concrete structures are effective and can be well designed to fit into urban schemes, but do not have the crevices and cracks which attract invertebrates, algae and mosses.

AFON GWYRFAI, NEAR CAERNARFON, GWYNEDD

OS Map: 115. NGR: SH 547564
Gwynedd Division, Welsh Water Authority, Penrhosgarnedd, Bangor, Gwynedd.
Telephone: Bangor (0248) 51144.

Site Summary

Water resource scheme, capital works, 1978-81.
Channel: 7-8 metres wide, 0.3-1.5 metres deep.
Substrate: fine gravel and bedrock.
Designers: P Parkinson, Fisheries, Recreation and Amenity Officer, and N Milner, Senior Fisheries Scientist.

Work Description

See Section **113** Riffle and Pool Reinstatement for a fuller description of channel works at this site.
Locally quarried blockstone was placed to form current deflectors, pointing upstream, to improve fish habitat through diversifying the local sediment and flow patterns. Individual boulders were also placed on the stream bed in the same reach, for the same purpose.
The groynes were constructed by positioning stones from the bank outwards to a point about halfway across the channel. There is a greater depth of water over them at midstream than at the bankside (figures overleaf; photograph below).

Afon Gwyrfai: Three large blockstones placed, uncemented, on the bed of the dredged river.

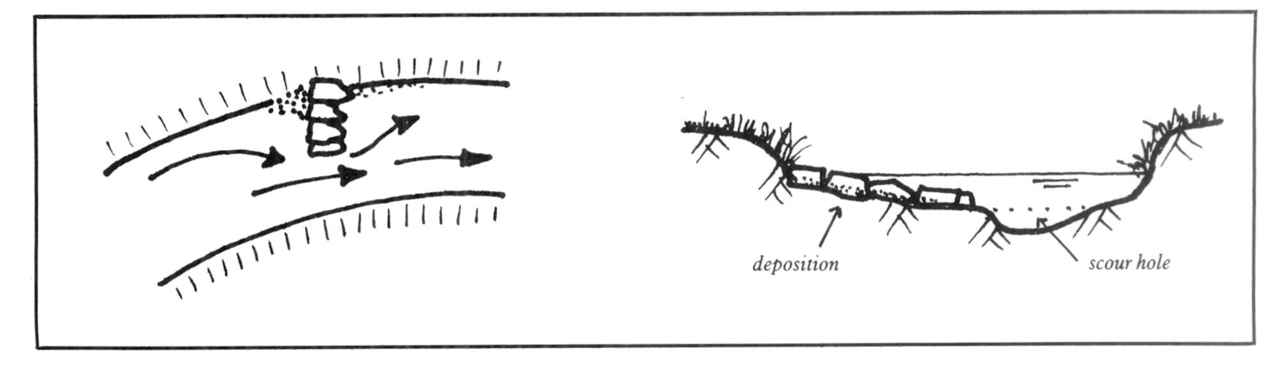

Afon Gwyrfai: An idealised plan and cross-section of the current deflectors.

Habitat Comments

1 An example of the effective and simple use of local materials to diversify a channel. Fish were seen holding position in the shelter downstream, and some mosses had begun to colonise the stones only 12 months after they were placed.

2 The use of local materials in an informal design is particularly appropriate to the moorland setting of this scheme.

RIVER TEME, LEINTWARDINE, HEREFORDSHIRE
OS Map: 137. NGR: SO 415928
Lower Severn Division, Severn Trent Water Authority, 64 Albert Road North, Great Malvern, Worcestershire.
Telephone: Malvern (06845) 61511.

Site Summary

Flood alleviation scheme, maintenance works, 1981.
Upland/lowland transition zone, rural location.
Channel: 0.5-2.5 metres high.
Substrate: cobbles, gravel, sand, alluvial and boulder clays.
Land-use: pasture.
Supervisor: B Draper.

Work Description

As part of river training maintenance work in 1980/81, current deflectors were constructed from blockstone and river gravels. It was intended they should protect the outer bank of a meander bend from further erosion; incidentally, it was hoped to protect a sand martin colony in the bank.

The groynes project across one-third of the width of the channel and are directed upstream, so that deposition in the angle reinforces the toe of the bank. Stone rip-rap was piled along the base of the bank for additional protection (figure below; photograph right).

The Teme is a valuable game fishing river, and the shelter provided by the groynes should improve fish habitat.

See page **110** for further information about this scheme.

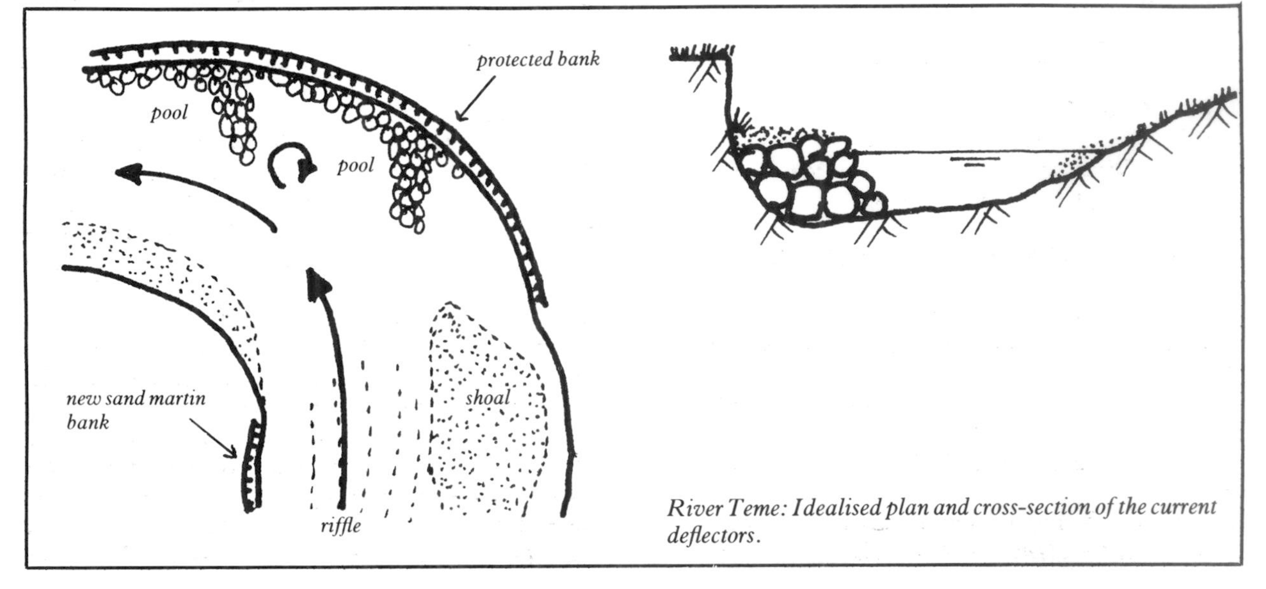

River Teme: Idealised plan and cross-section of the current deflectors.

River Teme: Blockstone and river gravels piled together to create current deflectors in front of a high eroding vertical earthbank.

Habitat Comments

1 The groynes have been effective in creating areas of still water in a turbulent gravelly reach of the Teme.

2 Sheep have access to the groynes and whilst sheep treading has helped to stabilise them, grazing has prevented the development of tall-herb vegetation. Fencing off some of the groynes with sheep netting to prevent grazing may be useful.

3 Once work was completed, the sand martin colony was deserted, a nearby unprotected bank being preferred. This may be because sand martins prefer to excavate the nest holes in eroding vertical earthbanks, ideally with water at the foot of the bank: once the groynes were constructed, these conditions were no longer satisfied (see page **285**).

RIVER RODING, ABRIDGE, ESSEX
OS Map: 177. NGR: TQ 466970
Eastern Division, Thames Water Authority, The Grange, Crossbrook Street, Waltham Cross, Herts.
Telephone: Waltham Cross (0992) 23611.

Site Summary

Flood alleviation scheme, capital works, 1980.
Rural location.
Channel: 8 metres wide, 0.2-0.6 metre deep (low water).
Substrate: clay, alluvial silt, concrete bank revetment.
Designers: D Wojcik, Project Engineer (New Works) and A Dearsley, Biologist.

Work Description

To diversify the flow of a 400 metre section of the Roding which had been straightened and canalised in 1973 during the construction of the M11 motorway, the opportunity was taken to introduce current deflectors and weirs as part of a wider flood alleviation scheme. The scheme is described in greater detail in Section **93** Multi-stage Channels. Being in a lowland clay catchment in eastern England, the use of blockstone for current deflectors would have been prohibitively expensive. Instead, gabion baskets and reno mattresses, filled with quarry stone and rubble, were used to create groynes in several designs. Larch poles driven vertically into the bed were also used. Groynes were positioned alternately on each side of the

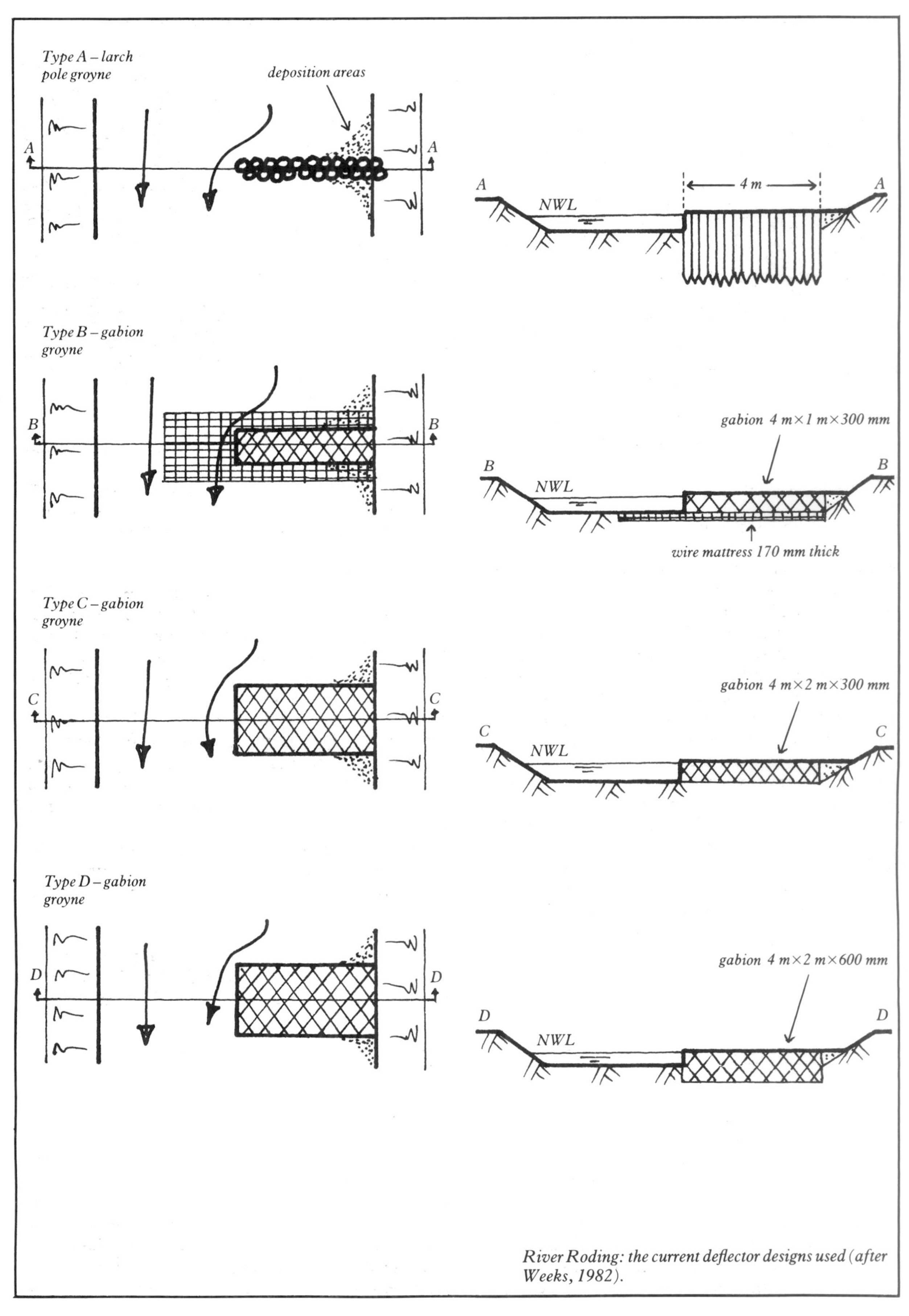

River Roding: the current deflector designs used (after Weeks, 1982).

River Roding: A typical gabion current deflector.

channel, so as to encourage a meandering flow pattern (figure left; photograph above).
Prior to the installation of the weir and groynes, the channel was very shallow during low flows, water passing uniformly over a silty bed between concrete banks. A survey of fish in the reach in 1978 showed that stone-loach were the most abundant species, (5.72 grams per cubic metre) with a smaller biomass of minnow, bullhead, stickleback species, and small chub, dace and roach, totalling only 9.5 grams per square metre overall. A year after the installation of the groynes and the weir (which increased water depth within the reach) the fish population had changed dramatically. All small fish classes (less than 10 centimetres in length) showed decreases in biomass while large and medium-sized (over 10 centimetres in length) chub, dace, roach, gudgeon, pike and large eels were recorded, all having been absent in the pre-scheme survey (Weeks, 1982). This suggests that conditions were improved for the growth of coarse fish which then replaced small fish typical of small, shallow streams.

Since they were installed, the gabion groynes have trapped silt, aiding the colonisation of waterside plants and helping to mask the wire mesh.

Habitat Comments

1 The fish surveys before and after the installation of the groynes amply demonstrate the increase in the variety of fish species which has resulted from the diversification of channel habitat.

2 The many crevices within the gabions probably increase the available habitat for stream invertebrates (more so than, say, a similar sized concrete structure) and, thereby, the available fish food.

3 The colonisation of the gabion tops by waterside plants benefits both the plant species and aerial insects – such as butterflies and hoverflies – which may feed on them.

4 The increase in bank (channel boundary length) may have benefited caddisfly, mayfly, dragonfly and damselfly, both as larvae and emerging adults.

Reference

Weeks, K G, 1982. Conservation aspects of river improvement schemes. Paper given to the Institute of Water Engineers and Scientists, 10 June 1982.

SHALLOW-WATER BERMS

The principle behind this technique is the creation of a shallow underwater marginal shelf to the river channel, to simulate a 'natural' single channel cross-section.
Engineering advantages include the provision of additional flood capacity, whilst maintaining a self-scouring low-flow channel (as in any multi-stage channel design) and bank toe protection through the establishment of marginal beds of emergent plants.
Biologically, berms increase the variety of water depth and flow conditions in the river channel. If left bare (which is only likely to occur on rivers with gravel substrates) feeding areas for common sandpiper and wagtails may be created. Elsewhere, the area available for aquatic plants – particularly emergent species – to colonise is increased, provid-

ing cover and food sources for invertebrates, fish and birds. Obviously, the process of colonisation can be speeded through planting (see Section **219**). As the following examples show, a wide variety of designs for berms are available. In designing a berm for any given site, the following points should be borne in mind:

A To be effective in increasing channel habitat variety, at least half the width of the berm should be submerged during times of lowest water flow.
B To encourage a range of aquatic plants, at least 20 centimetres of water should be over the lowest edge of the berm during lowest water flows.
C A 2 metre wide berm, with a slope of 1 in 4 or less, planted with emergent aquatic plants, is required to provide effective bank protection from erosion from boat wash (as recommended by Bonham (1980); see Section **171**).
D Riverside safety, especially where banks shelve deeply into deep water, may be improved by the construction of shallow water berms.
E If a shallow water berm is excavated as part of a multi-stage channel design, the protective margin of existing aquatic plants will be lost (contrast the Roding scheme **93**). The replanting of emergent aquatic plants may then be wise as a precaution againt bank erosion.

Reference

Bonham, A J, 1980. Bank protection using emergent plants against boat wash in rivers and canals. Hydraulics Research Station Report IT 206.

RIVER STORT NAVIGATION, NEAR BISHOPS STORTFORD, HERTFORDSHIRE
OS Map: 167. NGR: TL 495193 to 493203
Eastern Division, Thames Water Authority, The Grange, Crossbrook Street, Waltham Cross, Hertfordshire.
Telephone: Waltham Cross (0992) 23611.

Site Summary
Capital works, flood alleviation scheme, 1978-80.
Urban fringe, lowland location.
Channel: pounded navigation, 10-15 metres wide.
Berms: graded 1 in 3 to 1 in 4.5; 1.5 metres wide.
Substrate: clay.

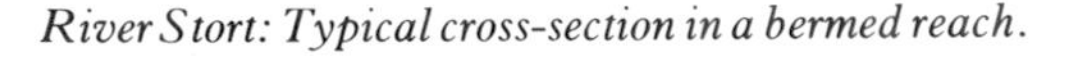

Work Description
The River Stort Navigation was remodelled between 1978 and 1980 by channel excavation and bank raising along 3,300 metres of channel; by the installation of 850 metres of steel sheet piling complete with concrete and stone bank protection; and by the construction of three flood discharge and water level control weirs.
During these operations, the opportunity was taken to construct, experimentally, a shallow water berm along a short length of the channel. As described in **219**, a research student was appointed to plant a variety of emergent aquatic plants, to monitor their establishment and to determine the impact of the works on the riverine environment.
The cross-section of an impounded navigation consists of steep banks above water level; a shallow shelf or beach just below water level; and a bed of silt gradually sloping to the deep, central boat channel. Such a profile develops gradually as a result of wave wash on the trapezoidal section that is left after dredging.
The intention of berm construction on the Stort was to increase the rate of recovery of the vegetation (by providing a new physical habitat for aquatic plants and through planting) and, secondly, to test the effectiveness of creating a vegetated berm to reduce bank erosion from boat wash (figure below; photograph right).

River Stort: Typical cross-section in a bermed reach.

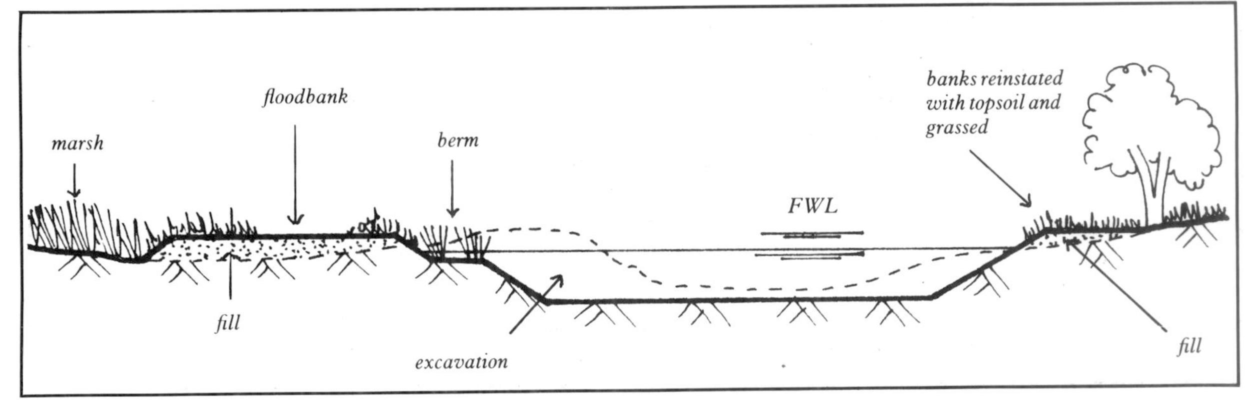

Because of access constraints in the town of Bishops Stortford, waterborne excavators were employed. To construct the berms, the channel of the Navigation had to be widened and the embankment and towpath were relocated along that reach. In this case, the berms were excavated after channel works had been completed.

Habitat Comments

1 The very steep batter left after regrading the banks of the Navigation severely limited the area available for marginal plants to colonise. The berm has increased the physical diversity of the channel and also the area available for aquatic vegetation to be planted and to colonise in future.

2 The berm was sited on the towpath side of the channel, and plants have been damaged in places by people.

3 The berm is about 1.5 metres wide, which although adequate to support plants to protect the bank from erosion, is barely enough to provide breeding cover for birds. It is difficult to assess the influence of this factor, however, because of disturbance from the adjacent footpath.

4 The design used here is, longitudinally, very uniform. As the water level is impounded there is little seasonal fluctuation which could create bays, shallows or muddy areas as additional variation in the channel habitat. It would have benefited wildlife to have designed the berm with variations in width and depth from place to place. This would probably be unnecessary in naturally fluctuating rivers.

River Stort: Showing the berm on the left, with well established emergent aquatic plants. In contrast, the far bank graded 1 in 1.5, has almost no emergents.

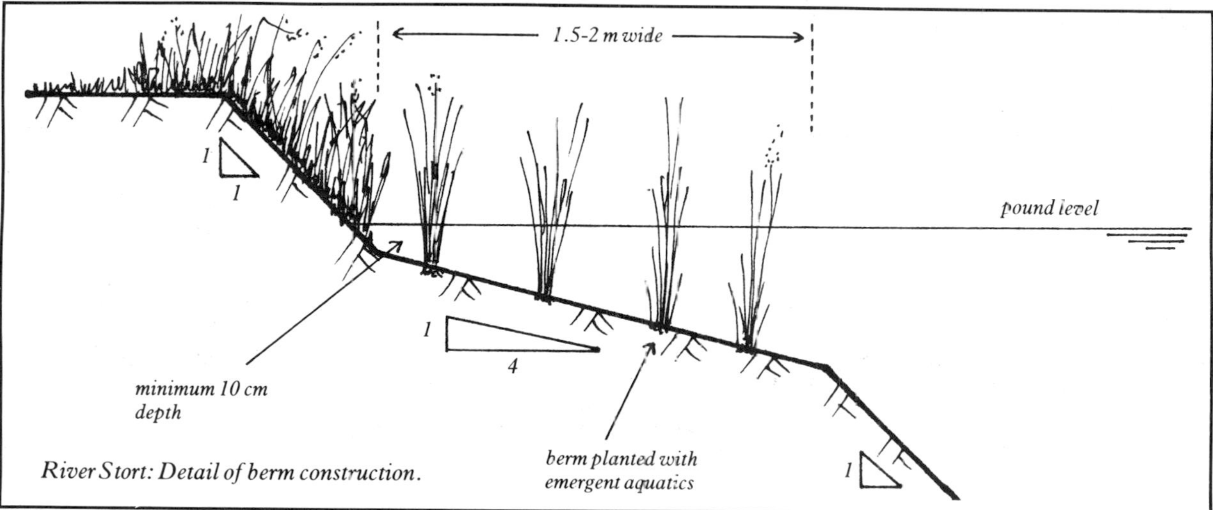

River Stort: Detail of berm construction.

RIVER TOVE, COSGROVE, MILTON KEYNES
OS Map: 152. NGR: SP 792439
Bedford Area Office, Cambridge Division, Anglian Water Authority, Cambridge Road, Bedford MK42 0LL.
Telephone: Bedford (0234) 63111.

Site Summary
Maintenance works, 1982.
Lowland, rural location.
Channel: 3-5 metres wide, depth variable.
Banks: 1-2.5 metres high, slopes vertical to 1 in 4.
Substrates: mud, soft silt, cemented gravel in riffles.

Work Description
Maintenance dredging of part of the River Tove carried out in 1982 has incorporated a wide range of conservation measures (see Sections **100** and **101**) since certain reaches were recognised as being of Site of Special Scientific Interest quality, although not yet notified under the Wildlife and Countryside Act 1981 (photograph below).
Dredging was carried out with a dragline excavator. Only short stretches were dredged, however, leaving patches of vegetation from which disturbed areas could be colonised. A smooth, uniform slope of 1 in 1.5 was left after dredging, unsuitable for rapid recolonisation since there are few sites for floating plant fragments to 'catch' and settle. The dragline operator was asked, therefore, to cut a narrow berm just below summer water level – although the berm is so narrow that 'notch' is perhaps a better description. Even in stiff clay, this was a difficult task: a hydraulic excavator would have done the work more easily and precisely. Once emergent plants have become established on the 'notch', they should provide the toe of the bank with some protection from erosion (figure below; photograph right).

River Tove: The rich emergent and floating plant community edging an untouched section.

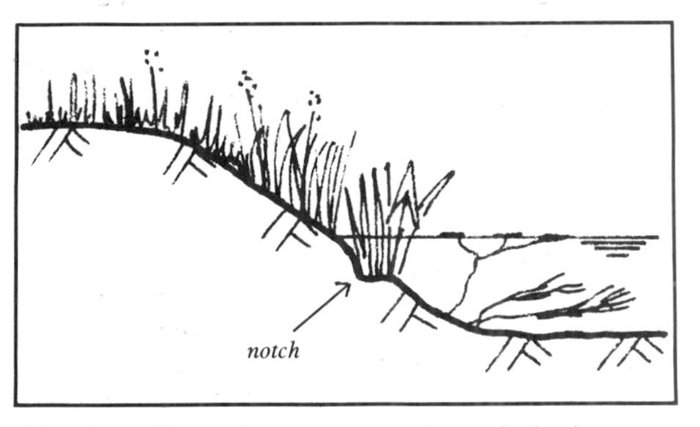

River Tove: Typical cross-section to show colonisation 'notch'.

Habitat Comments
1 Plants should readily colonise the 'notch' because care has been taken to retain undisturbed areas of aquatic and bank vegetation – sources of seeds and rhizomes are close at hand. The two *must* go hand in hand unless aquatic plants are deliberately planted in the notch after excavation.
2 Compared to excavating an even slope, both above and below water level, cutting even a narrow notch for plant colonisation is of benefit for wildlife.
3 On steeply sloping banks (of more than 1 in 3) adjacent to deep water, the notch may not be colonised by aquatic plants, since tall bank plants will tend to shade out growth. This problem is likely to be exacerbated on north-facing banks.

River Tove: Regraded bank on left (topsoiled but not yet seeded) with a notch cut below water level. Note that the lower 0.5-1 metre of the bank has not been topsoiled. Selective dredging has left many clumps of plants undisturbed (right), which will provide material for recolonisation.

RIVER ONNY, ONNIBURY, SHROPSHIRE

OS Map: 137. NGR: SO 453793
Lower Severn Division, Severn Trent Water Authority, 64 Albert Road North, Great Malvern, Worcestershire.
Telephone: Malvern (068 45) 61511.

Site Summary

Maintenance work, 1982.
Upland/lowland transition zone, rural location.
Channel: 8-12 metres wide; variable. Up to 1.5 metres deep, with good riffl/pool structure.
Substrate: gravel, cobble, bedrock, silt.
Supervisor: B Draper.

Work Description

The Onny is a gravelly river. At this point, it is in transition between the hills of the Welsh Marches and the alluvial lowlands of the Lower Severn Valley. Maintenance work was carried out in early 1982 to alleviate flooding and to protect a railway embankment endangered by the mobile river.
A new channel was excavated 20 metres from the old, in an asymmetric, multi-stage form. This incorporated a shallow, partly-submerged lower berm, and for flood flows, a broad upper berm. The intention was to create a deep, fast water channel with a gravelly, shallow margin on one side (to simulate the gravel shoals found naturally on such rivers) (figure overleaf).
The creation of the new channel required partial felling of an existing alder copse. The deep rooting habit of these trees was used to maintain a steep bank on that side, although several were coppiced to reduce their top-heaviness in case under-cutting occurred. Boulders weighing 500-750 kilograms were imported to the site to protect the 1 in 1.5 slopes of the railway embankment and the face of the upper berm.
Neither the lower nor the upper berm have been topsoiled or seeded, allowing temporary flower-rich plant communities to become established, benefiting both plants and terrestrial insects. Because of the gravelly nature of the river, it is unlikely that aquatic emergents will become established. The upper flood berm will be planted with ash, oak and beech and shrubs to reinstate the woodland/scrub habitat that was the main feature of the river corridor before work was carried out. Obviously, however, this will take at least 20 years to become established (photograph overleaf).

Habitat Comments

1 Total channel disturbance, such as this, is tolerable over short lengths of river – provided care is taken to restore a physically diverse channel.
2 The asymmetric channel provides an excellent variety of substrates and habitats for stream organisms.

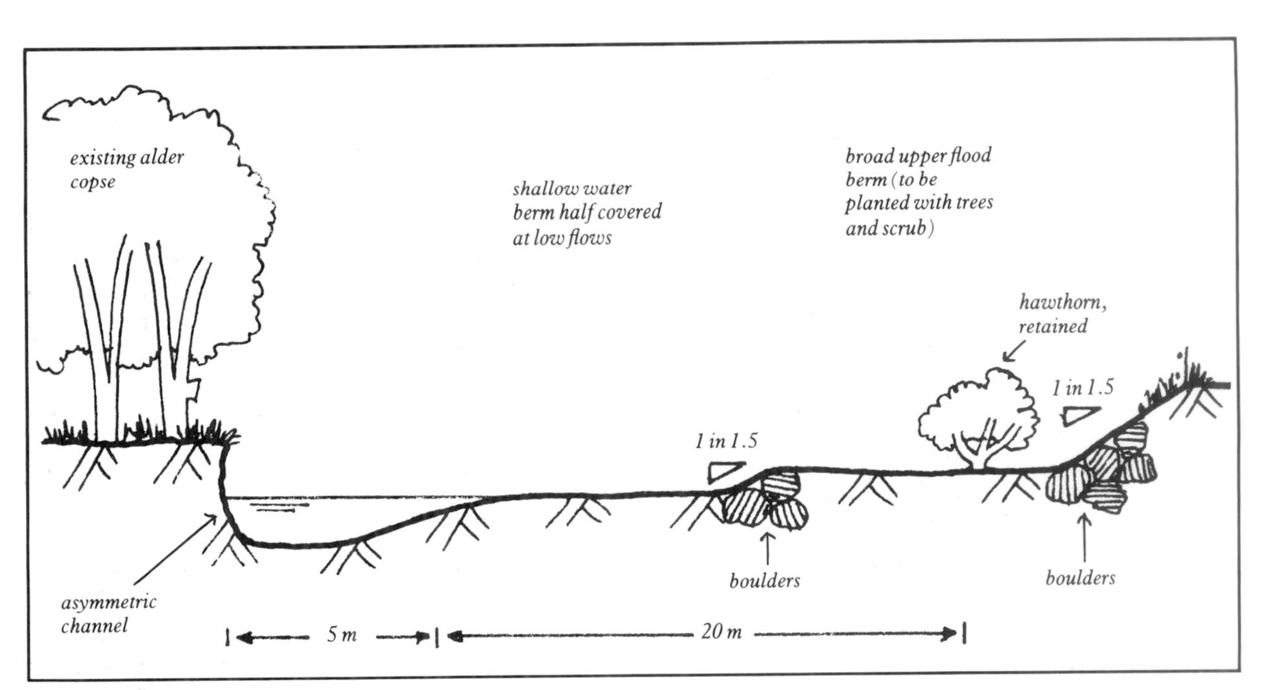

River Onny: Typical cross-section (not to scale).

River Onny: Looking downstream two months after work was completed. Note that the upper berm had not yet been planted.

3 The broad, shallow berms simulate natural shoals and beaches, typical of this type of river, and providing good feeding areas for upland riverine birds – especially dippers and wagtails. Temporary flower-rich communities can develop on the lower berm. Aquatic emergent plants are generally absent from gravelly rivers of this type; they are unlikely to colonise the lower berm, and should not be planted in this situation.

4 The alder roots in the steeper bank will provide shelter for caddisfly larvae and other stream invertebrates. Leaf and twig fall will increase organic matter in the stream, benefiting invertebrates, and providing food resources for fish.

SHALLOW BAYS

Sheltered from the main line of water flow, shallow bays add further to the diversity of river habitats. In summer, conditions become pond-like – the water warmed by the sun, rich in algae and plankton with snails, water beetles and pond skaters. Depending on the permanence of these conditions, dragonfly and damselfly larvae may be found. Fish fry benefit from the rich feeding conditions; the shallow water also protects them to a certain extent from large predators such as pike.
On 'natural' rivers, bays emerge as water levels fall. In trapezoidal channels with uniform bank slopes, however, this does not occur, and deliberate steps may be required to create them. The simplest and most effective bays are stock watering points – which diversify both channel and bank habitats. Alternatively, bays can be excavated in a bank, or created between two current deflectors.
On lowland rivers, especially chalk and limestone streams, shallow bays are likely to become dominated by aquatic plants – particularly emergent species – unless they are kept in check by cattle grazing (sheep will not graze aquatic plants below water level), or the bay is regularly cleaned out. Even a plant-dominated bay will benefit wildlife, however, and from the river management viewpoint, it should not encroach into the main river channel.
As two of the following examples show, shallow bays are attractive to people. Two points that need to be considered in scheme design, therefore, are safety for people and seclusion for wildlife.

RIVER STOUR, REDHILL, NEAR BOURNEMOUTH

OS Map: 195. NGR: SZ 091960
Avon and Dorset Division, Wessex Water Authority, 2 Nuffield Road, Poole, Dorset.
Telephone: Poole (0202) 671144.

Site Summary
Capital works, land drainage and flood alleviation.
Urban fringe location.
Lowland, clay-chalk river.
Channel: 15-20 metres wide.
Substrate: clay and silt.
Contact: M West.

Work Description
During the early 1970s, the River Stour between Throop and Longham was dredged and realigned by the late Avon and Dorset River Authority, to alleviate flooding and improve the drainage of the adjacent land. The river is a good coarse fishery, and the scheme was designed in close consultation with landowners and angling interests.
Near Redhill, a shallow bay, with banks graded to 1 in 4, was excavated in the outer bank of a realigned bend. Elsewhere, banks were uniformly graded to 1 in 1.5. No planting was done, since it was judged that plant fragments from upstream would quickly establish.
After ten years, the bay remains open. The margin of the pool has been colonised by bur-reed; when visited in July 1982, the shallow water of the bay was teeming with shoals of small fish. Bank vegetation is patchy with large areas of bare soil – due entirely to trampling by people. The bay is close to a housing estate, and is a popular fishing and play area for children (figures below).

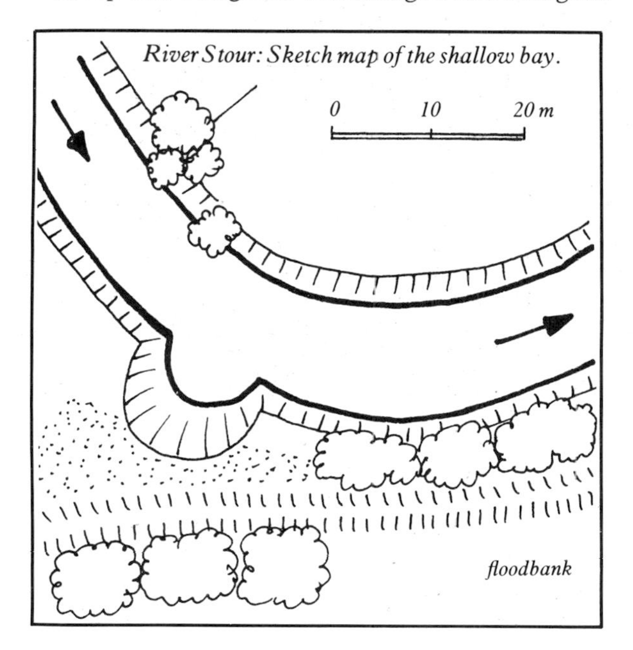

River Stour: Sketch map of the shallow bay.

River Stour: Field sketch of the shallow bay.

Elsewhere along the Stour, the graded banks have been eroded to a limited extent – creating vertical earth banks and, where they have slumped, natural berms, now colonised by bulrush, bur-reed and arrowhead.

Habitat Comments
1 The bay contributes to the variety of channel habitats on the Stour and benefits fish and invertebrates.
2 The bay has great human value: it is one of the few easily accessible sections of the Stour and attracts river users – especially children. Wildlife would have benefited even more if similar bays had been excavated elsewhere, at less accessible locations.

RIVER MEDEN, WARSOP, NOTTINGHAMSHIRE
OS Map: 120. NGR: SK 566683.
Lower Severn Division, Severn Trent Water Authority, Mapperley Hall, Lucknow Avenue, Nottingham.
Telephone: Nottingham (0602) 608161.

Site Summary
Land drainage improvement and flood alleviation scheme, capital works, 1981.
Lowland, urban location.
Channel: 3.5 metres bed width, c. 0.5 metre water depth.
Banks: 2-3 metres high, slope 1 in 1.5.
Substrate: silt and organic material overlying Bunter.
Designer: A Hallam, Senior Project Engineer.
Adviser: N Lewis, Conservation Officer, Nottinghamshire Trust for Nature Conservation.

Work Description
Subsidence resulting from coal mining adversely affected surface water sewers and caused frequent flooding of agricultural land and a recreation ground in Warsop. To remedy the situation, a scheme was carried out in 1981 over 1.4 kilometres of the Meden, which involved excavation in the river bed of up to 1.5 metres depth. The design allowed for the careful disposal of excavated spoil in adjacent areas (see **198**) and reinstatement of disturbed areas.
In order to minimise disturbance to wildlife, work was carried out from one side, the working bank being graded to a slope of 1 in 1.5. The opposite bank was generally retained undisturbed. The work followed the existing course of the river, and no channel straightening was carried out.
To provide a sheltered area for fish, and to aid colonisation by aquatic plants, a shallow bay was excavated with the sides graded to 1 in 1.5 (figure below). Elsewhere, fish holding pools were excavated and a gravel riffle replaced on the lowered bed.
The recovery of native bankside plants has been satisfactory since completion of the scheme, as the original top soil containing seeds and rhizomes of these plants was used for reinstatement of the working areas. An area was experimentally seeded with a wild-flower mixture, which unfortunately failed.
Being in a recreation ground, the river was attractive to children, although the steep banks made access difficult. Steps for easy access were built nearby, but the local authority eventually requested that, for safety reasons, certain lengths of the banktop should be fenced.

River Meden: Sketch of the shallow bay.

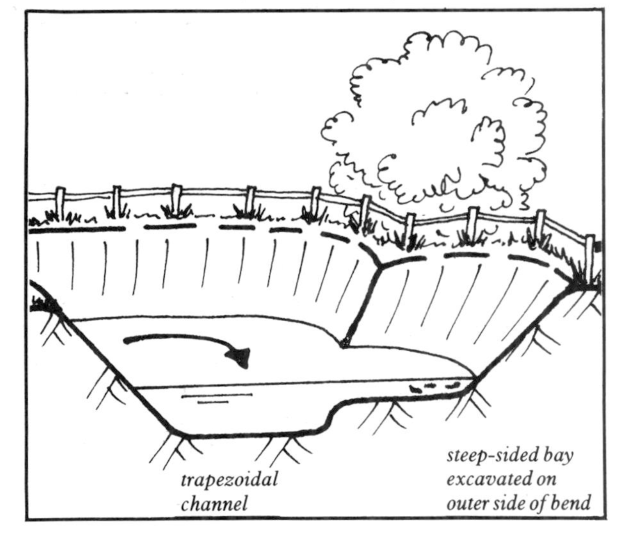

Habitat Comments
1 The bay provides variety in depth and flow for stream invertebrates and fish fry, and has probably enriched the animal community of this stretch of the Meden. Provision of more than one bay in the 1.4 kilometres of the scheme would have certainly benefited wildlife in the river corridor even more.
2 The problem of safety for children attracted to the bay could have been overcome by excavating gentler slopes around it (and, indeed, throughout the length of the park).
3 Water quality is probably the limiting factor on aquatic communities in rivers such as the Meden, but even so, attempts to diversify the physical environment of the channel, such as this, are admirable.

RIVER STOUR, TREDDINGTON, WORCESTERSHIRE
OS Map: 151. NGR: SP 260434
Avon Division, Severn Trent Water Authority, Finham Reclamation Works, St Martins Road, Finham, Coventry
Telephone: Coventry (0203) 415115.

Regional Architects' Department, STWA, Abelson House, 2297 Coventry Road, Sheldon, Birmingham.
Telephone: 021-743 4222.

Site Summary
Maintenance dredging, 1981.
Rural village-edge location.
Channel: 3-5 metres wide, depth 1 metre.
Banks: 2-3 metres high, now with a 1 in 2 batter.
Substrate: clay and gravel.
Engineers: D Alcott and W Garrad.
Landscape Architects: J Purseglove and M Ericcson.

Work Description
Maintenance dredging of the Stour in 1981 reduced bed levels by up to 1 metre. Throughout the work, care was taken to maintain the wildlife habitats and landscape features of the river corridor (see Sections **102**, **253** and **262**).
A shallow indent was excavated during dredging – simply a 'bite' out of the bank, graded to a shallow slope. The bay was cut in an ungrazed section of the bank, backed by scrub but not shaded (photograph below).
The banks were left to colonise naturally from local seed sources, and were not top-soiled.

Habitat Comments
1 The indent is well located – the site is remote and secluded in an ungrazed strip of land between a treeline and the river.
2 The bay helps to diversify bank as well as channel habitats.

River Stour: The shallow indent.

LADDON BROOK, IRON ACTON, AVON
OS Map: 172. NGR: ST 671844.
Bristol Avon Division, Wessex Water Authority, Box 95, Quay House, The Ambury, Bath, Avon.
Telephone: Bath (0225) 313500.

Site Summary
Land drainage scheme, capital works, 1979.
Lowland, rural location.
Channel: 2 metres wide at low water level, depth 1.5 metres.
Banks: 1-1.5 metres high, 1 in 1 slope or steeper.
Substrate: clay and gravel.

Work Description
The Brook drains agricultural land north of Bristol. It was dredged in 1979, care being taken to retain hedges on both banks (see **245**).
To provide cattle on adjacent pasture with access to the Brook, a stock watering point was constructed – incidentally forming a shallow bay. The water point provides a slightly different channel-edge habitat compared to the rest of the steep-sided Brook. Occasional cattle grazing and trampling keeps narrow-leaved emergent aquatic plants in check, which might otherwse dominate the area, and allows a mixed plant community of broad-

leaved species to flourish (figures and photograph below).

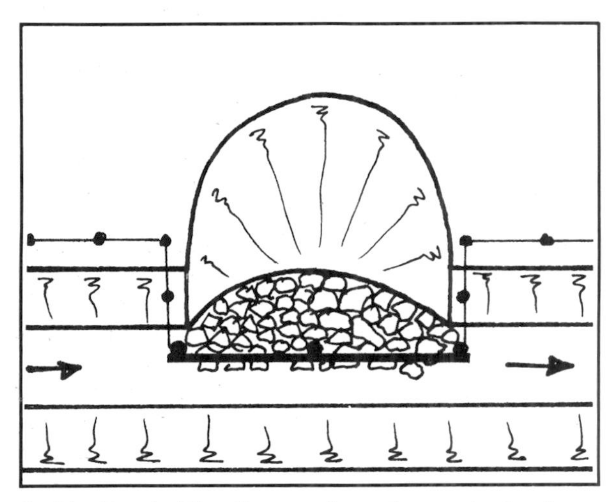

Laddon Brook: Plan diagram of a cattle-watering bay in a uniform channel.

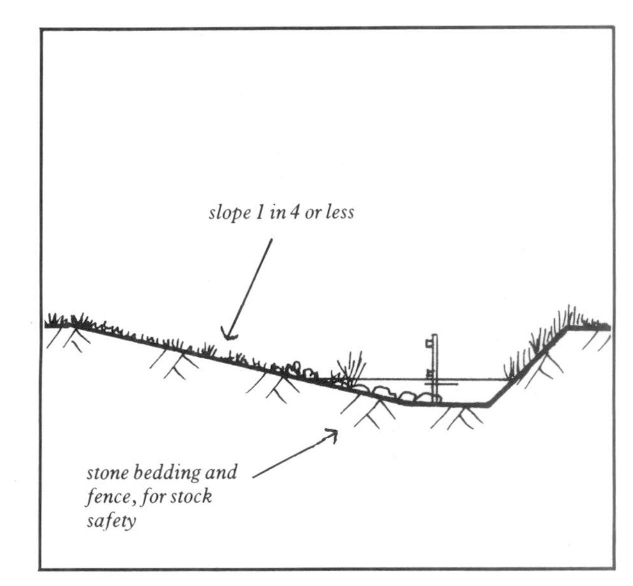

Laddon Brook: Cross-sectional diagram of a cattle-watering bay.

Laddon Brook: Securely fenced cattle-watering point, forming a shallow bay rich in emergent plants, in an otherwise steep-banked, partially shaded reach.

Habitat Comments

1 This is an attractive example of a common type of work which unintentionally diversifies channel habitats, thus aiding wildlife.

2 It is essential to fence the watering point securely, both to protect other parts of the channel from damage by stock, and to protect other vegetation on the bank and channel edge from grazing. Tipped stone, rubble or gravel on the bed of the watering point is both safer for stock and diversifies channel substrate. In some clay streams, such as the Cary in Somerset, stock watering bays are major wildlife habitat features – with a greater variety of aquatic plants than elsewhere and the rubble bed forming the only riffles for miles.

RIVER ALNE, WOOTTON WAWEN, WARWICKSHIRE
OS Map: 151. NGR: SP 159643
Avon Division, Severn Trent Water Authority, Finham Reclamation Works, St Martins Road, Finham, Coventry CU3 6PR.
Telephone: Coventry (0203) 415115.
Regional Architects' Department, STWA, Abelson House, 2297 Coventry Road, Sheldon, Birmingham.
Telephone: 021-743 4222.

Site Summary
Flood alleviation scheme, capital works, 1979/80.
Rural, lowland location.
Channel: 4-5 metres wide, depth variable.
Banks: variable slopes.
Substrate: sandy clay, gravel.
Engineer: R Tinley.
Landscape Architect: J Purseglove.

Work Description
Dredging for flood alleviation, carried out on the Alne in 1979/80, lowered bed levels by about 1 metre. To compensate for the steeper bank profiles this created, shallow bays were excavated at irregular intervals. The example illustrated here was about 10 metres long by 3 metres wide. The bay shelves gently such that there is about 0.5 metre depth of water at its mouth, before dropping steeply into the main channel, which is 1-1.5 metres deep. It is sited between two coppiced alders, which protect the exposed bank from erosion. The banks around the bay are graded to approximately 1 in 4, so that cattle can have access to drink safely (photograph below).
The bay is located immediately upstream of a meander which has been retained with a through-flow of water, where the main channel was realigned.

River Alne: The bay, on the right, looking upstream. The alder clump in the foreground protects the downstream edge of the bay from erosion.

Habitat Comments
1 Deepening and realignment leaves a uniform channel and bankside unless deliberate efforts are made to introduce physical variety.
2 The shallow bay can be colonised by a range of water plants, but these should not invade the main channel because of the sudden increase in depth and flow rate at its mouth. Aquatic plants from the original bank could be put on one side during excavation and then dumped back to speed colonisation.
3 Invertebrate and fish life will benefit from the additional cover, shelter and slower water flow velocities. Emergent aquatic and bank plants should also provide water birds such as moorhen, mallard and little grebe with cover for nesting.

WHOLE CHANNEL REALIGNMENT

Occasionally, works may be required to realign a river channel – such as when a motorway cuts across a meander loop. Often such realignment works result in the river channel being straightened; heavy bank and bed protection may then be required to reduce erosion and scour. Alternatives are available, however, as demonstrated by a scheme carried out on the River Roding at Passingford Bridge (below). Other examples which contribute ideas for natural channel realignment are Gum Branch (**115**) and Henley-in-Arden (**87** and **224**).

RIVER RODING, PASSINGFORD BRIDGE, ESSEX

OS Map: 167. NGR: TQ 508975
Eastern Division, Thames Water Authority, The Grange, Crossbrook Street, Waltham Cross, Hertfordshire.
Telephone: Waltham Cross (0992) 23611.

Site Summary
Channel diversion scheme, capital works, 1982.
Lowland, rural location.
Channel: 6-11 metres wide; 1.5-2.5 metres deep.
Banks: 1.5-2 metres high, batter varied.
Substrate: clay and imported gravel.
Designer: D Wojcik, Project Engineer, New Works.

Work Description
In 1973, during construction of the M11, a length of the River Roding near Loughton of about 400 metres had to be realigned, and a straight, concrete-lined diversion channel was constructed. This impoverished fish populations, and it was only by the installation of a low flow weir and current deflectors as part of the 1979-80 Abridge flood alleviation scheme (see **124** and **129**) that the fish community showed any signs of recovery.
When a similar diversion for 200 metres of the Roding was required 6 kilometres upstream, near Passingford Bridge, as a result of construction of the M25, the designers sought to construct as natural a channel as possible, in which the natural fish community (the Roding is noted for chub) could flourish.
The original motorway design involved construction of a wide, straight channel protected with Dytap concrete revetment, similar to that constructed in the 1973 M11 realignment. TWA decided that this was unacceptable and prepared a 'natural river design'. A reach of the Roding was sought which had entry and exit lines matching those of the realigned section and which was also of similar length. A matching section was found 4 kilometres downstream, near Brook House Farm, and taken as a blueprint for the diversion channel (figure below; photograph right).

River Roding: The 'adopted' river section at TQ 480977, near Brook House Farm.

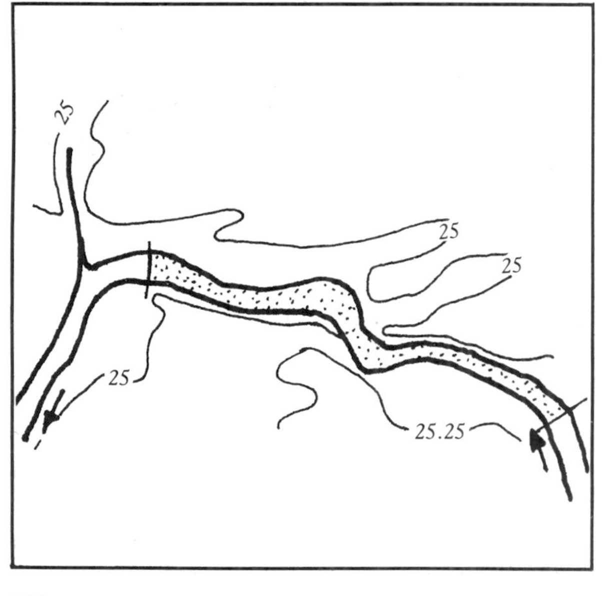

River Roding: Realigned river section at TQ 508975, near Passingford Bridge.

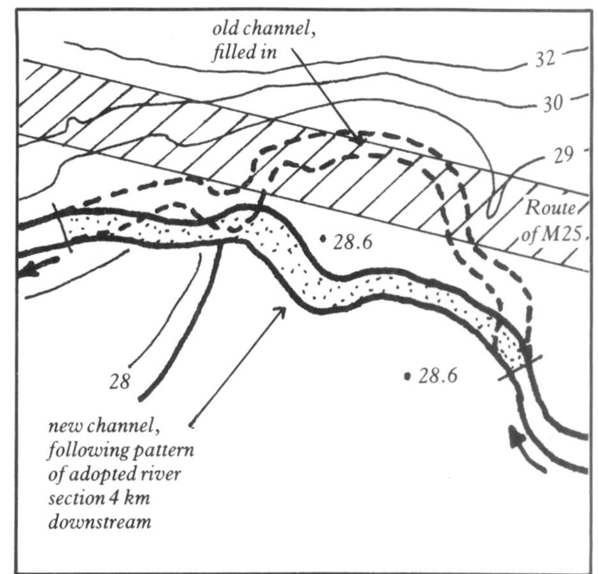

River Roding: Channel near Brook House Farm, used as a model for the realigned channel.

In early 1982, the contractor excavated the new channel reproducing the planform and bank slopes of the adapted section. The bed profile of the river was not matched exactly: this was considered to be unnecessary as long as the meandering pattern and slope of the banks was reproduced – natural processes would do the rest.

Ideally, gravel riffles should be created with material taken from the riffles of the old channel. Unfortunately, in this case the gravel was absent from the original river section. Instead, gravel was obtained from a natural gravel seam excavated during construction of the lower part of the diversion.

The natural river design occupied less land than the original motorway design and was probably cheaper, since the extensive revetment works were no longer required. The road engineers still requested extra bank protection with stone-filled gabions at the junctions with the old channel (figure below, photograph overleaf).

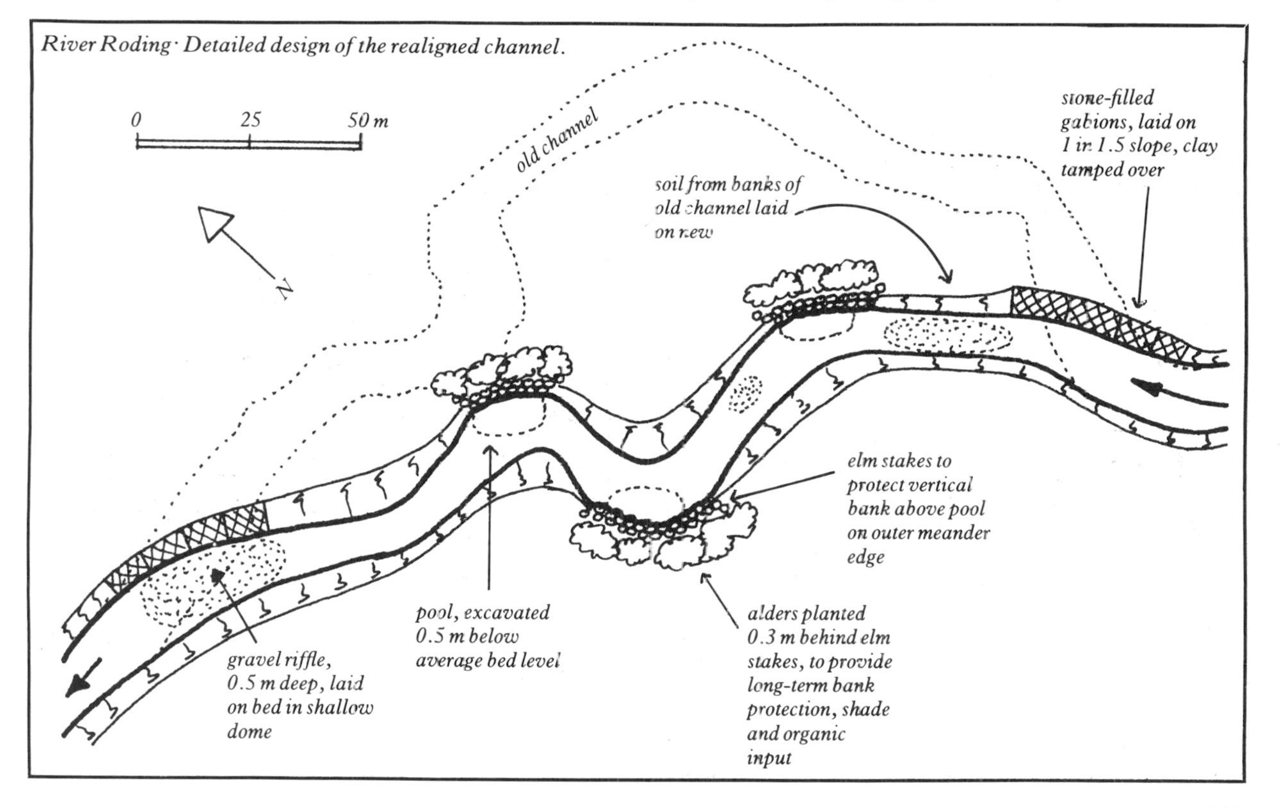

River Roding: Detailed design of the realigned channel.

River Roding: The new realigned channel near Passingford, four months after the completion of work.

Habitat Comments

1 Using a reach of the existing, natural channel as a blueprint for a new section of river provides a simple and elegant solution to a potentially complex river engineering problem.

2 The diverse channel and bank slopes provide a variety of habitats which, given time, should permit development of a balanced wildlife community.

3 The bank protection – using elm stakes and alders – to support a steep bank is sympathetic to plant and animal colonisation. The gabion protection may be unnecessary, but covering them with clay and topsoil should permit rapid plant colonisation.

4 Topsoil from the old river channel was spread on the banks of the new channel. This could help development of a similar marginal and bankside plant community in the new channel. For a few years, however, it is likely that dock and crucifers will dominate – weeds with long-lived seeds which respond to disturbance. Possibly, stripping turf from the banks of the old channel, and relaying them on the new, would help to reduce this aggressive weed growth (see **238**).

TECHNICAL 2: BANK FORM

Bank form – slopes, materials and their variability – is inseparably linked to channel form. In times of high flow, the banks are part of the river channel, and bank slope, in particular, influences erosion and depositional processes (see pages 115 and 142). For the purposes of this Handbook, however, we follow the convention of describing habitats at and below normal water level as 'channel' and those above as 'banks'.

For plants and animals living in the river corridor, the form of the riverbank is of considerable importance because:

- bankside habitats are of value to wildlife in their own right.
- bankside habitats may act as a buffer zone between the river and the adjacent land, helping to protect the river from undesirable influences such as spray drift from pesticides and fertilisers, and human disturbance.
- soil moisture content varies between the water surface of the river and the banktop, thus influencing the type and distribution of bank vegetation. Bank slope thus determines the width of this gradation.
- bank slopes influence channel scour and deposition.
- the frequency of bare, vertical earth banks determines the availability of habitat for bank-living species such as water vole, kingfisher and sand martin.

A wide range of practices are described in this section which either maintain or recreate the natural variation in banks and materials, so retaining or permitting the rapid re-establishment of natural plant and animal communities. As in 'Technical 1, Channel Form', non-uniformity is the key. Given that bank revetment is required, it is preferable on both aesthetic and wildlife conservation grounds to use natural materials – living or dead – than to use man-made materials and structures of concrete, nylon, plastic and steel.

In Britain, the use of plants, wood and stone is often regarded as being 'traditional' or 'labour intensive'. In Bavaria and Austria, the same methods have been examined and updated as the science of 'biotechnical engineering' – making use of the strengths of natural materials and exploiting their different growth forms so that they perform effectively to replace or complement man-made materials.

The benefits to wildlife are two-fold. Firstly, natural materials tend to be more variable in character, with different profiles, holes, crevices, nooks and crannies, so permitting the more rapid establishment of plant and animal communities. Secondly, the dynamic state of our watercourses inevitably means that materials will be washed out, eroded or otherwise deteriorate at some point in the short or long term future – with unpredictable consequences for the natural environment. The destruction or degradation of natural materials is likely to pose less of a hazard than that of man-made structures: gabion baskets, for example, may break open or rust over time, leaving an unsightly and dangerous tangle of wire which would be avoided by the use of a 'natural' technique.

The concept of biotechnical engineering is based on three principles:

- flexible structures should be employed to absorb erosive energy rather than to reflect it.
- plants can be used to provide a self-regenerating first line of protection from scour (or indeed, wave wash from boats), while inert materials underneath provide a second line of defence when and where necessary.
- bank protection should use the cheapest available local materials; the major costs are transferred from the purchase of materials and equipment to paying for labour, the latter perhaps involving long-term maintenance programmes.

The last principle requires expansion. Biotechnical engineering techniques tend to involve low capital expenditure on materials and equipment, and high revenue expenditure – mainly on labour for maintenance. In contrast, man-made techniques tend to be high on capital and low on revenue expenditure. At present, the financial, organisational and political pressures facing drainage authorities tend to favour capital investment in materials and equipment rather than investment in a skilled labour force. Despite this, a number of RWA Divisions are regularly using the biotechnical methods described. The wider and increased use of these methods, however, may demand a switch from capital to revenue expenditure to provide adequate staffing levels; to ensure the training of a labour force in biotechnical engineering skills; and to provide for the continuity of the labour force.

Bankside vegetation

The nature and management of bankside vegetation is a key part of 'Bank Form'. This is considered in detail in 'Technical 5 – Grass and Herbs' and 'Technical 6 – Trees and Scrub'. The key points are summarised here:

Bankside and banktop vegetation varies with height above low water level. Flowering herbs at the toe of the bank are usually able to survive in a temporary habitat, which may be occasionally destroyed by flooding. These plants can easily be re-established by planting or, by leaving refuges, will spread out to reach maturity again in a year or two. At the other end of the scale, trees and scrub on the

drier banktop survive flooding through their tenacity. The lifespan of individuals is measured in decades rather than single years and, after disturbance, the recovery of the community as a whole is a long, slow process perhaps taking centuries.
Because of the vital role of trees and scrub in providing shelter, cover, food and organic detritus for wildlife and plants around them – as well as gracing the landscape – and because the recovery rate is so slow, replanting trees and scrub is a very poor second to their conservation. Most water authorities already recognise this in their own guidelines, and recommend practices which help to retain trees during maintenance and capital works.

The scheme examples
Of the following schemes, those on pages **146** to **154** illustrate methods which help to conserve and retain bankside wildlife habitats. Those on pages **155** to **196** describe methods of bank protection which recreate holes, crevices, nooks and crannies – so allowing plant and animal communities to recover as rapidly as possible once river engineering operations have been carried out. As discussed above, non-uniformity, preferably through the use of natural materials, provides the key.
Unlike other sections of the manual, the use of some revetment materials has been illustrated with reference to sea defence works.

WORKING FROM ONE BANK

This is already standard practice for the maintenance operations of many drainage authorities, but the amount of environmental disturbance caused depends on two factors – the width of the channel and the reach of the equipment being used.
For the purpose of conserving diverse bank form, working from one bank means LEAVING THE OPPOSITE BANK ENTIRELY UNTOUCHED (photograph right). This combines well with partial dredging or weed-cutting of the channel to leave at least one-third untouched (see pages **98** and **146**).
Although it may be convenient to carry out all of a scheme from one side, there are advantages in alternating the working bank – to avoid sensitive wildlife habitats or to avoid complaints from a single landowner who has had all the spoil spread on his side. This may also help retention of trees which help to shade out weed growth (**214**).
With care and forethought, equipment can work between trees (**246**), over hedges (**244**) and track through brambles and rose scrub (**243**), without long-term damage to it – so that the worked bank is not necessarily denuded and less than 50 per cent of bank habitat is disturbed.
If significant widening is carried out, however, all the trees and scrub on the working bank will be lost. In these circumstances, the channel should be slightly over-widened and a flatter batter to the bank be incorporated, so that aquatic and herbaceous vegetation, trees and scrub can be replanted without the need for regular management to reduce hydraulic roughness and to restore the design cross-section.

A small river, deepened and widened in 1982. Work was carried out from one bank – but this has not conserved the bank habitat.

AFON EWENNY, BRIDGEND, MID GLAMORGAN
OS Map: 170. NGR: SS 903774
Gower Division, Welsh Water Authority, 86 The Kingsway, Swansea, Glamorgan. Telephone: Swansea (0792) 468000.

Site Summary
Flood alleviation scheme, capital works, 1978/79.
Urban fringe location.
Channel: 3-5 metres wide.
Banks: 1 in 2 on worked bank, variable on opposite bank.
Substrate: shale, clay, bedrock.
Engineer: E Petty.

Work Description
To alleviate flooding of houses and an adjacent main road, the Ewenny was deepened and slightly widened in 1978, forming a roughly trapezoidal channel. Work was done entirely from one side of the channel, leaving a row of mature alders and the far bank and bed undisturbed.
The worked bank was graded to a batter of 1 in 2, topsoiled and seeded (photograph below).
This small scheme also demonstrates the retention of tree cover: overhanging branches were kept; shrub and bramble cover beneath the alders was left; and the newly graded bank was stock fenced and planted with alder and other native trees. Eventually, the stream should have its original tree cover restored – at least over short stretches.

Habitat Comments
1 The tree and scrub-covered, uneven bank under the alders was preserved intact. Working from one bank in this manner also allows the margin of the channel, together with its wildlife community, to be retained (see page **98**).
2 The worked bank was left at a uniform slope. Scour in the past three years has steepened the outer bank of the bend – this could have been anticipated, and a steep bank cut and protected with stone or stakes if felt necessary, while regrading was being done.
3 Tree-planting on the right, worked bank, has had a poor success rate to date, because the stock-fence was placed too close to the young trees. Horses were able to reach over and eat them! More tree planting is due to be carried out which, hopefully, will be more successful.

Afon Ewenny: The left bank was untouched during deepening and widening for years prior to this photograph being taken. The right bank was regraded, seeded, fenced and planted with trees.

EAST FEN CATCHWATER, STICKFORD, LINCOLNSHIRE
OS Map: 122. NGR: TF 364605
Lincoln Division, Anglian Water Authority, 50 Wide Bargate, Boston, Lincolnshire.
Telephone: Boston (0205) 62661.

Site Summary
Annual maintenance.
Fenland drainage system.
Channel: 6 metres wide, 3-4 metres deep.
Bank slopes: 1 in 1.5 on worked bank, steeper and less even on opposite.
Substrate: clays.

Work Description
The East Fen Catchwater is a large carrier, gathering water from higher land to the west and re-routing it away from the rich arable land of the fens to the east. Regular maintenance of the catchwater is essential for drainage of the adjacent lowlands.
Annual bank maintenance and drain clearance has been carried out from one bank only for many years, allowing a tall, dense hedge of mixed tree species to grow up on the highland side. The worked bank is maintained at a batter of 1 in 1.5 and, with annual mowing, has a grassy plant cover of perennials – nettle, thistle, dock, hogweed and canary grass. On the rougher, less disturbed and more shaded bank grows an understorey of willow herb, false oatgrass, dock and St John's wort (photograph below).

Habitat Comments
1 The channel is artificial, but leaving one bank more or less untouched over the years has allowed the bank form to develop from a uniformly trapezoidal section, providing sheltered sites for a wide variety of plants and animals, including water vole.
2 In contrast to almost every other drain in the area, the East Fen Catchwater has dense, continuous tree cover on one bank and a woodland-type plant cover beneath it. The plant community is not very rich, and all are common species, but in contrast to the surrounding intensive arable land it provides cover, shelter and varied food sources for a wide variety of invertebrates, birds and mammals.

East Fen Catchwater: Ash, hawthorn, sycamore, poplar and sallow dominate the unworked bank, providing cover and food for wildlife in the channel as well as on the bank itself.

RIVER YEO, BRADFORD ABBAS TO SHERBORNE, DORSET
OS Map: 194. NGR: ST 600138
Somerset Division, Wessex Water Authority, Kings Square, Bridgwater, Somerset.
Telephone: Bridgwater (0278) 57333.

Site Summary
Land drainage scheme, capital works, 1979/80.
Rural location.
Channel: 2 metres wide.
Banks: 2-2.5 metres high.
Substrate: sand, silt, clay, gravel.

Work Description
The Yeo below Sherborne, Dorset, is a small meandering river. A land drainage scheme in 1979/80 lowered the bed by 1 to 1.5 metres and a number of meanders were infilled or 'eased'. Despite this drastic disturbance to bank and channel habitats and loss of channel length, care was taken to work from one bank, wherever possible to preserve the variation in bank slopes and in particular, steep sandy banks used by sand martins for nesting. On the inside bends of the few meanders that were retained, the angle of the regraded bank was reduced from 1 in 1.5 to approximately 1 in 3 – to aid reinstatement of a more natural meander cross-section (photograph below).

Habitat Comments
1 Working from one bank has conserved a diverse bank form over at least 30-40 per cent of the total length of bank. At the same time, the vegetation has acted as a refuge for birds, mammals and invertebrates and a source of seed to assist the natural regeneration of the plant community on the disturbed banks.
2 The scheme is commendable for attempting to reinstate varied bank slopes on some of the regraded sections.

River Yeo: A retained meander bend, with the steep outer bank (and its scrub cover) left untouched. Machines worked from the left bank, which was regraded to a more gentle slope than elsewhere. Note the contrast in vegetation between the regraded grassy bank and the established scrub and herbs on the untouched bank.

FENCING
Although fencing is primarily the responsibility of the landowner, the exclusion of stock can be a very effective 'passive' technique for stabilising banks, so reducing the amount of work a drainage authority might be asked to do, such as to dredge a silted channel or to protect an eroding bank.
Stock, particularly cattle and horses, may affect bank stability in two ways. Trampling causes direct mechanical damage, causing clods of earth to break away and fall into the channel. Damage to vegetation, by trampling, may expose bare soil and allow rapid erosion. Excessive grazing may also damage the vegetative cover, so encouraging erosion.
Thus, it may be in a drainage authority's interest to fence, or encourage landowners to fence, the bank-top to exclude animals from steep and marshy banks, with the aim of reducing the need for channel maintenance works and bank protection works. In pastoral areas of the country, wildlife will benefit from the additional cover provided by ungrazed tall herb and scrub communities. Fencing may also encourage the natural regeneration of trees.

RIVER GILPIN, SAMPOOL BRIDGE, LEVENS, CUMBRIA
OS Map: 97. NGR: SD 472856
Rivers Division, North West Water Authority, PO Box 12, New Town House, Buttermarket Street, Warrington WA1 2QG. Telephone: Warrington (0925) 53999.

Site Summary
Lowland, rural location.
Channel: c10 metres wide.
Banks: c2 metres high, slope 1 in 1 to 1 in 2.
Substrate: alluvial sands.

Work Description
The River Gilpin is tidal up to the A590 road bridge. Tidal doors are fitted to the bridge and, above, the river is tide locked during periods of high tide. The Gilpin is one of the main carrier watercourses through the extensive low lying 'fenland' area of the Lyth Valley, where the drainage system is currently being improved.
Upstream of the A590 Sampool Bridge, bank erosion has occurred where cattle have grazed and trampled the banks, but an ungrazed bank with a dense cover of tall grasses downstream of the grazed bank has resisted erosion more successfully (photograph below).

River Gilpin: Grazed and ungrazed banks.

River Gilpin: The grazed banks have had wooden piling and boards driven in during the past in an attempt to protect against erosion. A fence at the top of the bank might have protected the farmers' grazing land more effectively.

RIVER PIDDLE, WOODLANDS, DORSET
OS Map: 194. NGR: SY 860912
Dorchester Area, Avon and Dorset Division, Wessex Water Authority, Wessex Road, Dorchester.
Telephone: Dorchester (0305) 66811.

Site Summary
Lowland rural location.
Channel: 2.5-4 metres wide.
Banks: up to 0.5 metres.
Substrate: alluvial clay and gravel.

Work Description
The Piddle is a chalk stream with fine game fishing set in an attractive landscape of flower-rich banks and adjacent damp pastures.
The reach described here has a 2.5-4 metre wide channel and is partly fenced and partly unfenced. The fenced reach has a rich bankside and aquatic flora, including purple loosestrife, water mints, water dropworts, meadowsweet and sweet flag. In summer, the waterside is alive with insects – dragonflies, damselflies, hoverflies, and the caddis and mayflies which are so important to fish. The

River Piddle: Luxuriant bankside vegetation on the fenced reach – a diverse habitat of plants, insects, birds and mammals. ▲

River Piddle: The unfenced section, with bankside and marginal aquatic plant growth reduced by grazing. ▼

dense bankside and marginal vegetation provides cover for nesting moorhen and little grebe. The catchment as a whole is thought to support at least a transient otter population.
In contrast, cattle had encroached onto the damp pasture of the river edge of the unfenced reach, breaking down the banks. This section had a short grass cover and, compared to the fenced reach, appeared to support a less rich flora and fauna (photographs on previous page).

VERTICAL EARTH BANK PROTECTION

As one extreme of variation in bank form, natural vertical earth banks are worthy of conservation because of the wildlife habitats they provide both above and below the water-line.
Vertical earth banks commonly form the outer bank of a meander bend; the most effective way of conserving such a vertical earth bank is to retain the meander with a near-normal flow.
Earth banks are often used by kingfishers and sand martins for nesting (page **285**). Such banks frequently have deep pools beneath them, and may be undercut with holes – often used as fish-lies.

RIVER TEME, LEINTWARDINE, HEREFORDSHIRE

OS Map: 137. NGR: SO 412734
Lower Severn Division, Severn Trent Water Authority, 64 Albert Road North, Great Malvern, Worcestershire.
Telephone: Malvern (068 45) 61511.

Site Summary
Maintenance works, 1981.
Rural location, upland/lowland transition zone.
Channel: up to 15 metres wide.
Banks: 0.5-2.5 metres high.
Substrate: cobbles, gravel, sand, alluvial and boulder clays.
Supervisor: B Draper.

Work Description
This scheme is described in detail on page **110**. As part of a flood alleviation scheme, several meanders were 'eased', although the original channels were retained as cut-offs or ponds. Vertical earth banks were left untouched. Particular care was taken with those used by sand martins for nesting colonies.
Tipped quarry stone and river gravels were used to construct current deflectors to reduce erosion of a major earth bank (see page **128**).

Habitat Comments
1 The care taken throughout this reach to conserve the variation in bank slopes is excellent.

AFON CLWYD, RHUDDLAN, CLWYD

OS Map: 116. NGR: SJ 032767
Dee and Clwyd Division, Welsh Water Authority, Box 53, Shire Hall, Mold, Clwyd.
Telephone: Mold (0352) 58551.

Site Summary
Maintenance works, 1969/70.
Lowland, rural location.
Channel: 15 metres wide.
Banks: 4 metres high.
Substrate: sand, coarse gravel, glacial clays.

Work Description
A 4-metre high bank at the confluence of the Elwy and Clwyd was being rapidly eroded, slumping of the cliff causing siltation of a valuable fishing pool below.
Work was undertaken in 1969/70 by the late Dee and Clwyd River Authority to protect the bank. Buttresses of stone-filled gabions with tipped stone were used, held in place by 8-centimetre diameter willow poles (figure below).

Afon Clwyd: Gabion and tipped stone current deflectors, held in place with willow poles, protecting a steep bank.

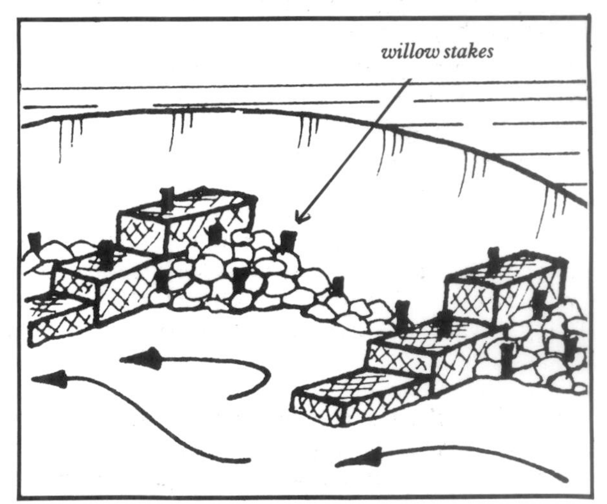

Since the work was completed, the gabions have become overgrown with bramble and scrub. The willow poles have also taken (photograph below).

Habitat Comments

1 Although the existing eroding bank was of wildlife value in its own right, given that it had to be protected, the method used was effective and helped to create a new wildlife habitat – the scrub providing dense cover for breeding birds.

2 Without the covering of willow, which became rapidly established from the stakes, the work would have been ugly and possibly less effective, since the gabion baskets would have provided the sole protection against erosion. The conservation value of the work would also have been much less without the willow.

Afon Clwyd: Twelve years after construction of the current deflectors, now well covered with native vegetation. The willow stakes have sprouted.

PARTIAL PROTECTION USING WOODEN PILING

Partial protection of an earth bank can be given by driving in wooden stakes, vertically shoulder to shoulder, to form a line of piling to protect the lower part of the bank. The area behind the stakes needs to be backfilled with local material from the river bed to prevent floodwater from flowing behind the stakes and pulling them out. To ensure the backfill does not push the piles over, they need to penetrate to a depth at least equal to the exposed length – and sometimes more depending on the bed material.

Protection of the toe of the bank in this manner – the half of the bank usually subjected to greatest erosion – leaves the upper half of the bank exposed as a habitat for bank nesting birds (figures left and overleaf).

Protection of the bank toe using timber piles. Toe of the outer bank of the meander protected by rough stakes.

Willow poles should not be used for staking, since they are likely to root and grow, so masking the bank. Larch poles, a recognised round-timber pile, are suitable and are quite durable.
Although this practice has been used by several drainage authorities to protect the whole face of a vertical earth bank (eg page **142**), it was not seen during the project as a technique to protect just the bank toe.

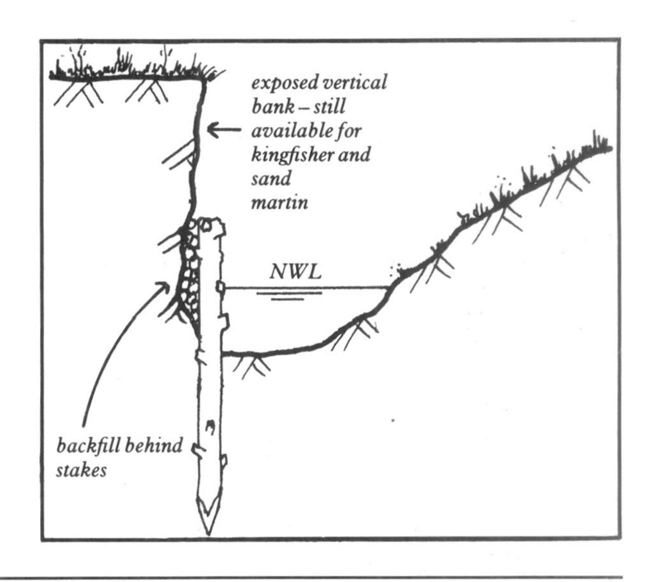

Protection of the bank toe using timber piles in cross-section.

ISLANDS

Islands, large or small, are important refuges for animals and plants. Remote from human disturbance and grazing animals, islands may support quite a different plant community, when compared to more accessible banks. Rare plant species may be given a foothold in an otherwise uniform landscape; common species may be able to flower and set seed when elsewhere they are grazed short. Insects feed on the flowers, and reptiles and amphibians benefit from dense tall vegetation in damp locations. Islands also provide animals with increased security from predators – ducks may breed more successfully. For otters, islands provide secure daytime resting sites.
By increasing the length of river bank, islands increase the richness and diversity of 'edge' habitats for wildlife. Often a zonation of plant communities can be seen, from established trees and scrub in the most stable areas to temporary flower-rich patches on downstream bars of accreting sediments.
Islands are such a valuable wildlife resource that they should be retained untouched in every possible location (figure right).

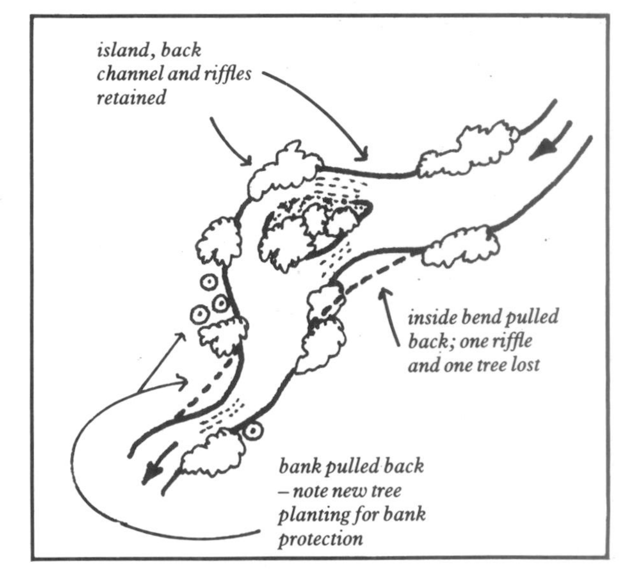

A theoretical example of island retention.

Islands are uncommon features of lowland British rivers – man-made islands are more common, eg between a mill-leat and a main river. These can also provide important wildlife refuges, although, because they are joined to the mainland, they may be more open to predators. The construction of flood by-pass channels provides an opportunity for creating new islands; there are British examples of this on pages **84** and **87**.

BANKTOP ALDER PLANTING

A steep, eroding river bank can be protected indirectly by planting alders on the banktop, at some distance from the channel. The tree roots grow down into the soil, even into waterlogged soils below the channel bed, binding and securing the bank against erosion. By the time the river cliff has cut back to the line of alders, they should be mature enough, with strong enough root systems, to halt further erosion.
Use of this method of control means that the landowner and river manager must be prepared to tolerate a certain degree of further erosion, rather than to preventing it immediately by using alternative bank revetment methods.
Advantages to wildlife conservation are that the river channel and banks are not disturbed, at least initially, so that plants and bank-living mammals

and birds are able to make use of the site as before. Once the trees have become established, and the bank has eroded back to the line of tree planting, conditions will be altered: the bank will be made up of twisted, exposed roots rather than bare earth. Trees will shade the site, and their leaves (when they fall) and the invertebrates they support will contribute to the organic productivity of the river. Their roots will also provide shelter for invertebrates, especially caddis and dragonfly larvae. Although initiated through man's action, this change will be gradual and 'natural' in character.
Planting alders for eventual bank protection is only likely to be successful where the banks are 2 metres or less above normal water level, and soils are sand or clay, without underlying gravel beds which may erode rapidly and cause the upper bank to collapse.
Young trees – whips supplied by a nursery or wild stock taken from a natural regeneration site nearby – should be planted at 1 metre centres, in a minimum of two rows, along the whole bank length to be protected. The distance between the banktop and the first row should take account of the rate of erosion at that point (it will vary along the bank length), bearing in mind that it will take at least 15 years for the alders to become well established. The site should be securely fenced, with at least 1 metre between the fence-line and outer row of trees. The usual maintenance for new tree-planting will be needed for the first three to five years (methods of tree planting and aftercare are detailed on pages **258-267**) (figure below).
No examples of this practice were seen, although the schemes for the Roding at Abridge (page **93**) and Passingford Bridge (page **142**) included alders being planted on the outer banktop of meander bends, as a secondary line of protection behind vertical larch and elm stakes.
Other types of bank protection using alders and willows are described elsewhere in Technical 2, see pages **152**, **155**, **158**, **165**, and **166**.

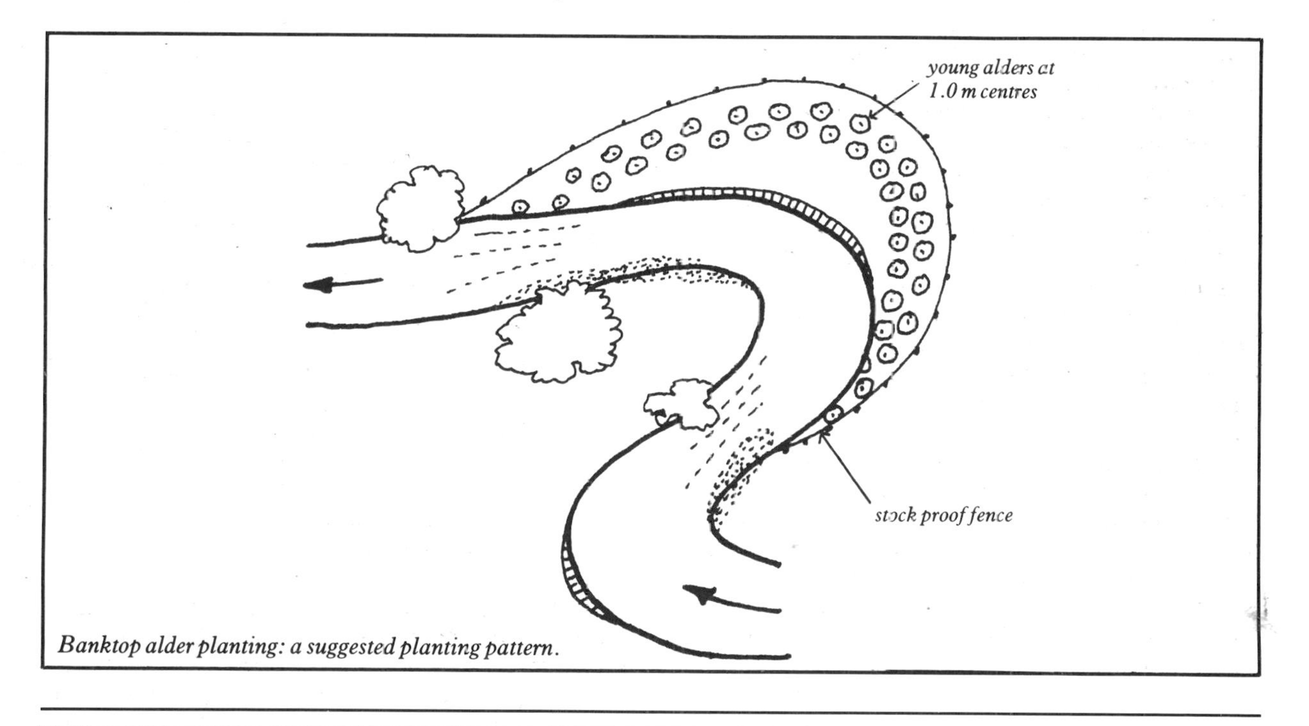

Banktop alder planting: a suggested planting pattern.

STUMPS AND LOGS

Tree management work generates large amounts of timber, which may cause problems in disposal. Using this timber for bank protection is a logical use of on-site materials, rather than importing alternatives.
The examples presented here show how effective this simple technique can be for a wide range of river types.

AFON CLWYD, PONT LLANNERCH, TREFNANT, CLWYD
OS Map: 116. NGR; SJ 059719
Dee and Clwyd Division, Welsh Water Authority, 25 Sandy Lane, Prestatyn, Clwyd.
Telephone: Prestatyn (074 56) 4384.

Site Summary
Maintenance work, 1982.
Rural location, upland/lowland transition zone.
Channel: 5-8 metres wide.
Banks: 1-3 metres high.
Substrate: clay and gravel.
Supervisor: A White, Area Controller (Rivers), Clwyd.

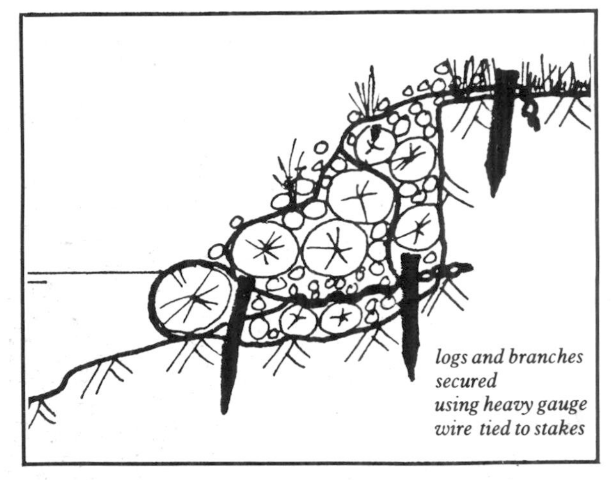

Afon Clwyd: Bank protection using logs and branches.

Work Description
As part of tree maintenance work, involving the removal of fallen trees and overhanging branches, limited bank protection work was also carried out, for example, to fill scour holes which threatened to topple mature trees.
Most of the trees present along the Afon Clwyd are alder or oak. The cut timber produced as a result of the maintenance work was taken and used for bank protection. The largest logs were laid at the bank line and secured with heavy gauge wire, strained against posts firmly embedded in the banktop. Further smaller logs and branches were laid on top, and also secured by wire tied to the posts in the banktop (figure above and photograph right).

Habitat Comments
1 Filling scour holes protects mature trees on the bank, so that they continue to play their part in the riverine community and the landscape.
2 The logs provide cover above and below the waterline for water voles, otters, and even stoats and weasels if dry enough.
3 The mass of branches also provide aquatic invertebrates and fish fry with shelter.

Afon Clwyd: Bank protection using logs and branches.

RIVER TEME, DOWNTON GORGE, HEREFORDSHIRE
OS Map: 137. NGR: SO 47
Lower Severn Division, Severn-Trent Water Authority, 64 Albert Road North, Great Malvern, Worcestershire.
Telephone: Malvern (0650 45) 61511.

Site Summary
Maintenance work.
Rural location.
Channel: up to 15 metres wide.
Banks: 0.5-2.5 metres high.
Substrate: cobbles, gravel, sand, alluvial and boulder clays.
Supervisor: B Draper.

Work Description
Otters are relatively numerous in the Welsh Marches, where clean rivers such as the Teme have good cover, abundant fish stocks and generally low recreational pressure.
The river management teams of STWA's Lower Severn Division, with the aid of the Otter Haven Project (see page **281**), have, where possible, sought to increase the numbers of lying-up places available to otters as part of their normal operations.
Logs and tree stumps are gathered from the River Teme as a routine clearance operation to reduce the risk of flooding, caused by log-jams in the channel during high flows. In the Downton Gorge, the logs and stumps so collected were secured to the bank with heavy gauge wire and stakes, both to fill a scour hole and to provide a resting place for otters (photograph below).

Habitat Comments
1 The comments made on the Afon Clwyd work (**156**) apply here also.
2 This is a simple, effective way of providing otters with additional cover. Even on rivers with a healthy otter population, it is worth providing such 'artificial' resting places, as future changes elsewhere along the river may reduce the number of natural sites.

River Teme: Timber removed from the river and tied into a scour hole with heavy gauge wire and stakes to provide a resting site for otters.

RIVER BRIDE, CHILCOMBE, DORSET
OS Map: 194. NGR: SY 540875
Dorchester Area, Avon and Dorset Division, Wessex Water Authority, Wessex Road, Dorchester.
Telephone: Dorchester (0305) 66811.

Site Summary
Maintenance work, 1981.
Rural location.

Channel: 2-3 metres wide.
Banks: 1-1.5 metres high.
Substrate: clay and gravel.

Work Description
This technique is not only applicable to upland rivers, as this example illustrates. In the Dorchester area, routine tree maintenance operations, clearing fallen alders and a proportion of overhanging branches to reduce flood risks, incorporates spot

bank repairs. This often prevents mature trees from being undercut and causing future problems. Staking and, if necessary, wiring in logs, stumps and brashings is standard practice where conditions allow.

River Bride: Alder logs and brashings wired into a scour hole in the right bank in front of the alder tree. The operation was carried out during the winter prior to the photograph being taken – the three stakes to the right of the tree are the only visible evidence of the work.

Habitat Comments

1 On lowland streams such as the Bride, lying-up sites for the otter are becoming increasingly scarce – mainly through habitat loss (see 'Biological 5: Mammals'). Practices such as this not only provide bank protection, but help to provide otters with additional cover, helping to replace lying-up sites lost elsewhere.

2 As the photograph below shows, in lowland rivers, such stick-piles quickly become overgrown and virtually invisible as the natural plant cover spreads over it, growing in silt trapped in the brashings.

FAGGOTING

Faggots, also known as 'kids' or 'raddles' in some parts of Britain, are brushwood or brashings tied into a bundle.

The Institution of Structural Engineers (1951) suggests that faggots are suitable for use on the banks of natural and artificial watercourses and for sea defences, as slope protection against weather, surface water flowing over a slope, water percolating through slopes, water currents, tidal effects and wave action.

The purpose of faggoting is to trap silt and sediment as the flow of water is retarded by the loose twigs and branches. The bank becomes consolidated through accretion and any subsequent scour is prevented by the woody branches buried in silt. Faggots can also be bound together to produce fascine mattresses and then sunk with stones onto the channel bed, to prevent scour. They are usually used to stabilise major eroding tidal river beds.

Faggots can be made of any brashings that are available. It must be remembered, however, that brashings of fresh willow are likely to take root and grow, especially if cut in winter. A careful choice

has to be made between using willow or non-willow faggots for different situations. In small water-courses (of say less than 5 metres width) a growth of willow from even a single bank is likely to cause a flood hazard, and alternative materials should be used. On larger channels, growing willows may be of benefit – their roots will help to stabilise the bank material and their shoots will provide a first line of defence against bank scour.
In recent years, the use of faggoting has declined, because of the relatively short life of some of the materials used when exposed to air; the loss of traditional skills; and the ease of installing alternative man-made materials with the same function at a higher capital cost, but lower labour and maintenance costs.

The major biological advantage of faggots are that they encourage the natural accumulation of silt in which aquatic invertebrates live, so that the natural processes of accumulation and decay continue. Above low water level, faggots allow plants to grow up through them, their roots and shoots unhindered, so that a natural bank plant community can become re-established. When willow faggots are used, the bushes growing from them will be an important additional habitat for fish, insects, mammals and birds.

Reference

Institution of Structural Engineers, 1951. Earth Retaining Structures. Civil Engineering Code of Practice Number 2. ISE.

RIVER URE, MIDDLEHAM, YORKSHIRE

OS Map: 99. NGR: SE 110889

Northern Area, Rivers Division, Yorkshire Water Authority, 48 Skeldergate, York YO1 1HL.
Telephone: York (0904) 36951.

Site Summary

Maintenance work, 1981.
Rural location, upland/lowland transition zone.
Channel: 20 metres or more wide, braided, shallow.
Banks: up to 2.5 metres high, of sand and gravel.
Substrate: coarse gravel.
Area Manager: R Ferguson.

Work Description

The Ure at Middleham is a large, gravelly river with sandy, unstable banks prone to undercutting and slumping. There are few mature trees on the banktop in this reach, probably due to rapid lateral erosion.

In March 1981, work was carried out to protect the outer bank toe of a large meander where the river was braiding. Following traditional practice for the area, osier faggots were used.
Material for the faggots was cut from other osier sites in the area in the two weeks before it was required, as part of normal four to six year maintenance. The osiers were gathered into bundles 2-3 metres long, about 30 centimetres thick and bound with wire. Where shorter bundles were required, the osiers were cut prior to bundling. The thicker osiers of 50-60 centimetre diameter were selected and cut to form stakes of at least 1 metre long.
The bank was first regraded. Stakes were then driven into the bank on a grid pattern where required.
The faggots were then laid parallel to the bank, at the bank toe, between the stakes, with the butt end of the osiers pointing upstream overlapping the leaf end of the adjacent faggot. The faggots were then tied down to the stakes using heavy gauge wire (figure below).

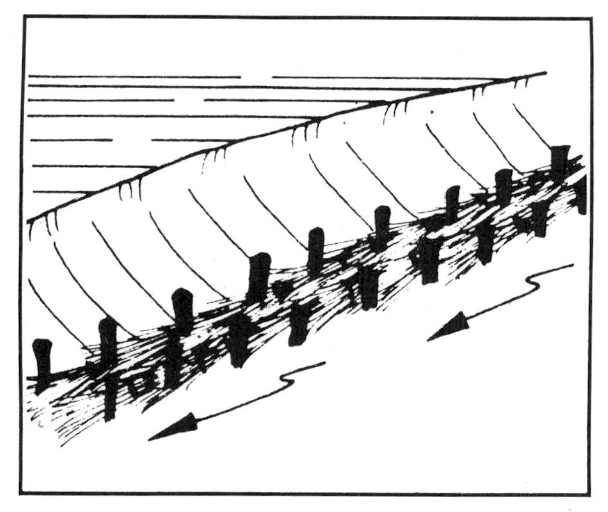

River Ure: Faggots staked parallel to the bank, butt end pointing upstream.

River Ure: In the case of deep erosion, additional faggots may be laid at right angles to the bank.

River Ure: Willow faggots laid horizontally and held with willow stakes to secure the toe of a regraded gravel bank. The photograph was taken after 18 months' growth. ▲

River Ure: Seen from the bank, the notepad highlights the coarseness of the gravel and the size of the willow stakes holding the faggots in place. ◀

River Ure: The line of osiers, grown from faggots and stakes, after 18 months' growth, protecting the toe of the regraded gravel bank. ▼

In areas subject to deep erosion, additional layers of faggots may be laid at right angles to the bank and again secured to the stakes (figure on **159**).
River gravels were then tipped over the completed faggot work, and graded. Finally, the area was fenced against stock.
The osiers rapidly root and grow into compact bushes, branching out from their base, and reaching a height of 5-7 metres at maturity (see photographs left). Cutting back every four to six years maintains the vigour of the stand, clears out trash, and provides new material for more faggot work.
Osiers (*Salix viminalis*) or goat willow and sallows (*S. capraea* and others) are the best types of willow for this work because they are bushy, relatively short, grow quickly to full height, and respond rapidly to coppicing, so that once established they provide a permanent, living revetment. Cutting back prolongs their life, but is not essential. In the Ure catchment, YWA extensively use the hybrid *Salix triandra × viminalis*.

Tree willows, such as crack willow (*S. fragilis*) or white willow (*S. alba*) are less suitable because, unless they are cut back periodically, they grow into large, single-trunked trees, which may cause scour if not protected by scrub and bushes. They *can* be successfully used as coppice, but are traditionally pollarded.

Habitat Comments

1 Willows are some of the most valuable tree species that can be planted along a river – contributing to both productivity and physical diversity, so that a wide range of organisms benefit.
2 Wherever possible, material for faggots should be from a site local to the place of use, to ensure that any local varieties of willow are maintained.
3 Again, where possible, a number of willow species should be used to add variety to the appearance of the osiers and to add to the diversity of habitats available for wildlife.

CANADIAN WILDLIFE SERVICE

Although not strictly faggoting, the Canadian Wildlife Service recommends a similar solution to the problem of bank slumping described on page **159**.
The slumped bank is regraded. Fresh winter-cut willow stakes are driven into the bank at regular intervals and it is then seeded with grass. Additional initial protection may be given by loose brashings wired down to the stakes, rather than bundled faggots (see figures below and right).

Reference

Canadian Wildlife Service, 1981. Wildlife habitat – a handbook for Canada's prairie and parklands. Western and Northern Region, Canadian Wildlife Service.

A stream bank badly slumped.

The bank regraded and stabilised with willow stakes.

The area fully recovered.

RIVER OUSE, YORKSHIRE
a *Poppleton. OS Map: 105. NGR: SE 571551*
b *Barlow Grange. OS Map: 106.*
NGR: SE 639303
c *Swinefleet. OS Map: 106. NGR: SE 765217*
Northern Area, Rivers Division, Yorkshire Water Authority, 48 Skeldergate, York YO1 1HL.
Telephone: York (0904) 36951.

River Ouse at Poppleton: Three-year old osiers grown from faggots at the water's edge. Note the section of faggoting which did not sprout – the bank toe, however, is still protected to some extent.

A POPPLETON
Site Summary
Maintenance work.
Rural location.
Channel: c25 metres wide.
Banks: up to 6 metres high.
Substrate: sand and gravel.
Area Manager: H H Ferguson.

Work Description
The non-tidal sections of the Ouse are similar to the Ure (see **159**), and willow faggoting has been used for many years to protect them from scour and slumping. At this site, faggoting was carried out in 1979 (photograph below).

B BARLOW GRANGE
Site Summary
Maintenance work.
Rural location.
Channel: c50 metres wide, tidal.
Banks: shallow foreshore.
Substrate: sand, alluvial and tidal silts.
Area Manager: H H Ferguson.

Work Description
On the embanked tidal sections of the Ouse below Selby, willow faggots have been used on the *river side* to stabilise and trap silt, protecting the base of floodbanks. They were first installed in about 1948 and have been maintained by coppicing on a cycle of four to five years. Faggots were used (see **159** for method of construction) bound by heavy gauge wire to stakes, and laid behind tipped stone brought in by barge (figure and photograph above right).

In the years since installation, the dense stand of willows has trapped silt on the foreshore, protected the floodbank behind, and provided an enriched habitat for birds, insects, and mammals in the area. The floodbank is not mown or grazed and a diverse, flower-rich meadow community has grown up, with meadow cranesbill, tufted vetch and field scabious being the most attractive in mid-summer, probably spreading in from nearby road verges (figure on right).

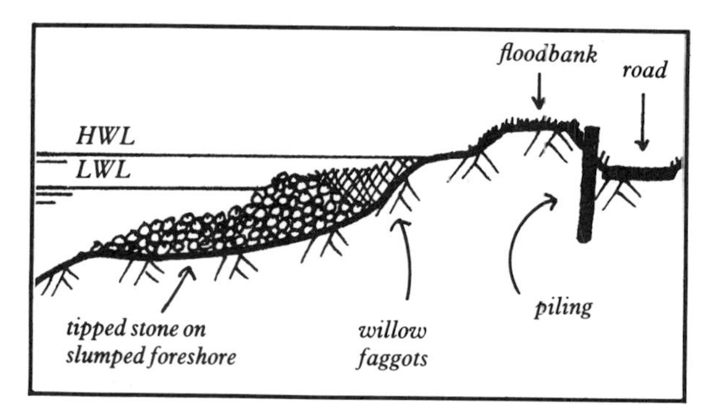

River Ouse at Barlow Grange – construction.

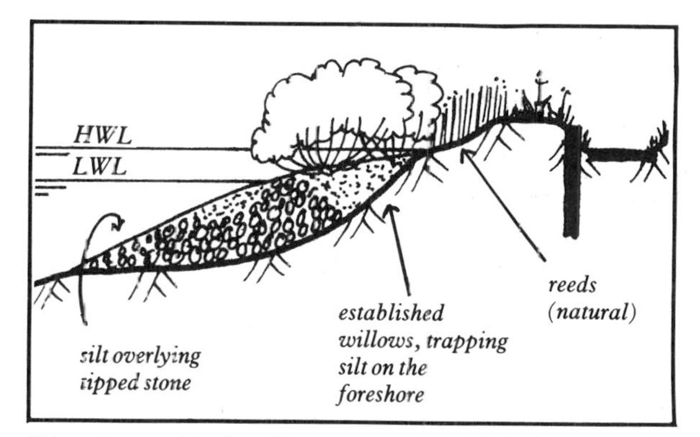

River Ouse at Barlow Grange – once established.

River Ouse at Barlow Grange: Established willow.

C SWINEFLEET

Site Summary

Maintenance work, 1974/75.
Rural estuarine location.
Channel: 210 metres wide plus, tidal, saline.
Banks: shallow foreshore.
Substrate: sand, alluvium and tidal silts.
Area Manager: H H Ferguson.

Work Description

Below Goole, the tidal Ouse becomes saline. Osiers will not grow in persistently salty conditions. The floodbank is protected in a similar manner as at Barlow Grange, except that the faggots were laid and stacked above high water level, where they are rarely inundated by tidal water. Clumps of common reed (*Phragmites*) were planted in the salty inter-tidal zone in front, and tipped stone secures the base of the foreshore from scour and slumping below low water (see figure on right). The work was carried out in 1974/75 and is ready for its first maintenance cut (see also **173**).

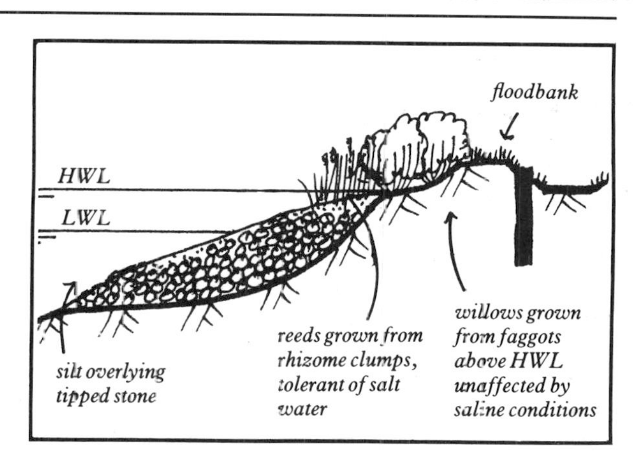

River Ouse at Swinefleet – once established.

Habitat Comments

1 These schemes illustrate a range of conditions under which willow faggoting has provided both an effective method of bank protection and a valuable habitat for wildlife – especially breeding and passage birds.

RIVER BRIDE, BURTON BRADSTOCK, DORSET

OS Map: 193. NGR: SY 487894
Dorchester Area, Avon and Dorset Division, Wessex Water Authority, Wessex Road, Dorchester
Telephone: Dorchester (0305) 66811.

Site Summary
Maintenance work.
Lowland, rural village-edge location.
Channel: 2-3 metres wide, shallow.
Banks: 3 metres high.
Substrate: gravel and clay.
Engineer: L Miles.

Work Description
In a narrow channel, such as the Bride at Burton Bradstock, the use of willow faggots for bank protection would create an unacceptable flood hazard as the willows would probably grow and restrict channel capacity.
Pine brashings and hazel underwood made available free by a local forestry firm as waste were used. Even so, close work study showed that to break even at £1.00 per faggot (at 1981 prices), they had to be made at the rate of one per 13 minutes, on site, with unusable wood left stacked aside.
The brushwood was bound into 25-kilogram bundles using baler twine (polypropylene string). Pine stakes, also made available free as forestry thinnings, were driven in a line and the faggots packed behind, three deep. The completed work was covered with river gravel, but top-soil was not applied.
Within a few weeks, the area was colonised by plants – mainly weed species – and even the stakes were hidden from view. By the following summer silt trapped in a narrow band by the faggots at the water's edge had been colonised by fool's watercress and brooklime (photograph below).

Habitat Comments
1 The pine and hazel faggots – and the practice of not topsoiling the regraded bank – allows a native plant community to develop unrestricted. Although it is likely to be dominated by weeds for several years, this is far preferable to seeding with an agricultural grass mix in this situation.
2 The faggots trap silt in the channel edge, and encourage marginal plant growth.
3 By *not* sprouting and growing, the faggots allow a diverse bank and channel edge plant community to develop in full sunlight. Willows are not always appropriate from the conservation viewpoint. Other material could be used, as available, in the same way as pine and hazel were used here. Thorn brashings were traditionally favoured for sites where silt-trapping was the main intention of faggot work, eg in fascine mattresses.

River Bride: 18 months after installation, the pine faggots and stakes are almost hidden by grasses and herbs.

SPILING

A variation on the use of willow for faggots for bank protection is the craft of 'spiling' or weaving willow withies around fresh winter-cut willow stakes. The technique requires a little more skill than faggot work, but has the advantage that it uses less material. It is appropriate for the protection of steep or vertical banks.

Ideally, the willow stakes will take root and sprout to provide living, permanent protection. Fencing of the bank top to prevent grazing of the new growth by stock will help this. Without this, the impact of grazing may cause the stakes to die and eventually rot.

See also example **168**, the Upper Lugg scheme.

MEECE BROOK, NORTON BRIDGE, STAFFORDSHIRE

OS Map: 127. NGR: SJ 868306

Upper Trent Division, Severn Trent Water Authority, Trinity Square, Horninglow Street, Burton-on-Trent DE14 1BL.
Telephone: Burton-on-Trent (0283) 44511.
Regional Architects' Department, Severn Trent Water Authority, Abelson House, 2297 Coventry Road, Sheldon, Birmingham B26 3PU.
Telephone: 021-743 4222.

Site Summary

Land drainage scheme, capital works, 1981.
Lowland, rural location.
Channel: 3-4 metres wide.
Banks: up to 2 metres high, irregular slopes.
Substrate: gravel, clay, sandy alluvium.
Engineers: S Powers, D Pinnegar.
Landscape Architect: M Ericsson.

Work Description

The Meece Brook is a small, attractive river. In 1981, the bed of a part of it was lowered and regraded to improve land drainage.

In a number of places, spiling was used to protect eroding outer meander bends. Sharpened willow stakes were driven vertically into the river bed at the bank toe, and withies were wound around them (figure and photograph below). The area behind the spiling was then backfilled and the upper bank graded.

Meece Brook: Spiling – top view (above); face view (below).

Meece Brook: Spiling. Willow stakes have been driven into the river bed and withies are being woven around them. (The work was filmed for the RSPB production The Vital River*).*

The top of the bank was not fenced and cattle had access. A year later, the willows had sprouted from the stakes and formed a bushy protection for the bank. The growth at the top of the stakes was kept short by grazing. Watercress and brooklime were growing at the foot of the spiling, and the bank was stabilised (photograph below).

Meece Brook: 18 months later the bank, protected at its toe by the spiling, has grown over. Cattle have grazed off the growing tops of the willow, but have not been able to reach the face.

Habitat Comments

1 The willow spiling has completely naturalised, benefitting landscape and diversifying the habitat available to wildlife.

2 Supporting a steep bank, the channel below the willow spiling has formed a small pool, again adding diversity to the habitat.

3 As it is exposed to grazing, the growth of willow from the stakes has been curtailed, so reducing its effectiveness for protecting the upper bank and its value as wildlife habitat. If the willow was not grazed, however, the growth would have to be cut back every six to eight years.

WIRE MESH AND WILLOW

There are less traditional ways of using willows for effective bank protection – where the use of imagination and cheap, easily available materials provides the key.

Once fresh, winter-cut willow stakes, logs or brashings have rooted, and shoots have started to grow, a revetment will be secure. Only periodic coppicing will be required to maintain its effectiveness. Initially, however, logs and brashings have to be kept in place: wiring, using chicken wire, wire netting or gabion mesh, is the most common method. The examples given here are not particularly special; no one is better than any other, but they are all effective revetment techniques, carried out by maintenance gangs or contractors, using the cheapest and easiest available materials – often left-overs from other jobs.

The following points are essential to success:

1 Willow material should be winter-cut and used fresh, within two weeks of cutting.

2 Stakes should be driven down to the water table. Horizontal logs and brashings should be laid within 1 metre of normal water level.

3 The bank should be fenced against stock for at least three years, using sheep netting if there is *any* likelihood of the adjacent land being grazed. The fencing should be periodically checked, especially after high flows.

It is preferable to use a mixture of willow types and species so that the bank does not end up with a very uniform appearance. A mixture of species is easily made just by taking logs, branches and brashings from a variety of local willows – it doesn't need a botanist to see the differences! Wildlife will benefit from the greater variety of insects that a mixed stand will support. Native black poplar will regenerate in the same way as willow and, if locally available, it can be planted at the same time, towards the top of the bank.

AFON CLWYD, BROOK HOUSE, DENBIGH, CLWYD
OS Map: 116. NGR: SJ 069657
Dee and Clwyd Division, Welsh Water Authority, 25 Sandy Lane, Prestatyn, Clwyd.
Telephone: Prestatyn (074 56) 4384.

Site Summary
Maintenance works, 1977.
Rural location, upland/lowland transition zone.
Channel: 2-3 metres wide, shallow.
Banks: 1-1.5 metres high, slopes variable.
Substrate: cobbles, gravel, sandy alluvium.
Engineer: A White, Area Controller (Rivers), Clwyd.

Work Description
This small stony stream was undercutting the foot of a floodbank which protects the hamlet of Brook House. Stone-filled gabions were laid in the stream bed, with willow logs held by more gabion mesh laid horizontally on top. The willows now form continuous bank protection, at the foot of the floodbank. Tree growth on the bank itself is prevented by normal mowing.
Dense willow growth can be tolerated on this small stream because fields on the opposite bank are floodable, and it does not require maintenance dredging (photograph below).
Alternatively, gabion baskets can be filled as usual with river gravels or quarry stone, 'fronted' with willow brashings and logs. The latter will quickly sprout, masking the wire mesh, binding the stone and securing the gabions in place (see figure below).

Habitat Comments
1 This well-established willow bank protection shows how a tree-shaded bank and channel habitat can be created by sympathetic river management. The ground flora beneath the willows has naturalised as a mossy, grassy bank community. The willows themselves provide additional cover and feeding sites for small birds, and many insect species.

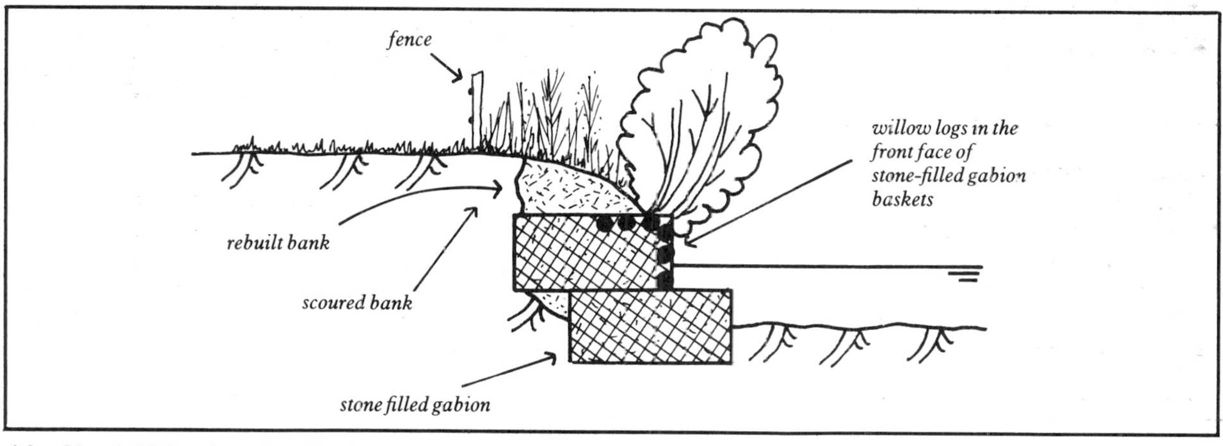

Afon Clwyd: Willow logs placed in the front-face of stone filled gabion baskets.

Afon Clwyd: A line of osier and crack willows grown from logs laid horizontally over gabion baskets and held in place with gabion mesh, after five years of growth.

UPPER LUGG, LEOMINSTER, HEREFORDSHIRE
OS Map: 149. NGR: SO 451621
Wye Division, Welsh Water Authority, St Nicholas House, St Nicholas Street, Hereford HR4 0BB.
Telephone: Hereford (0432) 57411.

Site Summary
Flood alleviation scheme, capital works, 1980-81.
Rural location, upland/lowland transition zone.
Channel: 10-12 metres wide, 1-2 metres deep.
Banks: variable, up to 3 metres high.
Substrate: alluvial and glacial sands, clay and gravel.
Engineer: R Vivash.

Upper Lugg: Spiling and coppice willow stumps protecting a river cliff.

Work Description
For a detailed description of this scheme, see pages **75** and **96**. A variety of techniques of bank protection with willow were used, material being obtained from willows cleared from shoals in the channel.
Spiling was used to protect the toe of regraded banks where spoil had been tipped in front of eroding meander cliffs and planted with coppiced willow stumps (figure on right). The bank has been graded to a rounded profile, steeper at the base. This, with the additional drop in flow caused by the spiling, should help to reduce scour.
Elsewhere, willow logs, gained from selective coppicing, were pinned to sheep netting, pegged into

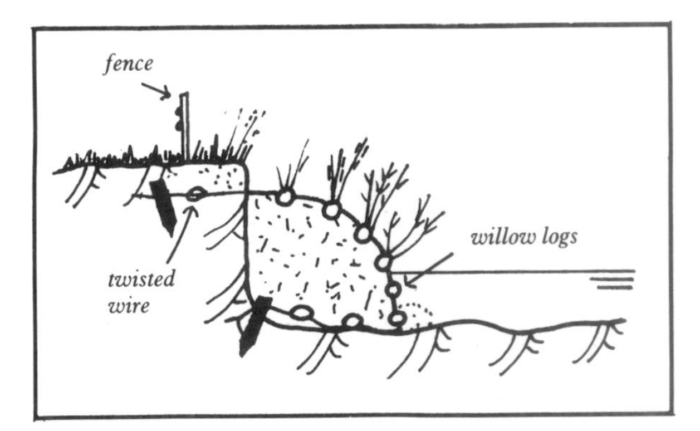

Upper Lugg: Willow logs stapled to sheep netting, pegged down over spoil.

Upper Lugg: Young willows uprooted during channel works were selectively wired down against the face of an outer meander bank and covered with spoil. With good fencing to exclude sheep and cattle, they have grown well, to provide attractive and effective bank protection.

the base of the bank, spoil back-filled over it, graded and the wire and willow pulled back over it and pegged again into the bank top. The work was then fenced to exclude stock. Within a few months of installation, the logs sprouted and took root (figure left and photograph below). In deep water the log mattress can be sunk with the weight of spoil over it, so avoiding the need for staking.

Stock fencing is normally an integral part of bank protection works using willow. In each of the cases above, it was essential to put in secure stock fencing at the bank top, and to maintain it for the first three years. On the Lugg, several stretches of willow bank protection have not grown because sheep were able to get in where high water had broken the fences down. Wherever the fencing is sound, the willows have grown well, protecting the bank, softening the landscape and improving wildlife habitat.

Habitat Comments

1 The extensive use of willow has provided several effective methods of bank protection which offer considerable benefits for wildlife – contributing both to the productivity and physical diversity of habitats of the river.

Upper Lugg: Willow logs stapled to sheep netting and pegged down over back-filled spoil. These have suffered damage because sheep got in through broken fencing and ate the shoots. Elsewhere growth has been successful.

HURDLES

Another traditional use of local wood for bank revetment is in woven hurdles – a traditional means of providing initial protection until living plant cover has become re-established. Usually made of hazel, these will not grow, but will protect a regraded bank from wash and scour while a natural plant community re-colonises and germinates to grow up through the basket weave. Over a period of 10 years or so, the wood will rot, but by this time the plant community should have developed well enough to ensure the bank remains stable (figure on left).

Hurdles are the forerunner of many 'new' bank protection products using fabrics, meshes of jute, nylon, plastic, tropical hardwoods and concrete. From the wildlife conservation viewpoint hurdles have the major advantage (shared only with jute meshes) that they are biodegradable.

Hurdles of tropical hardwoods (such as ekki wood) are not biodegradable under British conditions and their use cannot therefore be recommended for conservation purposes. Furthermore, the exploitation of such wood for European use is threatening the ecology and very existence of tropical rain forests – the most fragile of all the world's ecosystems.

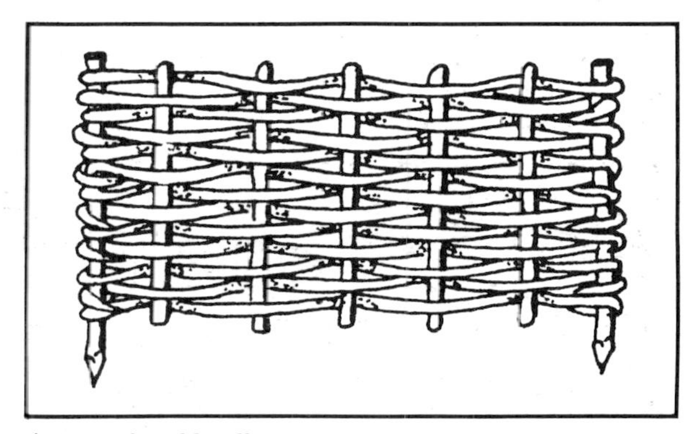

A woven hazel hurdle.

Hurdles are the product of woodland coppicing, which still continues in some parts of Britain. They can be bought at garden suppliers, but a cheaper source would be to order direct from the producer. County Forestry Officers should be able to supply the names of people still carrying out coppicing for

hurdle-making. Many local Nature Conservation Trusts are interested in managing their woodland reserves under traditional coppice systems: it may be possible to use them as a source of wood for hurdles, so furthering the conservation of two types of habitat at once!

As an example of commercial prices, Barker and Geary, Forest Products Craft Centre, Romsey Road, Kings Sombourne, Hampshire sell hurdles from £6.20 (for 1.8 metre×0.9 metre) to £8.70 (for 1.8 metre×1.8 metre) plus VAT, at 1982 prices.

HEDGE END, NEAR SOUTHAMPTON

OS Map: 196. NGR: SU 495136
Hampshire River and Water Division, Southern Water Authority, Marland House, Civic Centre Road, Southampton, Hampshire. Telephone: Southampton (0703) 34731.

Site Summary

Maintenance work, 1978.
Lowland, urban fringe location.
Channel: 1.5 metres wide.
Banks: 1-1.5 metres high; 1-1.5 batter.
Substrate: clay and gravel.
River Manager: J Shorthose.

Work Description

This small un-named stream was cleaned out and regraded in 1978. The sides were protected with 2 metre×1.5 metre hurdles, laid end to end on the lower face of the banks and pegged into place. The hurdles were obtained from local suppliers (photographs below).

Hedge End: The stream with the hazel hurdles laid and pegged in place (late 1978).

Habitat Comments

1 The use of hurdles benefits wildlife by allowing bank and channel edge plants to grow back unhindered, and providing crevices and shelter for colonisation by stream invertebrates.

Hedge End: The same reach in summer 1982, with the banks now well protected by plants, even where grazed and trampled by horses. The hurdles can only be seen by searching!

2 The gradual decomposition of the hurdles will itself act as a 'soil improver', benefitting plant growth over the years. Certainly, protection of the bare soil surface will aid initial germination of native seeds in the soil below. Restoration of the natural plant community may be aided if some of the *original* topsoil is spread on the bank, before the hurdles are laid and fixed in place.
3 Although probably only suitable for small streams, non-turbulent rivers, canals and backwaters, hurdles deserve to be used more widely for bank protection. Their use promotes the establishment of natural plant cover. Their cost is competitive with more modern bank protection systems; they are easy to handle and install; and are ecologically much more acceptable than the use of persistent, artificial or tropical materials.

REED PLANTING FOR BANK PROTECTION

Establishing aquatic plants in general is considered in 'Technical 4' on **219-228**, and, for the detail of planting techniques, reference should be made to it. This section, however, covers the use of emergent aquatic plants ('reeds') for bank protection.
Although 'reeds' have frequently been used in coastal locations for sea defence work (such as planting cord grass on mudflats or marram grass on sand dunes), much less work has been carried out in relation to bank protection on inland streams, rivers and canals. Indeed, the emphasis has been on controlling and reducing reed growth rather than encouraging it. At several locations, however, drainage authorities have experimented with the use of reed planting to protect regraded banks or the banks of navigations from scour and boat wave wash.

There are several advantages in using 'reeds' for bank protection rather than inert piling:

1 'Reeds' absorb wave-wash energy, rather than reflecting it.
2 Root mats of 'reeds' prevent scour of the substrate.
3 The dense stems of 'reeds' encourage sediment accumulation.
4 'Reeds' regenerate and maintain their own stability – although this is dependent on the prevailing conditions. If wave-wash from boats is too severe, the 'reeds' will be battered, damaged and, with silt sucked out from around by backwash, will degenerate and die. To re-establish emergent aquatic plants, additional flexible protection may be required.
Bonham, in his key paper on reed planting for bank protection, looked at the value of a number of species of emergent aquatic plants for protection against boat wash on the Thames and Norfolk Broads. Common reed, bulrush, reedmace and sweet-flag appeared to be the best species, each dissipating wave-wash energy to slightly different degrees (see table overleaf).
The riverine community clearly benefits when emergent aquatic plants are used for bank protection, rather than inert pilings. A reedbed will immediately increase the productivity of a reach – both through its own leaf production, and by providing a habitat for other wildlife. As a result, invertebrates increase and, in turn, feed fish, mammals, birds and other invertebrates. Dragonflies and damselflies are often seen haunting the edges of reedbeds. The 'reeds', if in a wide enough band, will provide cover for birds and mammals and a site for other plant species to invade and grow.
The various projects described here have tended to use whatever plants were locally abundant and easy to propagate.
An additional simple establishment technique used widely in southern Germany, but as far as we are aware not used in Britain, is to take clumps of common reed rhizomes and to put them as the top layer in otherwise stone-filled gabion baskets, set at normal water level (figure below) (Burkle, 1978).

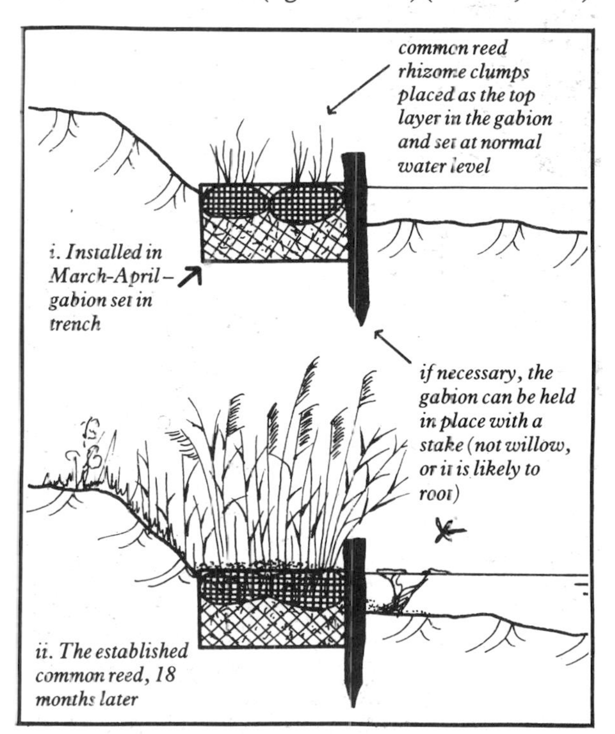

Bank protection using rhizome clumps of common reed in stone filled gabions.

References
Bonham, A J, 1980. Bank protection using emergent plants against boatwash in rivers and canals. Hydraulic Research Station Report, IT 206.

Burkle, F, 1978. Lebendau an Wasserläufen. Grundsätze und Beispiele aus dem süddeutschen Hügelland. (Natural construction on watercourses, principles and examples from the south German highlands). Garten und Landschaft 1/78: 18-24.

Shipwave dissipation by reedbeds, on bed slope of 1 in 4 (after Bonham, 1980)

Reed species	*Width of reedbed*	*'Shipwave' energy dissipated*
Common reed	2 m	60%
Reedmace	2.3 m	66%
Sweet-flag	2.4 m	75%
Bulrush	2.5 m	70%

LEE NAVIGATION, WARE, HERTFORDSHIRE
OS Map: 166. NGR: TL 377128
Eastern Division, Thames Water Authority, The Grange, Crossbrook Street, Waltham Cross, Hertfordshire.
Telephone: Waltham Cross (0992) 23611.

Site Summary
Maintenance work, 1978.
Lowland, rural location.
Channel: c15 metres wide, impounded navigation.
Banks: c1 metre high.
Substrate: clay.

Work Description
A two kilometre length of the Navigation has one bank protected with clumps of great pond sedge (*Carex riparia*) planted on a 1-metre wide berm in 10-60 centimetres depth of water. Planting was done in 1978. Since then, the pond sedge has spread and grown over the whole length into a dense fringe of plants, up to 50 centimetres high, persistent through the winter. The sedge cannot invade the deep water channel, nor encroach onto the dry bank. A few other plants have grown in the belt of pond sedge, such as rushes, and willowherbs, but its dominance is not threatened (photograph below).
The bank above the berm was graded to 1 in 1 and seeded with a dry grassland mix including fescues. Fabric was used to stabilise the bank during the establishment period, and has since degraded as the grass has spread.

Lee Navigation: Great pond sedge, planted in 1978 on a 1 m berm, pictured in 1982.

Lee Navigation: The opposite bank of the same reach, protected by boarding.

The opposite bank of the navigation is vertical, protected with wooden boarding. Soil has washed out of the bank in places behind the boards, but 60 per cent of the boarding is masked by an overgrowth of great willowherb, nettle and soft rush, some in the edge of the channel (photograph above).

Habitat Comments

1 The sedge planting has clearly performed well in protecting the bank against boatwash, apparently better than the boarding on the opposite bank.

2 The sedge planting is very uniform – mixing in a few other species at intervals would have diversified the habitat, and been visually more pleasing.

3 Invertebrates will have benefited from the planting. A berm of greater width than 1 metre, however, would have encouraged more breeding birds – especially as the adjacent towpath creates frequent disturbance.

4 In time, it is possible that other plants will invade the 'reed bed,' particularly as clumps of sedge age and decay, and this should benefit wildlife, while maintaining plant cover for bank protection.

RIVER OUSE, SWINEFLEET, YORKSHIRE
OS Map: 106. NGR: SE 765217
Northern Area, Rivers Division, Yorkshire Water Authority, 48 Skeldergate, York YO1 1HL.
Telephone: York (0904) 36951.

Site Summary
Maintenance work, 1974/5.
Rural estuarine location.
Channel: 210 metres wide plus, tidal, saline.
Banks: shallow foreshore.
Substrate: sand, alluvium and tidal silts.
Area Manager: H H Ferguson.

Work Description

Below Goole, the Ouse is estuarine in character, with brackish to saline water and a tidal range of six metres. The river is embanked – the floodbank being protected by a combination of tipped stone, planted common reed, and willow faggots and stakes (see **163**, example C).

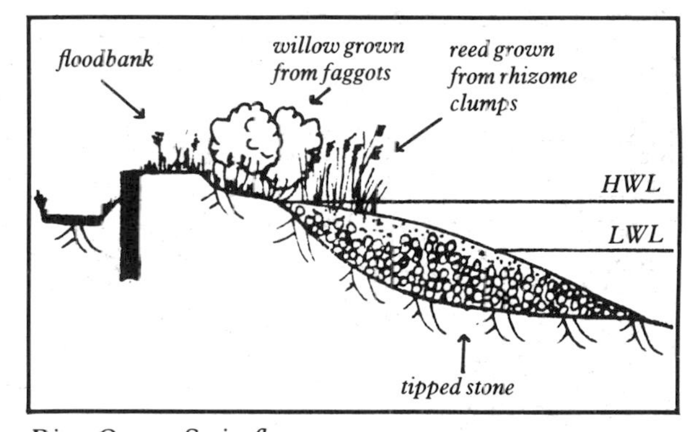

River Ouse at Swinefleet.

Common reed was planted to trap silt and help prevent scour. It can tolerate occasional inundation with saline or brackish water. Reed rhizome clumps were dug from nearby reedbeds in adjacent drains and on the banks of the Ouse, and replanted at about 50 centimetre intervals at high water level

River Ouse at Swinefleet: Common reed established from rhizome clumps, after eight years' growth. From initial plantings at and above high water level, the reedbed has grown downslope.

and just above. Once established, common reed grows into water, but establishment in water is not usually successful (figure on **173**; photograph above).
For other establishment methods for common reed, see page **222**.

Habitat Comments
1 Common reed is frequently found in estuarine locations such as this. Planting of this kind is very welcome since many extensive reedbeds have been lost through land drainage and land claim schemes in recent years. Both invertebrate and bird populations (especially breeding species such as sedge warbler and reed warbler) will benefit.

River Stort Navigation: Great pond sedge, in spring, two growing seasons after planting.

RIVER STORT NAVIGATION, NEAR BISHOP'S STORTFORD, HERTFORDSHIRE
OS Map: 167. NGR: TL 495193 to 493203
Eastern Division, Thames Water Authority, The Grange, Crossbrook Street, Waltham Cross, Hertfordshire.
Telephone: Waltham Cross (0992) 23611.

Site Summary
Flood alleviation scheme, capital works 1978-80.
Lowland, urban fringe location.
Channel: 10-15 metres wide, impounded navigation.
Berms: graded 1 in 3 to 1 in 4.5; 1.5 metres wide.
Substrate: clay

Work Description
See page **132** for details of the scheme and construction of shallow-water berms, 1.5 metres wide graded 1 in 3 to 1 in 4.5.
The berms, on an outer bend of the navigation, were planted during 1980 with a variety of emergent aquatic plants. Details of the planting are given on page **219**.
The most successful species were great pond sedge, lesser pond sedge and reed sweetgrass, but all grew well except common reed, yellow flag and reed canary-grass – which failed for avoidable reasons. Again, details will be found on page **219** (photographs left and right).

Habitat Comments
1 Although the berm was cut and planting carried out to encourage and speed vegetative recovery, the work has been of value in providing bank protection. The opposite unplanted bank, graded to 1 in 1.5 and steeper, without berms, has not been colonised by any emergent aquatic plants in two years, and is showing signs of erosion from boat wash within two years of dredging.
2 See pages **133** and **221** for additional comments.

River Stort Navigation: The planted berm in spring, after two seasons' growth. The left bank is unplanted.

NATURAL STONE

Bank protection using natural stone as large blockstones or tipped quarry stone is, together with the biological materials described on pages **155** to **175**, the most sympathetic material for wildlife habitat conservation.
Natural stone has the advantage over concrete, 'reconstituted' stone or steel for wildlife that it has many crevices, spaces and rough surfaces – places where invertebrates can shelter, soil can develop and plants grow. Where bedrock or cobble substrates are already present in a river, stone revetment increases the habitats available to the existing plant and animal community. Elsewhere, where substrates are sand, silt, clay or unstable gravels, the use of stone revetment provides new habitats for wildlife and the species diversity of the reach will probably be increased.
Soil and silt may develop or be trapped between the stones permitting plants to grow; this provides an additional defence against scour and the roots help to stabilise the stonework.
Aesthetically, natural stone usually looks attractive – even when new – and when weathered and colonised by mosses, lichens and other plants, it blends into the landscape.

The main disadvantages to the use of stone for revetment are cost and the equipment required for handling. In the lowlands of England, stone may have to be transported over long distances, making it prohibitively expensive. Very large blockstones, perhaps weighing several tons each, clearly present handling problems and may damage excavators and lorries. At least one contractor fits old, already battered, bodies to his lorries when carrying large stones for water authority projects! Smaller sizes of stone, for rip-rap, do not have this problem. Costs are so different around the country, and sizes of material used so variable, that no prices are given here.

Concrete or steel has replaced stone for bank revetment in many situations in recent years for reasons of cheapness, ease of installation and predictability. This last factor refers to the fact that the performance of smooth structures, when built as designed, can be calculated and predicted more accurately than for works using natural stone. The increasing use of computers in scheme design, however, may help improve the reliability of such predictions.

For each of the following schemes, which illustrate the use of natural stone in a variety of locations in England and Wales, the **Habitat Comments** are similar:

1 The use of natural stone has permitted natural plant communities to establish themselves. Because of differences in geographical location and physical conditions, the nature of the plant cover is different – from wetland plants on the sluice apron of the Skipton Bypass Compensatory Washland scheme, to lowland bank plants at Shallowford Gauging Station and the sparse mosses and upland grasses of the Afon Gwyrfai in Snowdonia. By increasing the diversity of habitats on the banks of the river, both above and below water level, the plants directly benefit animal life.

2 The rough surface, cracks and crevices of natural stone, both above and below the water-line, benefit invertebrates by increasing the surface area of rock available to them and providing those which require it with shelter from fast water flow velocities.

3 The use of natural stone, as opposed to other inert materials, is usually acceptable aesthetically.

AFON GWYRFAI, NEAR CAERNARFON, GWYNEDD

OS Map: 115. NGR: SH 552556 to 547564
Gwynedd Division, Welsh Water Authority, Penrhos Road, Penrhosgarnedd, Bangor, Gwynedd.
Telephone: Bangor (0258) 51144.

Site Summary

Water resource scheme, capital works, 1978-81.
Upland location.
Channel: 7-8 metres wide, 0.3-1.5 metres deep.
Substrate: fine gravel and bedrock.
Designers: P Parkinson, Fisheries, Recreation and Amenity Officer and N Milner, Senior Fisheries Scientist.

Work Description

This scheme is described in detail in Sections **113** and **119**.

The outer bank of a bend in which a pool had been excavated was reveted with locally quarried blockstones, laid on a slope of 1 in 1. The stone was slate, which can be easily laid as slabs, with smaller pieces fitted in between.

A feature of the reinstatement of this section of channel was the number of trees which were planted. These were mainly alder and goat willow, planted at 1 to 3 metre spacing along the tops of both banks, including between the stones of the bank revetment shown here. Once grown, the trees will densely shade the channel and secure the banks. Since the channel should not need maintenance dredging, trees on both banks could be tolerated (photograph below).

Afon Gwyrfai: Revetment using blocks of slate. The measuring stick is divided into 10 cm sections. Note the young alder planted between the stones.

RIVER KENT, KENDAL, CUMBRIA
OS Map: 97. NGR: SD 5192
Rivers Division, North West Water Authority,
PO Box 12, New Town House,
Buttermarket Street, Warrington WA1 2QG.
Telephone: Warrington (0925) 53999.

Site Summary
Flood alleviation scheme, capital works, 1971-79.
Urban location, upland/lowland transition zone.
Channel: about 30 metres wide, less than 1 metre deep.
Banks: 2-3 metres high, with higher masonry walls in places.
Substrate: coarse gravels.

Work Description
The scheme is described in more detail on page **120**.
The river is the focal point of the town of Kendal and the design of the flood alleviation scheme had to take into account visual and aesthetic as well as engineering requirements. Natural stone was chosen for revetment of most of the banks, in the form of large blocks of limestone (up to 3m×1m×2m) set, uncemented, as rough steps with smaller stones set between to fill the largest gaps (photograph below).
Ragwort and willowherb has already grown in soil accumulated in gaps between the blocks, softening the starkness of the stonework and, in summer at least, brightening the river edge with flowers. In time, the stones will also be colonised by mosses and lichens. It is likely that pied and grey wagtails are nesting in crevices in the stonework in undisturbed areas (photograph below).
The blockstone gives a semi-formal edge to the river – appropriate in a country market town – allowing people safe access to the water if they wish, and loafing and roosting spots for the mallards which come to feed.

River Kent: Very large blocks of limestone ('blockstone') set in a stepped fashion, uncemented, with smaller pieces fitted between as required. ▲

River Kent: The uncemented large blocks of limestone make an attractive semi-formal edge to the river. Ragwort and willowherb have colonised it. ▼

MEECE BROOK, SHALLOWFORD, STAFFORDSHIRE
OS Map: 127. NGR: SJ 875293
Upper Trent Division, Severn Trent Water Authority, Trinity Square, Horninglow Street, Burton-on-Trent DE14 1BL.
Telephone: Burton-on-Trent (0283) 44511.
Regional Architects' Department, Severn Trent Water Authority, Abelson House, 2297 Coventry Road, Sheldon, Birmingham B26 3PU.
Telephone: 021-743 4222.

Site Summary
Land drainage scheme, capital works, 1981.
Lowland, rural location.
Channel: 3-4 metres wide.
Banks: Up to 2 metres high, slope 1 in 1.5.
Substrate: sand, alluvial silt, clay.
Engineers: S Powers, D Pinnegar.
Landscape Architects: J Purseglove, M Ericsson.

Work Description
Bank protection work downstream of a gauging station on the Meece Brook, regraded for land drainage purposes in 1981, used uncemented stone from a local quarry, to form a slope of cl in 1.5. By the second summer, the stone was completely hidden by bankside plants growing through and on it (photograph below).

Meece Brook: Bur-reed, willowherb and purple loosestrife growing on tipped stone revetment below Shallowford Gauging Station.

RIVER COLY, COLYTON, DEVON
OS Map: 192. NGR: SY 249943
Environmental Services (East Area), South West Water Authority, Manley House, Kestrel Way, Sowton Industrial Estate, Exeter.
Telephone: Exeter (0392) 76201.

Site Summary
Flood alleviation, capital works, 1980.
Lowland, rural village-edge location.
Channel: 2-3 metres wide.
Banks: 0.5-1 metres high.
Substrate: clay and fine gravel.
Area Engineer: N Grundy.

Work Description
Flooding of the village of Colyton was alleviated by construction of a two stage channel, the river bed also being lowered by 0.5 to 1 metre. To check scour of the new bed and banks, blockstone was placed along the edge of the channel and as low weirs at intervals along the channel (see **123**). Local stone was bought in as 1,250-1,525 kilogram blocks and tipped where required (photograph right).

River Coly: Blockstone bank protection and weir, two years after construction.

RIVER AIRE, SKIPTON BYPASS COMPENSATORY WASHLAND SCHEME, YORKSHIRE
OS Map: 103. NGR: SD 9552

Western District, Southern Area,
Rivers Division, Yorkshire Water Authority,
21 Park Square South, Leeds LS1 2QG.
Telephone: Leeds (0532) 440191.

Site Summary
Flood alleviation scheme, capital works, 1975-83.
Rural location, upland/lowland transition zone.
Channel: 10-15 metres wide.
Substrate: gravel, sands and silt.
Designer: YWA, Rivers Division.

Work Description
See page 77 for details of the overall scheme.
The outfall structure of the washland into the Aire used tipped stone as the 'apron' between the base of the outfall and the river. Silt which has accumulated

River Aire: The bed and sides of the outfall channel between the sluice and the river are protected with loose, tipped stone, permitting a wetland plant community to flourish.

amongst the rock supports a temporary and rich community of common marsh plants – 14 species were counted in a July visit. This has created a small wetland, diversifying the riverbank habitat and providing more varied food sources and soil conditions for invertebrates. Several common frogs were found in the area, indicating that the damp conditions suit them as well (photograph on **179**). The plants should be washed out by discharges from the outfall (designed to operate on average once every two years), so there should be little risk of vegetation choking the outfall channel in the event of dense vegetation growth developing; however, occasional clearance may become necessary.

GABIONS

Gabions – wire mesh cages, filled with loose stone – provide flexible structures for bank protection, which allow smaller sizes of quarry stone, or even coarse river gravels, to be used where otherwise they might be unstable. Their flexibility comes from their porosity; water flows through the spaces between the stones, and the stones are able to shift slightly within the cage, so deflecting flows to a limited extent to accommodate erosion, reducing velocities through friction and dissipating erosive energy.

Gabions can be used in many situations for bank and bed protection, and to build small dams, weirs and groynes. They can be 'home-made' from wire mesh of suitable strength, such as galvanised chain-link fencing, or obtained commercially in sections for construction on site, in various strengths of galvanised and polythene-coated wire.

Newly constructed gabions look unattractive, and if plant growth is prevented by scouring or heavily polluted water, they remain so. The habitat offered to wildlife by gabions, however, improves as silt collects in the spaces between the stones and plants grow over the wire mesh. Underwater, algae and invertebrates may colonise the gabions, sheltered from the force of the current.

A danger in using gabions for bank protection, however, is that sooner or later the wire cage will corrode or fail through metal fatigue, and the cage will break open. Immediately the gabion loses its effectiveness against scour and a mass of broken, tangled, rusty wire is left in the river. Galvanised and plastic gabions have a longer, but still finite, life. The useful life of a gabion is shortened by poor installation (eg filling too loosely, or misguided attempts to make them stronger by covering them with concrete or impervious sheeting, so causing them to lose their flexibility) or inappropriate use (eg in spatey rivers carrying mobile, coarse gravels).

Until overgrown by plants, gabions have a low roughness factor. As a result, scour is frequently seen to develop at the downstream end of a gabion wall, say on the outer bank of a meander. This could be prevented by planting willow stakes in, or in front of, the last few gabions, so that the growing shoots break up the force of flow into smaller, less erosive eddies. Indeed, in many situations, the use of gabions could probably be avoided altogether,

If gabions are to be successfully used for bank protection, they must be correctly installed in appropriate locations. This line of gabions, on the River Rea, Ten Acres, Birmingham, failed within a year of installation. The base of the gabions was undercut, causing them to slump forward.

since most of the benefits for river bank or bed protection offered by their use can also be derived by the use of alternative materials described in

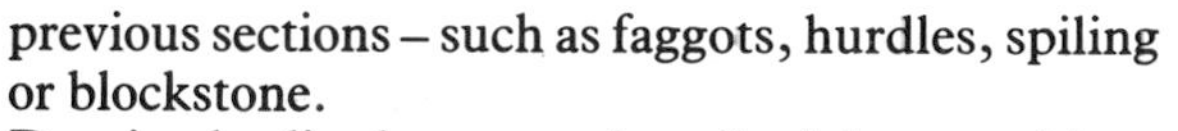

previous sections – such as faggots, hurdles, spiling or blockstone.
Despite the disadvantages described above, gabions are widely used by all water authorities. The examples described here illustrate the sensitive use of gabions, generally where they have become well colonised by plants. Examples using a combination of stone-filled gabions and willow logs are given on pages **167** and **168**, and a combination of stone and common reed rhizome clumps on page **171**.

RIVER RODING, PASSINGFORD BRIDGE, ESSEX
OS Map: 167. NGR: TQ 508975
Eastern Division, Thames Water Authority, The Grange, Crossbrook Street, Waltham Cross, Hertfordshire.
Telephone: Waltham Cross (0992) 23611.

Site Summary
Channel diversion scheme, capital works, 1982.
Lowland, rural location.
Channel: 6-11 metres wide; 1.5-2.5 metres deep.
Banks: 1.5-2 metres high, batter varied.
Substrate: clay and imported gravel.
Designer: D Wojcik, Project Engineer, New Works.

Work Description
See page **142** for a detailed description of this scheme. Two hundred metres of the Roding had to be diverted because of the construction of the M25. At the request of the motorway engineers, the new embankment closing off the old channel was protected with gabion mattresses laid on a 1 in 1.5 slope, filled with limestone or gravel rejects and covered by 100 millimetres of clay, compacted into it. Top soil from the original banks was spread on top, to encourage rapid regeneration from rhizomes and seeds of the original vegetation (figure right).

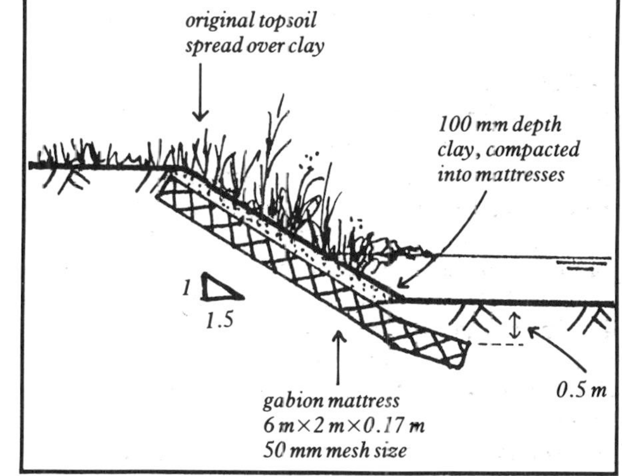

River Roding: The use of gabion mattresses and compacted clay for bank protection.

Habitat Comments
1 Covering the gabion mattress with compacted clay and topsoil ensures rapid recolonisation by plants, hopefully quickly and densely enough to resist scour and prevent the rock and wire being exposed to erosion.
2 Varying the bank angle and using other forms of bank protection within the short stretch of the scheme builds in variation to the physical habitat, which is excellent.

LECK BECK, KIRKBY LONSDALE, LANCASHIRE
OS Map: 97. NGR: SD 611753
Unknown.

Site Summary
Rural location, upland/lowland transition zone.
Channel: 8-15 metres wide.
Banks: 1-3 metres high, slopes variable.
Substrate: coarse gravels and large cobbles.

Work Description
This example has been included to illustrate how gabions can be successfully used to protect the banks of coarse gravel rivers. It is not known who carried out the work or when – although we estimate that it was at least 10 years ago.
This site is at the confluence of the River Lune and the Leck Beck. Regularly, the Lune floods back up the Beck, causing local flooding, impeded drainage, and depositing coarse gravels. The Beck has been widened and deepened periodically to alleviate this problem. Fifty millimetre gabion wire mesh was used to hold down 120-150 millimetre cobbles into the bank, so helping to stabilise it as part of such works.
The use of the gabion mesh has been successful, in that both the bank and the bank protection have remained intact. Perhaps a key factor for this success is that flooding has deposited silt and sand over the gabions, to become trapped between the cobbles, providing a medium in which plants can root. Grasses and gorse have since colonised. Sheep grazing and trampling has helped to consolidate the grass sward. Sheep will not eat unpalatable plants such as gorse (which in this area typically invades permanent pasture), so providing virtually immovable bank protection (photograph overleaf).

Leck Beck: Coarse river cobbles stabilised by gabion mesh, now well covered with sheep grazed turf and gorse.

Habitat Comments

1 The gabion mesh has stabilised the cobbles so that a soil has been able to develop, and the local plant cover of grassland and gorse has spread over it. This seems excellent from all points of view. Gorse scrub, for example, is good wildlife cover in areas such as this.

RIVER ALNE, HENLEY-IN-ARDEN, WARWICKSHIRE
OS Map: 151. NGR: SP 154665
Avon Division, Severn-Trent Water Authority, Finham Reclamation Ground, St Martin's Road, Finham, Coventry.
Telephone: Coventry (0203) 415115.
Regional Architects' Department, Severn-Trent Water Authority, Abelson House, 2297 Coventry Road, Sheldon, Birmingham.
Telephone: 021-743 4222.

Site Summary
Flood alleviation scheme, capital works, 1979-80.

River Alne: Commercial gabions, 1 m×1 m×3 m, filled with local stone, stacked two high and secured with iron bars. Rosa longicuspes, *planted two years previously, now trails down over the gabions.*

Lowland, urban location.
Channel: 4-5 metres wide, depth variable.
Banks: variable, man-made in this reach.
Substrate: sandy clay, gravel.
Engineer: R Tinley.
Landscape Architect: J Purseglove.

Work Description
The Alne was deepened by up to 1 metre in 1980-81 to alleviate flooding in Henley-in-Arden. An old bridge and adjacent property were protected in a narrow part of the channel by a wall made with gabion baskets, 1m×1m×3m, stacked two high and staked in place with iron bars. The top of the gabion wall was covered with topsoil and planted. Being in an urban setting, where a quick-growing attractive plant cover was needed, the landscape architect recommended *Rosa longicuspes*, which in two years has rapidly spread down over the wire and stone (photograph left).

Habitat Comments
1 The gabions have been used as a cheap but effective substitute for stone walling. When well covered by the trailing 'dog rose,' it fits in well with its urban surroundings and does not look out of place.
2 The gabions will make additional habitat for invertebrates. Mosses and small plants should be able to colonise crevices above water level.
3 *Rosa longicuspes* is an attractive rambling rose suitable for town settings. It is an alien species, however, and not suitable for planting in rural locations.

FARLINGTON MARSHES, LANGSTONE HARBOUR, PORTSMOUTH, HAMPSHIRE
OS Map: 196. NGR: SU 690049
Hampshire River and Water Division, Southern Water Authority, Marland House, Civic Centre Road, Southampton SO9 4XT.
Telephone: Southampton (0703) 34731.

Site Summary
Sea defence scheme, capital works, 1979-80.
Estuarine, rural location.
River Manager: J Shorthose.

Work Description
Sea defences for Farlington Marshes – a nature reserve managed by the Hampshire and Isle of Wight Naturalists' Trust – were improved in 1979-80.

The most exposed lengths of the earth embankment are faced with in-situ concrete slabs. The most sheltered lengths, however, are protected by 300 millimetre thick Reno wire mattresses filled with imported limestone, laid at a slope of 1 in 5, and covered with mud dredged from in front of the embankment. Between the two types of protection is a short transition section of stone-filled gabion mattresses, secured in concrete frames set at a slope of 1 in 1 and covered in spoil dredged from a drain on the inner side of the sea wall.
Both the 'sheltered' and the 'transition' sections have developed saltmarsh plant communities. The water authority report that they are particularly pleased with the 'sheltered' section protected by buried Reno mattresses as there has been very little

Farlington Marshes: The 'sheltered' section, protected by buried Reno wire mattresses.

scour to date (which they attribute to the flat 1 in 5 slope); before improvement, this length of embankment had 15 minor breaches along it due to wave erosion (photographs on **183** and above).

Farlington Marshes: The 'transition' section, protected by Reno mattresses set in concrete frames. The zonation (in terms of salt-tolerance) of the salt marsh plant community can be seen, from glasswort at the base to fescues and yarrow at the bank-top.

Habitat Comments

1 Use of Reno mattresses in this manner has permitted the development of a saltmarsh plant community on the seaward face of the embankment.

FABRIC AND MESH REVETMENT FABRICS

Although relatively new in Britain, man-made fabric and mesh products are being used more and more widely for bank protection and soil stabilisation, as alternatives to the traditional hazel hurdles **169**. Such products have been in use for a greater period of time in the Netherlands, generally satisfactorily, particularly for the establishment of common reed as permanent bank protection on polders.

For nature conservation, biodegradable soil stabilisers are clearly preferable to persistent ones. Concern has been expressed, for example, that decaying nylon products may eventually wash out of the river bank to pose a threat to waterbirds similar to that of discarded mono-filament nylon fishing line (by getting tangled around their feet, bills, wings and neck). Nearly all plastic and nylon products are UV stabilised to protect them from degradation by sunlight, if and when they become exposed. The use of any of these products must be qualified by this concern.

Rather than commenting on the full (and increasing) range of products on the market, outlined below are the criteria which will favour the restoration of a natural plant community over fabric or mesh revetment:

1 Many bankside plants develop robust rhizomes. The material should permit rhizomes to grow through it.

2 The material should not inhibit the growth of grasses and other herbaceous vegetation.

3 The material should either be stable, to function

effectively as long-term bank protection, or be biodegradable, functioning as short-term bank protection until dense vegetative cover has developed. For the reasons above, the latter is probably preferable.

4 The breakdown products of the material should be non-toxic, physically unobtrusive and unobstructive, and should pose no physical hazard to wildlife.

The choice of revetment or soil stabilisation system will depend on site conditions and flow regime, as well as cost, availability and ease of construction. A comparative table of some fabric, mesh and cellular concrete products is given below. The table is not intended to be comprehensive. *Inclusion of a product in the table or mention of a product in the examples which follow should not be taken as endorsement of the use of that material by RSPB or RSNC.*

Hydraseeding techniques, using mixtures of bitumen, organic mulch and seeds, may help to establish good plant cover rapidly.

Finally, the use of such revetment products is likely to results in less erosion and slumping – put another way, the river channel is less likely to develop the diverse physical structure required by wildlife. While this feature may be desirable from the river engineering viewpoint, it is undesirable for wildlife conservation. Efforts should be made, therefore, to increase the physical diversity of the channel by introducing channel and bank features such as berms, asymmetrical channels and shallow bays on which the revetment materials can then be laid.

A comparative table of some fabric, mesh and cellular concrete revetment products

Supplier	Product	Price/m² (1982)	m² Laid per Man Hour	Description
Brooklyns Westbrick Ltd, Manor House, Cossington,	Dytap	£19	4-5	Solid interlocking concrete blocks, either finished in plain concrete or faced with natural stone. Can be laid with either dry or grouted joints.
Bridgwater, Somerset TA7 8JR	Dymex	£12	7	Interlocking concrete cellular revetment blocks. Cavities can be filled with soil and seeded. 25% concrete:75% cavity.
Chilton Polden (0278) 722888	Grasscel	£12.80	7	Cavity forming interconnecting concrete grid with localised upstands. The cavities and channels can be filled with soil and seeded. 25% concrete:75% cavity.
	Dycel	£12.50-£14	7	Cellular concrete blocks designed specifically for river bank revetment, which can be pre-assembled into articulated panels. The cells can be filled with sand, gravel or soil and seeded. 49% concrete:51% cavity.
Nicolon Ltd, PO Box 137, Cambridge CB1 2PH	Gobimat	£10-£11	c36	Concrete blocks, available individually or as flexible matting with the blocks bonded to woven nylon filter cloth. If used as matting, the cells can be filled with soil and seeded. 80% concrete:20% cavity.
Cambridge (0223) 316667	Pocket Fabrics	£1.50-£2.50	not available	Woven polyethylene filter fabric, with rows of prefabricated pockets each 30×30 cm in size, either made of the same material as the ballast pockets or reed pocket fabric – made of 3-4 cm open weave polyethylene mesh, intended to allow vegetative growth.
MMG Erosion Control Systems, Waterloo House,	Enkamat	£1.60-£2.40	Up to 40	Matting, consisting of a mesh formed from crinkly high tenacity nylon threads, fused where they cross. 90% of the volume of the matting is air. Once laid, the web can be filled with soil and seeded.
King's Lynn, Norfolk PE30 1PA King's Lynn (0553) 4423	Enkamat A	£7.20-£8.60	Up to 40	Prefilled Enkamat matting, with a gravel and bitumen filling. Plants are able to grow through the material.

FOUR CANAL SITES:
A *ASHBY-DE-LA-ZOUCH CANAL, NEAR MARKET BOSWORTH, LEICESTERSHIRE*
OS Map: 140. NGR: SK 395004

B *GRAND UNION CANAL, WELFORD, NORTHAMPTONSHIRE*
OS Map: 140. NGR: SP 617808

C *RUSHALL CANAL, NEAR ALDRIDGE, WEST MIDLANDS*
OS Map: 139. NGR: SK 045023

D *STAFFORDSHIRE AND WORCESTERSHIRE CANAL, WOLVERHAMPTON, WEST MIDLANDS*
OS Map: 139. NGR: SO 885992

British Waterways Board,
Engineering Department, Dock Office,
Gloucester GL1 2EJ.
Telephone: Gloucester (0452) 25524

Site Summary
Bank protection works, 1982.
Canal system.
Rural and urban locations.
Substrate: clay.
BWB Water Scientist: R G Hanbury.
Supplier: Nicolon Ltd, PO Box 137,
Cambridge CB1 2PH. Cambridge (0223) 316667.

Work Description
'Reeds' – usually *Carex* species, such as greater and lesser pond sedge – were planted on canal banks until the early part of this century. Direct replanting into recently regraded banks, however, is now considered impractical as the exposed banks are likely to be eroded by boatwash before the plants are established.
Trials were begun in 1982, by BWB, to protect regraded canal banks using 'Nicolon' pocket fabric. The fabric was supplied to the Board's specification, with large-mesh pockets at the water line, in which clumps of pond sedge rhizomes were planted. Mainly greater pond sedge was planted, with some lesser pond sedge.
Four sites were selected for the trials, each experiencing different levels of boat traffic:

Site	Boats/ha/ year (1977)	Traffic
D Staffordshire & Worcestershire	4001-5000	very heavy
B Grand Union	3001-4000	heavy
A Ashby-de-la-Zouch	1001-2000	medium
C Rushall	1-1000	light

Once the bank had been graded as required (to a 1 in 1.5 slope or less), the roll of pocket fabric was laid at the top, pegged down and unrolled so that the upper pocket of yellow reed mesh ('Nicolon' code 66380) fell at the water line. The lowest pockets were filled with rubble as ballast, and the upper pockets with pond sedge rhizomes recently dug from a BWB-owned site at Leicester where it is abundant. Spoil was tipped over the pocket fabric, seeded and, where there was stock access, fenced to prevent grazing of young plants. A three-man direct labour gang carried out the work, at an overall cost of £12 per metre (1982 prices) (figure below).

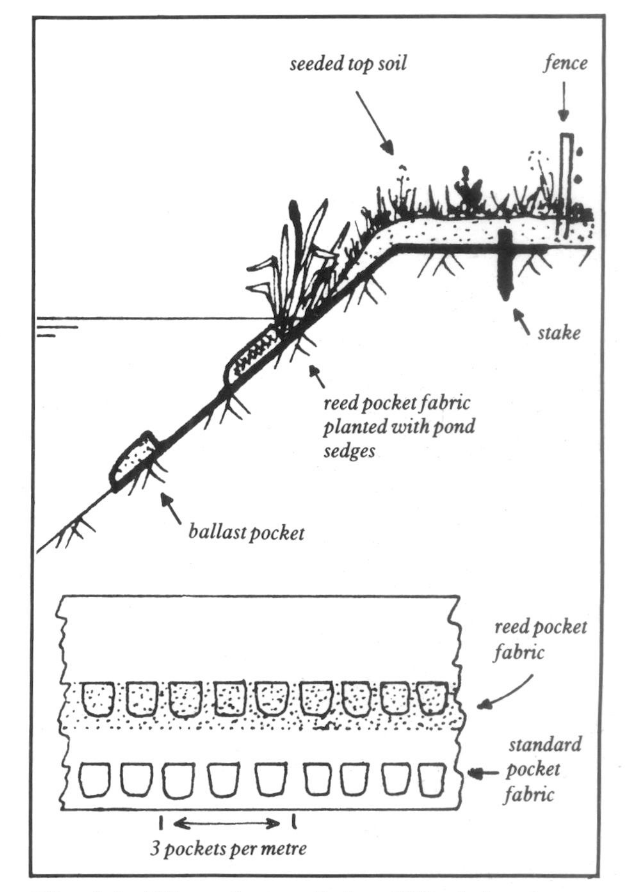

'Canal sites' illustrating installation of 'Nicolon' pocket fabric.

Plantings in April showed a 90 per cent take within six weeks, although later plantings in June 'got away' less quickly. All are now well established (photographs on right).

Habitat Comments
1 This technique has permitted development of natural plant cover, allowing the space for colonisation of additional species and benefiting animal life at the canal edge, whilst providing the bank with protection against scour.
2 Pond sedge rhizomes were seen growing outside the reed mesh pockets within three months of plant-

ing, demonstrating that the 'clumpy' appearance of the bank vegetation would quickly disappear. (In Holland, common reed has been planted in similar mesh pockets and forms a uniform reedbed within a year or so.)

3 Ideally, for wildlife habitat creation purposes, a range of aquatic plant species should have been planted – although other species may not have been so suitable for bank protection purposes. See pages **21** and **219** for additional practical and legal information about the planting of aquatic species.

Rushall Canal: Pond sedges planted into 'Nicolon' pocket fabric, one month after planting. ▶

Staffordshire and Worcestershire Canal: Pond sedges planted into 'Nicolon' pocket fabric, one week after planting. ▲

Ashby-de-la-Zouch Canal: Pond sedges planted into 'Nicolon' pocket fabric, three months after planting. ▶

Ashby-de-la-Zouch Canal: Three months after planting.

BY BROOK, BOX, NEAR BATH, WILTSHIRE
OS Map: 173. NGR: ST 814688
Bristol Avon Division, Wessex Water Authority, PO Box 95, The Ambury, Bath, Avon.
Telephone: Bath (0225) 313500.

Site Summary
Capital works, 1982.
Rural, lowland location.
Channel: 7-10 metres wide.
Banks: 2.5 metres high, graded 1 in 1.5.
Substrate: clay and silt.
Engineer: M A Hillyer, Divisional Planning Engineer.
Supplier: Nicolon Ltd, PO Box 137, Cambridge CB1 2PH. Cambridge (0223) 316667.

Work Description
Revetment works to protect regraded banks around a new gauging station made use of two types of 'Nicolon' pocket fabric and 'Gobimat' – concrete blocks bonded to 'Nicolon' nylon mesh. The two types of pocket fabric were made from black 'Nicolon' fabric code 66339 with a very small mesh, and from white 'Nicolon' reed fabric code 66380 with a large mesh. Both had two rows of pockets above normal water level and two below.
An agricultural seed-mix was sown on the graded bank before the revetment materials were put in place. The pocket fabrics were installed as for the BWB trials (page **186**), although no planting was carried out, spoil and topsoil being dropped into the pockets as ballast instead. The fabric was not covered by spoil, except on the crest of the bank.

Three weeks after installation in May, germination was very patchy, although slightly greater through the large mesh white 'reed' fabric than the small mesh black fabric. Three months after installation, in July, there was about 60 per cent of ryegrass over the white fabric. At the end of the summer, vegetative cover of the white 'reed' fabric was nearly complete, but cover of the black fabric was still poor (photographs below and right).
The 'Gobimat', installed on the outer bank of a

By Brook: White 'reed' 'Nicolon' pocket fabric, three weeks after installation on a graded bank with patchy germination of ryegrass from seed spread underneath.

By Brook: The same site three months after installation. On the left is the black fine mesh pocket fabric; in the centre, the white 'reed' coarse mesh pocket fabric; and on the right, the 'Gobimat' concrete block revetment.

bend, had plant growth in the recesses between the blocks at the top of the slope after only three months; by the end of the summer, there was some growth in the recesses over the full slope.

Habitat Comments

1 Development of full plant cover has been slow, particularly through the fine mesh pocket fabric. Indeed, use of the fine mesh fabric will probably prevent perennial bankside plants from colonising the bank, until sufficient silt has accumulated in which they can root. Use of the wide mesh reed fabric, combined with deliberate planting of aquatic and bankside plants in the pockets and spreading of the original topsoil, would seem to offer a better method for quickly establishing a 'natural', diverse and abundant plant community.

2 Seeding with an agricultural grass mix (on banks too steep to be grazed) reduces the chances of a natural plant community developing for many years.

3 Although the fabric may look unattractive initially, once plant cover has developed fully, it should blend into the landscape.

4 The shaping of the bank is rather unimaginative. Use of revetment materials in this manner is likely to hold the bank to its graded profile, again inhibiting the colonisation of emergent aquatic plants.

SELSMORE SALTERN, HAYLING ISLAND, HAMPSHIRE

OS Map: 197. NGR: SZ 736993

Hampshire River and Water Division, Southern Water Authority, Marland House, Civic Centre Road, Southampton SO9 4XT. Telephone: Southampton (0703) 34731.

Site Summary

Sea defence scheme, capital works, 1982.
Estuarine, rural location.
River Manager: J Shorthose.
Suppliers:* Gobimat: *Nicolon Ltd, PO Box 137, Cambridge CB1 2PH. Cambridge (0223) 316667.
Enkamat: *MMG Erosion Control Systems, Waterloo House, King's Lynn, Norfolk PE30 1PA. King's Lynn (0553) 4423.*

Work Description

'Gobimat' – concrete blocks bonded to 'Nicolon' nylon mesh – and 'Enkamat A' – a mat of crinkly, high-tenacity nylon threads, fused where they cross and filled with gravel and asphalt – were used in combination to repair a low sea wall.

The 'Gobimat' was laid first to protect the bank toe, with the 'Enkamat A' above. The 'Enkamat' was covered with 10 centimetres of topsoil and seeded with sea couch grass – a native grass appropriate for the location. In principle, this is the same technique recommended for the use of 'Enkamat' on freshwater rivers and streams. Within a matter of weeks, a strong growth of grass had developed (photograph overleaf).

Interestingly, the 'Gobimat' at the base of the slope seemed to cause a change in the size of sediment deposited below the slope, from mud to gravels. This was possibly a result of the reflection of wave energy from the concrete surface.

Selsmore Saltern: The seawall, three weeks after completion of the work. The 'Gobimat' is at the base of the wall, with 'Enkamat A' – covered with topsoil and re-seeded with sea couch grass – above.

Habitat Comments

1 The sea couch grass seed mixture took well. Within three weeks of topsoiling, other saltmarsh plants (such as sea beet and wild carrot) were colonising the 'Enkamat' protected area of the bank as well. A natural native plant community seems likely to develop quite rapidly.

2 The 'Gobimat' at the base of the sea wall is unlikely to develop a permanent plant community because it is so exposed to wave wash. Some areas had already been colonised, at least temporarily, by sea beet, glasswort and wild carrot.

3 Colonisation of the bank was probably aided by the areas of native plants which remained undisturbed nearby, providing sources of seed, rhizomes and plant fragments.

SANDWELL VALLEY BALANCING LAKE, BIRMINGHAM

OS Map: 139. NGR: SP 0392

Tame Division, Severn Trent Water Authority, Tame House, 156/170 Newhall Street, Birmingham B3 1SE.

Telephone: 021-233 1616.

Site Summary

Flood alleviation scheme, capital works, 1982.

Lowland, urban-fringe location.

Design: Divisional Engineers Department, Tame Division.

Suppliers: **Netlon:** ***Netlon Ltd, Kelly Street, Mill Hill, Blackburn, Lancashire. Blackburn (0254) 62431.***

Dymex: ***see page 185.***

Work Description

Care has been taken throughout the design and construction of the balancing lake to minimise disturbance and to ensure the area will recover rapidly. Tree planting, choice of grass mixtures and choice of erosion protection materials have all contributed to habitat reinstatement, while design has ensured that important wetland, ditch and hedgerow habitats have been retained (see pages **81** and **200** for additional information).

Erosion protection around the control and inlet structures of the balancing lake made use of 'Netlon', described here, and 'Dymex', described on page **193**. The lake side of the inlet structure was protected with 'Netlon' type CE111 – a black coloured, low density polyethylene polymer mesh, with a mesh thickness of 2.9 millimetres and mesh

aperture of 7 millimetres – placed over the naturally occurring layers of sand, gravel and clay. Seed was applied directly to the subsoil prior to laying the 'Netlon'. The area was not topsoiled (photograph below).
The inlet structure is expected to be overtopped by 1 in 10 year floods, so the 'Netlon' protected slope will only have to withstand relatively infrequent overland flow. The established grass cover should be able to withstand such events, but the 'Netlon' provides additional protection against scour and gullying.

Habitat Comments
1 Use of a mesh revetment provides a basis for the reinstatement of wildlife habitats on the lake edge. The seed mixture used contains a mixture of species which should allow other plants to invade and diversify the sward in the future.

Sandwell Valley Balancing Lake: 'Netlon' being rolled out and pegged down at the foot of the inlet structure.

CELLULAR CONCRETE REVETMENTS

Concrete revetment should only be used in limited locations where plant cover alone cannot give sufficient protection against scour and the failure of the bank would be serious, or where the smoothness of concrete is required for hydraulic efficiency and to minimise roughness in areas with moderate or high water flow velocities.
The use of smooth concrete for bank revetment, however, produces an even, uniform bank profile – of little value to wildlife, inhibiting, and possibly even preventing, colonisation by plants, invertebrates and other animals. In general, therefore, cellular concrete revetments may be welcomed as providing a practical alternative to the use of smooth concrete which is more acceptable environmentally.
There are a number of cellular concrete revetment systems now available, laid either as interlocking blocks or attached to a backing mesh. The table on page **185** describes a limited selection of these. *Inclusion of a product in the table or mention of a product in the examples which follow should not be taken as endorsement of the use of that material by RSPB or RSNC.*
The most objectionable aspect, from the wildlife and aesthetic viewpoints, is that cellular blocks tend to be used to stabilise and protect uniform, evenly graded slopes. In some locations, such uniformity may be required for hydraulic reasons – equally, however, it may be possible to design reveted banks with rounded tops, ledges, berms, bays and bends, in an imitation of natural bank forms.
Although the establishment of tall herb, scrubby or emergent aquatic vegetation may be unacceptable for hydraulic reasons, there is no reason why banks protected with cellular blocks should not be planted up and sown with grasses and short herbaceous plants, in the same way as other banks (see planting aquatic plants, **219**; natural recolonisation of grasses and herbs, **234**; grass and herb seed mixtures, **235**; transplanting turves of grass and herbs, **238**).
If good plant cover is to develop on such reveted banks, it is important to leave a good depth of soil both below and within the blocks. Concrete grouting below, for example, 'Dymex' means plants are

effectively in a shallow pot in some 10 centimetres of soil, without free drainage, and with excessive root constriction. Scrappy poor and unattractive plant growth is likely to result.

RIVER AIRE, INGHEY BRIDGE, YORKSHIRE
OS Map: 103. NGR: SD 961517
Department of Transport, Yorkshire and Humberside Regional Office, Windsor House, Cornwall Road, Harrogate, North Yorkshire HG1 2PW.
Telephone: Harrogate (0423) 68903.

Site Summary
Bridge revetment works, 1980/81.
Rural location, upland/lowland transition zone.
Channel: 8-12 metres wide.
Substrate: gravels, sand and silt.
Design and construction: Western District, Southern Area, Rivers Division, Yorkshire Water Authority,

River Aire: Detail of the flood berm protected by 'Grasscrete' (right) and the bank slope protected by tipped stone (left). ▲

River Aire: The flood berm protected with 'Grasscrete,' laid two seasons previously, pictured in August 1982. ▼

21 Park Square South, Leeds LS1 2QG.
Telephone: Leeds (0532) 440191.
Supplier: Grass Concrete Ltd,
Walker House, 22 Bond Street, Wakefield.
Telephone: Wakefield (0924) 375997.

Work Description
The supports of a bridge constructed by the Department of Transport to carry the new Skipton bypass across the river Aire required protection against scour.
The Aire is a coarse gravel river with mobile sediments, shaped into a two-stage channel in this reach. 'Grasscrete' – formed by pouring concrete in situ into a special plastic former – was used to protect the upper flood berm from scour; the bank slope is protected with large tipped stone. It was (and still is) intended that the cavities in the 'Grasscrete' should be filled with topsoil and be seeded with grass to give complete grass cover over the whole area – although it was recognised that repeated scouring and deposition might inhibit this – but the contractor has not completed the work yet. In the meantime the cavities have filled with gravel and silt and (two growing seasons on) have been colonised naturally by indigenous plants – predominantly willowherb, ragwort, dandelion, grasses and mosses. Total cover is patchy – varying from 0 to 95 per cent. The best plant cover has developed where sand and gravel had been deposited over the concrete by flood flows (photographs on left).
The 'Grasscrete' also delineates the design profile of the flood berms, providing a hard surface down to which the channel can be cleared when sediments have accumulated unacceptably.

Habitat Comments
1 'Grasscrete' has a high percentage area of concrete in relation to spaces, so it is only slowly covered by plants spreading out from the spaces.
2 The smoothness of the concrete of this system reduces friction at the surface, and may increase scour of soil from the spaces, so inhibiting plant growth.
3 From the wildlife viewpoint, it is probably better to permit materials such as this to colonise naturally (although the area may not be so attractive visually) rather than seeding with an agricultural grass mixture – which may result in the production of a dense, lush sward which indigenous plants cannot colonise.

RIVER TAME, SANDWELL VALLEY BALANCING LAKE, BIRMINGHAM
OS Map: 139. NGR: SP 0392
Tame Division, Severn Trent Water Authority,
Tame House, 156/170 Newhall Street,
Birmingham B3 1SE.
Telephone: 021-233 1616.

River Tame: A close-up of the 'Dymex' cellular blocks, recently laid and seeded, showing the high proportion of soil to concrete at the surface.

Site Summary
Flood alleviation scheme, capital works, 1981-82.
Lowland, urban-fringe location.
Channel: 9 metres wide.
Banks: 4 metres high, 1 in 2 slope.
Substrate: sand, silt.
Design: Divisional Engineers' Department, Tame Division.
Supplier: Brooklyns Westbrick Ltd,

Manor House, Cossington, Bridgwater, Somerset TA7 8JR. Chilton Polden (0278) 722888.

Work Description
See pages **81**, **190** and **200** for additional information about this scheme.
The approach to a flood control structure on the river Tame was protected with 'Dytap' solid concrete interlocking revetment blocks at the bank toe and 'Dymex' cellular concrete blocks and grass above. The blocks were laid on graded banks on a 1 in 3 slope. The spaces of the 'Dymex' blocks were filled with topsoil and sown with the grass and herb seed mixture used elsewhere in the scheme (photographs on **193** and below).

River Tame: 'Dymex' recently laid on the banks of the Tame and its confluence with a small tributary, upstream of the flood control structure. 'Dytap' was laid at the bank toe.

Habitat Comments
1 The low proportion of concrete to soil in 'Dymex' at the surface means that a complete plant cover can rapidly develop, from seed or planting.
2 Use of 'Dytap' at the bank toe will do little to encourage the colonisation of aquatic emergent vegetation, although the fast flow velocities in this reach may have made use of such a material unavoidable.

BY BROOK, BOX, NEAR BATH, WILTSHIRE
OS Map: 173. NGR: ST 814688
Bristol Avon Division, Wessex Water Authority, PO Box 95, The Ambury, Bath, Avon. Telephone: Bath (0225) 313500.

Site Summary
Capital works, 1982.
Rural, lowland location.
Channel: 7-10 metres wide.
Banks: 2.5 metres high, graded 1 in 1.5.
Substrate: clay and silt.
Engineer: M A Hillyer, Divisional Planning Engineer.
Supplier: Nicolon Ltd, PO Box 137, Cambridge CB1 2PH. Cambridge (0223) 316667.

Work Description
Bank protection work around a gauging station made use of 'Gobimat' and pocket fabric revetment materials (see also **188**).
'Gobimat' – concrete blocks bonded to 'Nicolon' nylon mesh – was laid on the outer bank of a bend immediately downstream of the gauging station, where it was expected that scour would be at its greatest.
The bank was graded to 1 in 1.5, seeded with an agricultural mixture, and the 'Gobimat' laid in place. Within a few months, plants were growing up through the 'Gobimat,' although the metre above normal water level remained unvegetated, probably as a result of the high flow velocities experienced in that zone (photograph on right).
For an example of 'Gobimat' used in sea defence work, see **189**.

By Brook: 'Gobimat,' with grass beginning to grow through the upper edge of the mat.

Habitat Comments

1 The cellular blocks will allow natural plant growth, as would similar block systems, and provide crevices and crannies for invertebrates below the water line, which is preferable to smooth concrete.

2 As high velocities on the outer bank of the bend are likely to prevent plant growth at the water-line, the 'Gobimat' is likely to remain visible – rather unattractive in this rural setting.

RIVER RODING, LOUGHTON, ESSEX
OS Map: 177. NGR: TQ 452964

Eastern Division, Thames Water Authority,
The Grange, Crossbrook Street, Waltham Cross, Hertfordshire.
Telephone: Waltham Cross (0992) 23611.

Site Summary

Channel diversion scheme, capital works, 1973.
Lowland, rural location.
Channel: 8 metres wide; 0.2-0.6 metres deep (low water flows).
Substrate: clay, alluvial silt, concrete bank revetment.
Suppliers: Brooklyns Westbrick Ltd, Manor House, Cossington, Bridgwater, Somerset TA7 8JR. Chilton Polden (0278) 722888.

Work Description

Although not an open cellular block, the 'Dytap' revetment system is included here as it is widely used to give a 'natural' appearance to protected banks. The solid interlocking revetment blocks are available with a smooth concrete or a natural stone face. When installed dry-jointed, it allows plants to colonise and grow through the spaces between the stones, partially masking the surface.

A four hundred metre reach of the river Roding was diverted in 1973 during construction works for the M11 motorway. A straight, two-stage, shallow trapezoidal channel was constructed and the banks faced with dry-jointed Dytap blocks. The growth of bankside plants between the unmortared Dytap blocks has softened the starkness of the design and improved the habitat for bankside flora and fauna (photograph above).

River Roding: 'Dytap' blocks – laid dry joined – colonised by bankside plants where silt has accumulated at the channel edge. A similar 'Dytap' face at a higher level (behind) has not been colonised so well.

The uniform, shallow flow of water through the evenly-shaped trapezoidal channel, however, supported little wildlife. As part of the Abridge flood alleviation scheme, measures were taken to diversify the channel to benefit fisheries and wildlife (see pages **124** and **129**). Indeed, a subsequent scheme has shown that it is possible to create channel diversions much more sympathetic to wildlife – see page **142**.

Habitat Comments

1 The dry-joined blocks allow plant growth between, and, given time and silt accumulation, a 'natural' bank edge plant community can develop.

2 Compared to tipped stone revetment, gabions, or open cellular concrete blocks, this system provides fewer niches for aquatic invertebrates, and therefore benefits the overall wildlife community less.

3 When set in concrete, 'Dytap' blocks have little, if any, benefit for wildlife.

4 This scheme also demonstrates how revetment materials can be used to protect and maintain bank and channel profiles which are unsympathetic to wildlife. Hopefully, such designs are now of the past and, at the very least, if trapezoidal channels are required, in-channel structures will be used to diversify flow patterns to the benefit of wildlife.

TECHNICAL 3: SPOIL DISPOSAL

Spoil disposal is a problem. Frequently spoil is used to infill irregularities in adjacent fields, which may marginally increase agricultural productivity, but at the same time destroy a small damp hollow – perhaps a valuable habitat for wetland plants and birds.

The Water Space Amenity Commission's 'Conservation and Land Drainage Guidelines' (1980) suggest that 'where the spoil is not likely to have a serious injurious effect on the top soil it should be spread evenly over the adjoining land beyond the channel, to a depth not exceeding 0.15 metres, unless this action is more harmful to conservation than by creating mounds'. These guidelines also recognise the need to consult the farmer 'on the method and timing of disposal' and the need to take care to 'avoid damage to flora particularly rare species'. Spreading spoil is common practice and is successful, effective and non-harmful in most cases. But what if spreading is harmful to wildlife? How can this situation be recognised?

Because flooding and high water-tables may have restricted the use of fertilisers and herbicides on river-side meadows, they are often rich botanically – both for wetland plants such as water mint, meadowsweet, marsh thistle, and marsh marigold and as a refuge for meadow species such as snake's head fritillary and orchids. Botanically rich meadows are also likely to support rich invertebrate communities, attracting butterflies, moths, damselflies and dragonflies to feed. Areas of wet pasture may be feeding and breeding areas for wildfowl and waders – especially snipe and redshank – now scarce in lowland England and Wales.

Spoil disposal may, therefore, be harmful to wildlife in a number of ways:

– if spread so as to smother botanically rich grassland including meadows and wetland plants.

– by being spread or heaped around the bases of trees so causing their death.

– by being spread over, or used to fill, wet hollows in fields.

Obviously, in determining how spoil should be disposed of the wishes of the landowner and occupier have to be taken into account. If a landowner wishes to infill hollows then as long as the land is not within a Site of Special Scientific Interest he may do so, but in our view it is not within a drainage authority's remit to aid him – even as part-compensation for disturbance elsewhere.

In operational terms, the statutory requirements of Section 22 of the Water Act 1973 as amended by Section 48 of the Wildlife and Countryside Act 1981, mean that every spoil disposal operation should be critically examined on site, in relation to both operational and wildlife conservation needs, to find an option acceptable from both viewpoints.

The alternatives are:

– Careful spoil spreading on adjacent land, avoiding sensitive wetland habitats **197**.

– Use of spoil to construct floodbanks, or the retention of spoil in heaps **201**.

– Carting spoil from the site, using for fill and floodbanks in nearby schemes proceeding simultaneously or for disposal at an alternative suitable site elsewhere **202**.

In addition, spoil disposal in relation to trees and scrub is also considered on page **202**.

SPOIL SPREADING

There are several forms of spoil spreading which are commonly practised:

1 Dredged material is left on the bank to de-water for a few months before being spread over the adjacent land. This may cause operational difficulties, because frequently the spoil does not de-water sufficiently to be spread easily; often the spoil may grow nettles and other 'undesirable' plant species: and, if the spoil is gravelly, soil capability may be reduced. From the wildlife viewpoint, this practice may be damaging if botanically rich meadows are smothered with spoil and if irregularities are smoothed out.

2 By trenching: where small quantities of spoil are to be disposed of, a trench may be excavated into which the material is put. Sub- and topsoil is then replaced and the ground reseeded. This minimises disturbance from both the agricultural and ecological viewpoints. In the case of botanically important meadows, however, even this degree of disruption may be unacceptable.

3 By removing the topsoil before spreading the spoil, then replacing the topsoil and re-seeding – a method frequently used where there are large quantities of spoil to be disposed of and where soil capability would be lost if spoil was spread as in 1, above. Whilst this minimises the after-effects of spreading on agriculture, this method of disposal would seriously disrupt the wildlife of ecologically important areas.

Descriptions follow of three schemes where spoil spreading was planned around, or was modified to take account of, significant wildlife habitats.

RIVER MEDEN, WARSOP, NOTTINGHAMSHIRE
OS Map 120. NGR: SK 568685
Lower Trent Division,
Severn Trent Water Authority,
Mapperley Hall, Lucknow Avenue,
Nottingham.
Telephone: Nottingham (0602) 608161

Site Summary
Land drainage improvement and flood alleviation, capital works, 1981.
Lowland, urban location.
Banks: 2-3 metres high, batter 1 in 1.5.

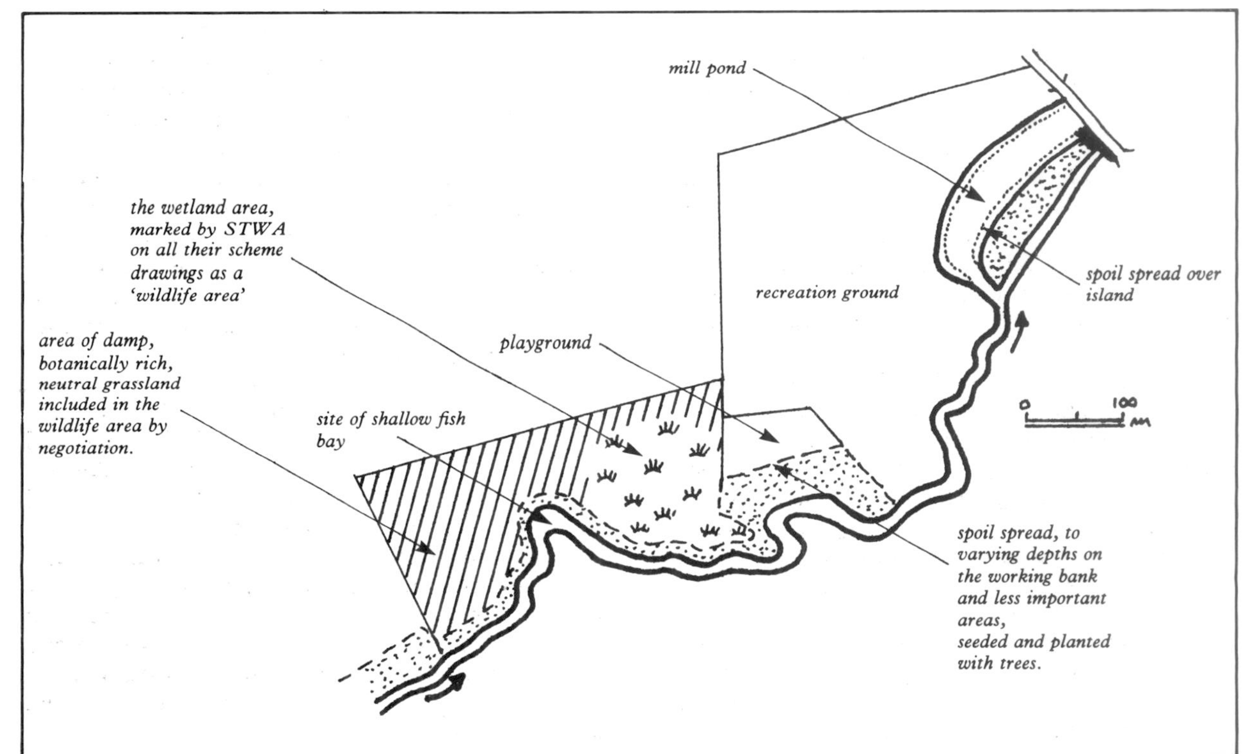

River Meden: Sympathetic spoil spreading

River Meden: The mill pond in the park at Warsop, desilted in 1982. The spoil was spread on the island at the right. The pond was excavated with shallow-water berms along each bank, to encourage the development of a broad band of natural emergent vegetation.

Substrate: silt and organic material over lying Bunter Sandstone.
Designer: A Hallam, Senior Project Engineer.
Adviser: Norman Lewis, Conservation Officer, Nottinghamshire Trust for Nature Conservation.

Work Description
The deepening of a 1.4km stretch of the Meden in 1981 (for additional details see **138**) included desilting a large mill pond (below left). In order to minimise costs, excavated spoil had to be disposed of on adjacent land, which is a playground and recreation area. Most of the park is mown grass, but the fringe along the river has scrub, rough grass and 'wild' patches, and a small rushy wetland with meadowsweet, giant horsetail, cuckooflower, marsh marigold and lesser spearwort amongst others.
The wet area was an obvious hollow in which to dispose of soil; the site could then have been seeded down to grass, and the recreation ground acreage of smooth grassland would have been increased and management standardised. Instead the wetland was left intact, and spoil was spread elsewhere, predominantly along the top of the worked bank, and on the island adjacent to the mill pond. To ensure that spoil was *not* spread on the small area of wetland, it was labelled as a 'wildlife area' on the scheme drawings which demarcated the intended disposal areas. During the consultation phase, prior to work starting, the wildlife area was doubled in size through negotiation with all the parties concerned, to include a further area of botanically rich grassland. (see figure on left). Reinstatement works included reseeding the spoil – in one experimental area a wildflower mix was used – and planting many native trees. Again, the wetland was left untouched.

Habitat Comments
1 The small wetland, which is particularly rich in plant species, is a fascinating relic of a wild area adjacent to the town, and it is excellent that it has been preserved untouched during channel works.
2 Disposal of spoil on the island has, of course, involved disturbance to what would otherwise have been a refuge for wildlife and plants during channel works and the period of restablishment. However, in this case the water authority was advised that the wetland was the more important and 'fragile' habitat, whilst the island community could be reinstated easily.
3 If a plant-rich site is wet because of periodic flooding, clearly using spoil to build up a bank between it and the river may limit flooding and damage the habitat as it dries out. Likewise deepening a river for improved arterial land drainage may have a similar effect.
In this case, disposal of the the spoil as a bund along the margin of the wetland area should not have this effect. Rainwater and water issuing from a spring line out of the Magnesian Limestone should be trapped behind it, so ensuring that the wetland area continues to receive an adequate supply of water.

RIVER GREAT OUSE,
NEAR WILLINGTON, BEDFORDSHIRE
OS Map 153. Location witheld by request.
Cambridge Division, Bedford Area Office, Anglian Water, Cambridge Road, Bedford. Telephone: Bedford (0234) 63111.

Site Summary
Capital works, improvements for navigation, 1977.
Rural, lowland location
Channel: 6-7 metres wide, depth variable
Banks: Slope 1 in 2, c2 metres high
Substrate: gravel and silt
Area Engineer: John Hesp.

Work Description
This section of the Great Ouse was dredged in 1977, to widen and deepen the main channel for navigation. Work was carried out from one bank, which was cut back by approximately 3 metres. Spoil was spread on hollows and the banks built up as necessary. At this site a pond and marshy area beside the river (remnants of an old river loop) would have been used as a spoil disposal area, except that the landowner wanted it to be retained. As the opposite bank had trees growing on it (a commercial plantation) work had to continue from the pond side. This required that a bank be built up between the pond and the river so as to bear the weight of the dragline, and later covered (as normal practice) with top soil and reseeded.
Since the work was done, the landowner has fenced the pond area against sheep. The wetland remains much as it was, with common reed, teazel, hawthorn and willow.

Habitat Comments
1 Although the pond has been retained, together with its wetland flora and fauna, and water levels in the pond still fluctuate with levels in the main river channel, the loss of the marshy strip between the pond and river – buried under spoil to allow the machine access – has almost certainly changed the ecology of the pond and possibly of the adjacent river. In times of high flow the pond was directly linked to the river. Fish would have used the

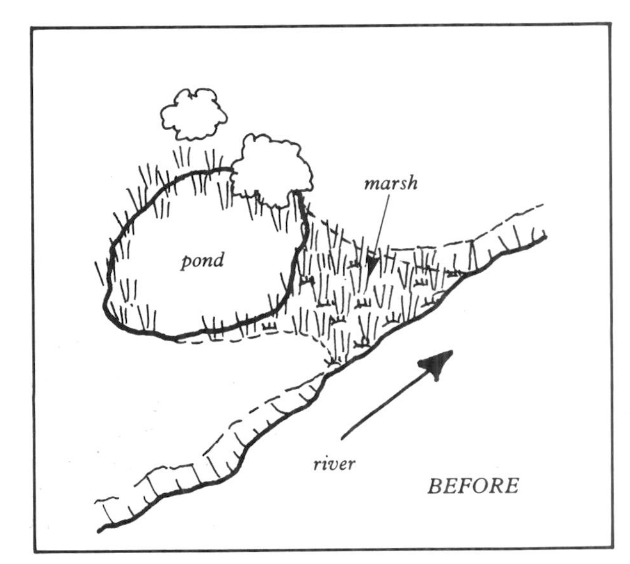

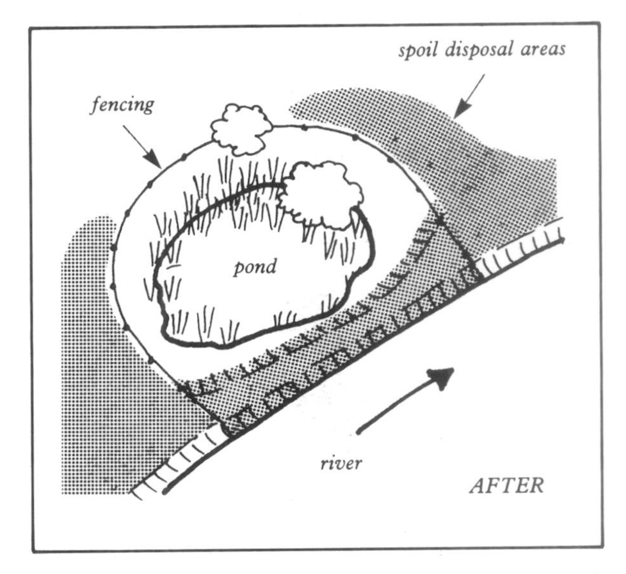

Great Ouse: Before and after spoil spreading.

backwater as a breeding site and young fry may have been safer from predators in the flooded reedbeds. Now this link has been blocked, the pond is not accessible to the fish.

2 Was the infilling of the marsh really necessary? It might have been possible to avoid it by excavating the bank from the sides of the pond, rather than immediately between the pond and the river; the channel bed could have been deepened from stations either side, much like working round a group of trees. This would have retained at least some of the marsh. Alternatively, if an embankment had to be built, a pipe could have been laid through it to maintain access to the pond for fish from the river.

SANDWELL VALLEY BALANCING LAKE, BIRMINGHAM.
OS Map 139. NGR: SP 0392
Tame Division,
Severn Trent Water Authority,

Sandwell Valley: A section of old hedge and ditch, undamaged although excavated spoil has been spread all round.

Tame House, 156-170 Newhall Street,
Birmingham B3 1SE.
Telephone: 021-233 1616

Site Summary
Flood alleviation scheme, capital works, 1982.
Lowland, urban fringe location.
Design: Divisional Engineers' Department, Tame Division.

Work Description
This scheme is described in more detail on page **81**. The excavated spoil from the lake was tipped on site on the slopes above the marshy washland, care being taken to leave as much as possible of the existing hedges and ditches undisturbed (below left) (see **81** for sketch map). Excess spoil was carried off site, and used to fill in pits where there was neither wildlife nor conservation interest.

Habitat Comment
1. As the area is being developed as a country park, there was an additional incentive to retain mature trees as landscape features. Trees and hedges, however, also act as important refuges for wildlife and plant populations, which may then spread out into the regraded areas, as they mature.
2. Although more than 90 per cent of established wildlife habitat has been totally disturbed during the implementation of this scheme, efforts have been made to retain patches undisturbed on the fringes and in the central area of the site. No rare species are present, but the conservation of common species is just as important, especially in city areas like this.

SPOIL DISPOSAL IN BANKS

Where there are flood meadows rich in flora and fauna, which would be damaged if spoil were spread, it may be possible to dispose of it through incorporating it into flood-banks – either if these are being constructed as part of a scheme or if they are already present.

The 'overdesign' of flood embankments is another alternative – that is, increasing the volume of the banks beyond that critically required for flood protection (see figure below). Although no examples were seen, this practice was discussed by several Water Authorities. One additional advantage is that over-large embankments do not require such high standards of maintenance, as failure is less likely. Tall vegetation can be permitted to grow, without the need for frequent checks for vermin damage. Scrub could be planted, at least on the side away from the river, without fear of the roots causing weakness to the bank.

Another possibility is to retain the spoil in special banks located in areas which are neither agriculturally nor ecologically important. An example of this technique is provided by the capital works carried out on the Great Ouse downstream of Great Barford in 1973/74, by the ex-Great Ouse River Division of Anglian Water Authority (OS Map 153: NGR TL 141526 – 149534). Spoil of a very gravelly nature from dredging for navigation works was retained in banks bordering the Great Ouse, instead of spreading it over the adjacent agricultural land. In this case, the reason for retaining the material in banks was an agricultural rather than a nature conservation one: the principle, however, remains the same.

A theoretical design for an over-large flood embankment. The low gradient and rounded top allows farm machinery and stock unhindered access, which compensates for land taken for the bank. Tree planting – at least on the side away from the river – is also possible.

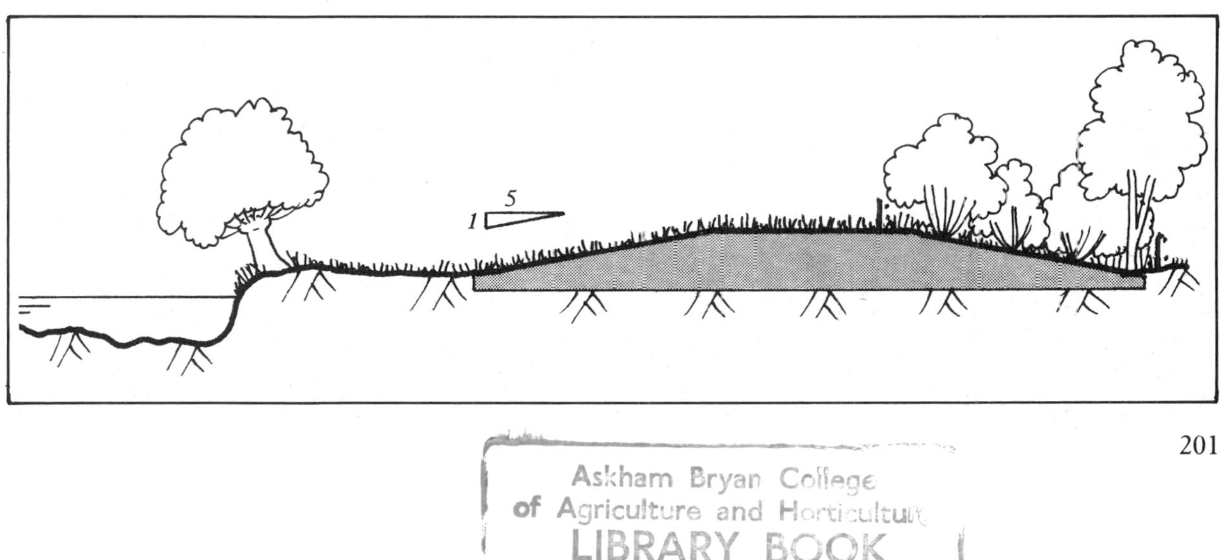

OFF-SITE DUMPING OF SPOIL

Schemes are described elsewhere in the manual, where excavated spoil has been disposed of off-site, so avoiding infilling wetlands or meanders. See, for example:

90 – Bradpole Flood Alleviation Scheme, in which spoil excess to the floodbank requirement was used in another scheme being carried out simultaneously nearby.

81 – Sandwell Valley Balancing Lake, where excess spoil was used to infill hollows on a derelict site on water authority land nearby.

SPOIL DISPOSAL AND TREES

Spoil disposal may be harmful if material is heaped up around the bases of trees: frequently the tree will be killed, since the tree roots will be unable to obtain enough oxygen.

This problem can easily be foreseen and avoided. If spoil does have to be dumped in the vicinity of trees and scrub, a three-metre radius should be marked around each tree and no spoil at all dumped within that zone.

TECHNICAL 4: AQUATIC PLANTS

Previous sections have dealt only with the non-living part of the river – with conserving or reinstating the variety of the physical form of the river channel and its banks, and with minimising damage from spoil disposal. These following sections look at direct management of the *living* part of the system – in particular plants – with exactly the same intention: to conserve and reinstate variety so that a natural community can quickly develop.

Aquatic plants are the foundation of life in streams and rivers – they are the primary food source in all food chains, and their structure adds to the physical diversity of the environment. The plant community is the most valuable element of the river ecosystem, on which every other living things depends; the more varied its structure and composition, the greater the diversity of other wildlife it can support.

There is no doubt, however, that some plants, at particular locations and times of year, can be a nuisance to man. The river manager therefore needs to know the plants and their growth habits, to be able to recognise those which will cause a nuisance in a given situation.

Large emergents such as branched bur-reed or bulrush finish growing in August, but since they persist more or less through the winter as clumps of brown leaves, they may present a winter flood hazard. Arrowhead or flowering rush, which produces similar growth in summer, decays rapidly after September, however, leaving only underground parts. Cutting the first may be important for winter flood prevention, but cutting the second would be a waste of effort!

Water crowfoots may present a summer flood hazard, but if cut before they reach their maximum size the regrowth is vigorous and a greater bulk than before can result. Other species, such as water starworts, can be effectively controlled by an early cut.

If ecological damage is to be minimised, it is also important to recognise types of plant community. At any site, all types of submerged, floating and emergent plants which are present should be conserved to safeguard associated invertebrates as well as the plant species.

Data presented in 'Biological 1: Plants' should help managers to recognise which plants could cause problems in their particular rivers, but personal observation of plant regrowth in rivers throughout the years is the only sound basis for aquatic plant control and management.

The control of aquatic plants is complex. The plant species present are a product of site conditions, so there are two alternative approaches:

A To remove the plants periodically.
B To change site conditions, so growth is reduced or prevented.

The first method implies a commitment to maintenance year after year, the second a one-off physical change which should reduce plant growth for the foreseeable future. Both, however, should be based on a sound knowledge of the responses by the plants and of the possible effects on non-target organisms. Aquatic plants are favoured by slow flows, shallow water, stable substrates, nutrient-rich water (either natural or from fertiliser run-off) and an absence of shade. Treeless lowland rivers and drainage channels with negligible flow are bound to have vigorous, dense plant growth. If only one site factor is changed, plant growth will be reduced.

In the UK, all drainage authorities carry out plant control programmes to a greater or lesser extent, but mechanical cutting or chemical herbicide treatment are the only methods generally used. In many areas, weed control is the major part of annual maintenance expenditure. It also gives rise to regular complaint from local people because of the disturbance to wildlife and angling.

Because of the on-going costs of weed control, drainage authorities are looking for alternative practices which might be as effective, cheaper and less damaging to the environment. Wessex and Yorkshire Water Authorities, for example, have begun tree-planting trials to see if shading out hazardous weed growth is effective. Southern, Anglian and Wessex Water Authorities have experimented with grass carp, to graze out excessive weed in enclosed water. Most authorities have tried new methods or practices from time to time, but fundamentally little has changed.

In studying river management methods in 1982, so few sites were seen where weed control also took habitat conservation into account that this section is the most poorly illustrated of all – despite being one of the most important and of relevance to many miles of lowland rivers and watercourses. Most of the ideas presented here are theoretical – although all have been demonstrated or researched abroad.

The habitat retention practices follow the two alternatives outlined above:

Periodic removal of plants –	(**204**)	cutting and dredging
	(**209**)	herbicides
	(**214**)	grazing
Change site conditions –	(**214**)	increase shade
	(**218**)	enlarge channel

The principles which underlie all of these are that:

– Not all plants are hazardous, since many die back before floods arise.

– Any treatment should leave significant areas, representative of the complete community, untouched as a refuge and source of recolonising material.
– Certain conditions are bound to encourage dense plant growth (eg: unshaded, nutrient rich, shallow, slow-flowing ditches and watercourses), and the only effective means of reducing growth is to change the conditions.

A final habitat creation section (**219**) looks at successful methods of replanting aquatics in sites which have been drastically disturbed.

WEED CUTTING AND DREDGING

Depending on flow conditions, weed growth in streams may cause silt accumulation, the two combining to reduce flood capacity. To restore capacity, weeds can be cut by hand (rarely done these days) or by machine, once or more during the growing season. A weed cutting boat or a Bradshaw bucket mounted on a hydraulic excavator (which usually, but undesirably, scoops out some silt along with cut weed) are two machines used. When too much silt has accumulated, maintenance dredging down to the previous hard bed is needed. This removes all the plants including the underground stems, rhizomes and roots. It may take 5-10 years for the plant community to recover fully from the effects of dredging.

The initial effect of disturbance is to reduce drastically the numbers of species and individuals present. Recovery is helped if cutting or dredging is carried out working *upstream* so that plant fragments and invertebrates drift down to recolonise the already worked section. Often, however, cutting and dredging is worked *downstream* in order to prevent dislodged silt from refilling the worked stretches.

Various studies of invertebrate populations have shown that the community has returned to the pre-dredging composition within two years – but this was in rivers which were regularly cut and dredged, so that the only invertebrate species which were present when the studies began were ones which could tolerate dredging or recolonise quickly. Sections of rivers which have been reduced to a trapezoidal channel still only support an impoverished fauna compared with downstream 'natural' sections even five years after dredging. Work in Denmark has shown that if patches of plants are left undisturbed during cutting or dredging, the invertebrate community will recover within a few months. From ecological first principles (see 'Introduction 3') you would also expect the reach to have more species, after a few years, than similar reaches that had been cut or clean dredged. Leaving patches undisturbed as refuges during regular maintenance work aids the rapid and complete recovery of the community (figure right).

This does not necessarily mean that the weed problem will recur equally quickly to become as bad as ever. Both community diversity and river management benefit from the reduction of the most vigorous plant species. The example of the Cary in Somerset (**207**) shows how the selective cutting

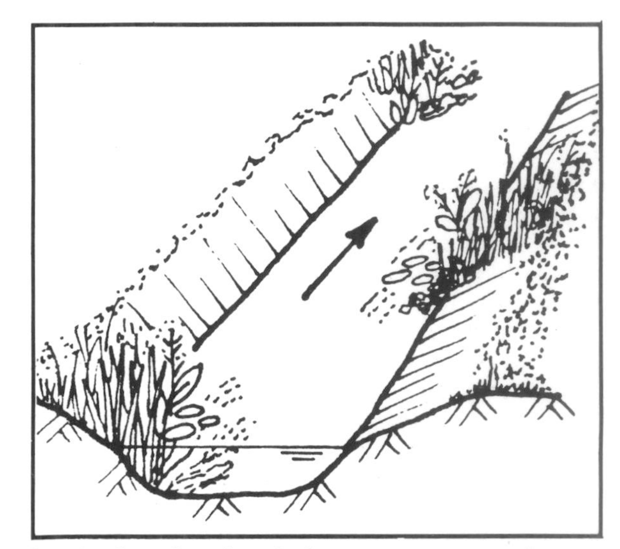

Leaving lateral patches of submergent, emergent and bankside communities undisturbed.

Leaving central patches of less common plants (such as water plantains and flowering rush) in small, plant-filled channels.

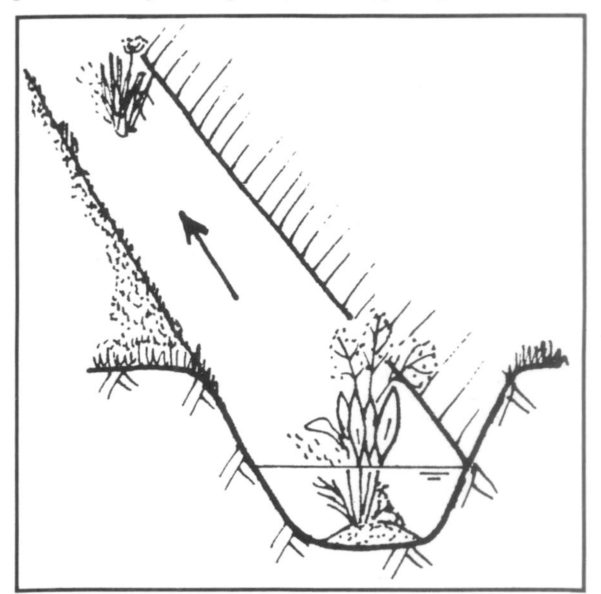

of the most aggressive and troublesome weed, branched bur-reed, allowed more local and attractive plants to flourish in its place (figure left). Weed cutting reduces competition from the aggressive plants, which otherwise would exclude rarer species.

To cut weeds selectively there needs to be a good basic knowledge of the plants by either the machine operator or his supervisor, preferably both. This requires on-site training by a biologist or ecologist. It would be a relatively simple job to draw up an identification card, to fit in the cab window possibly, for the operators to use as a guide. For each area and river type there is likely to be a different set of 'weed' and 'valued' plants. Local sets would therefore be more useful and easily made for areas within each drainage authority, rather than national sets.

The alternative to leaving small patches as refuges is to leave whole stretches uncut, and then to return to cut them another year. Alternate 200 metre lengths of uncut and cut river will provide a ready source of organisms to recolonise the lengths which have been cut (figure below). Clearly this is not feasible where there is an annual, severe, flood risk from plants choking the whole channel, but in stretches where weed and silt are cleaned out, say every 10 years, then managing long stretches on alternate five-year cycles would allow long-lived aquatic invertebrates such as dragonflies to become more abundant.

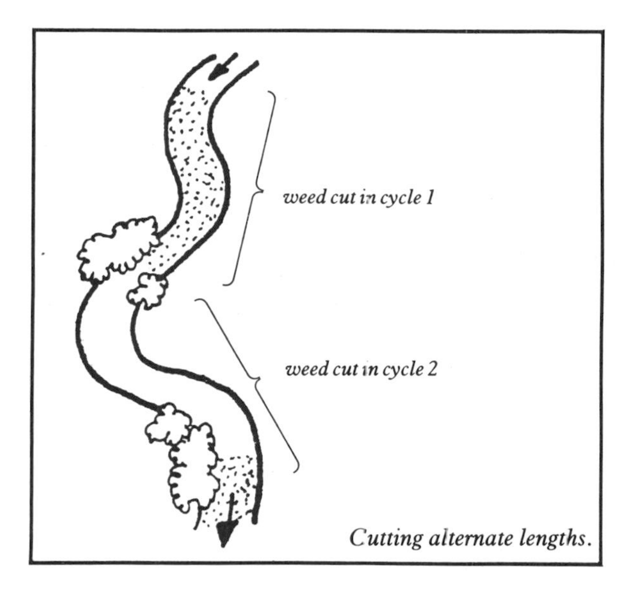

Cutting alternate lengths.

Timing of cutting is important, not only to the regrowth of plants from roots and rhizomes, but also because of its effects on wildlife breeding on or amongst the plants. For birds, disturbance in April, May and June is most damaging, when they are rearing first broods. Similarly, for aquatic invertebrates, weed cutting before July is most damaging since then individuals are largest and numbers fewest. Different species of course have different life cycles, and disturbance at *any* time of year will destroy some of them, but in general late summer or autumn is the least damaging time, when most are present in large numbers as small nymphs, larvae or eggs.

The depth to which dredging takes place and thus the depth to which the river bed is disturbed is also important. Dredging any depth of the bed will remove large numbers and many species of invertebrates, leaving worms and midge larvae predominating in the newly dredged bed.

Weed cut in a water course must be removed. Not only do loose, floating weed masses present more of a flood hazard than the rooted weed, but also decomposing weed deoxygenates the water and is effectively a pollutant. Similarly very large masses of cut weed should not be dumped on one spot of the bank, as the nutrient-rich water running out of it as it decomposes might enrich the watercourse – and stimulate plant regrowth.

In the Ouse Washes, in Cambridgeshire, an investigation of the influence of time since the ditches were last cleaned out in relation to the number of plant species showed that four species increased with ditch age, 14 decreased with ditch age, and seven showed little change in frequency, so demonstrating that it is not in the interests of plant conservation to leave ditches untouched (Thomas, Allen and Grose, 1981). Cleaning out recreates habitat for some plants which would not otherwise be present. But equally it is important to maintain a varied pattern of habitats within an area: too efficient cleaning out, over too large an area all at one time leads to a uniformity – disastrous for wildlife and plant populations.

Reference

Thomas, G J, Allen, D A, and Grose, M P B, 1981. The demography and flora of the Ouse Washes, England. Biol Cons, **21**, 197-229.

RIVER TOVE, COSGROVE, MILTON KEYNES
OS Map: 152. NGR: SP 792439
Bedford Area Office, Cambridge Division, Anglian Water, Cambridge Road, Bedford. Telephone: Bedford (0234) 63111.

Site Summary
Maintenance work, 1982.
Lowland clay river, rural location.
Channel width: 3-5 metres, depth variable.
Banks: 1-2 metres high.
Substrate: mud, silt, cemented gravel in riffles.
Channel vegetation: very rich in emergent and submerged species. River water dropwort is found here, an infrequent part-submergent plant of slow flowing streams.

Work Description
See Sections on **100** and **101** for a fuller description of this work. The Tove is a clay lowland stream, with a rich and varied plant community. Part of it is of Site of Special Scientific Interest grade, although it has not yet been notified under Section 28 of the Wildlife and Countryside Act 1981. When maintenance dredging was carried out in 1982, efforts were made by Anglian Water Authority, in conjunction with the Nature Conservancy Council's Assistant Regional Officer, to conserve patches of the plant communities undisturbed. On average one-third of the channel width was left untouched, so that submerged plants in the middle of the channel were retained, as well as the emergent edge plants (photograph below). Leaving an equal amount of vegetation as a 'fringe' on each bank would not have been so valuable, as the deeper water plants would have all been removed.
Other practices included retaining almost all gravel riffles, deep pools and steep banks, and cutting a 'recolonisation notch' below water level on all regraded banks, to encourage edge plants to grow there, helping stabilise the bank toe (see **134**).

Habitat Comments
1 Leaving approximately 30 per cent of the vegetation as untouched patches has clearly maintained a significant portion of wildlife habitat in the river. This ensures that the community retains a degree of stability, and, with other practices, should enable the disturbed areas to recover quickly.
2 The work was done to improve land drainage and, to date, no landowner has complained that insufficient work was done. The Water Authority has commented that desilting may be necessary more frequently (perhaps in 10 years instead of 20, as was the last interval). Although this has obvious financial consequences, for habitat conservation, little but often is preferable to 100 per cent disturbance at long intervals.
3 The skill of the machine operator was a vital factor. He was involved in all site meetings with the Nature Conservancy Council and other Anglian Water Authority staff and landowners, and was supervised quite closely during the early stages of the work by the NCC Assistant Regional Officer. He now carries out similar careful desilting on other reaches of the Tove, with less close supervision.

River Tove: Patches of emergent and submergent plants retained on a bend. A dragline excavator was used.

RIVER CARY, CARY FITZPAINE, SOMERSET
OS Map: 183. NGR: ST 5527
Somerset Division, Wessex Water Authority, Box 9, King Square, Bridgwater, Somerset.
Telephone: Bridgwater (0278) 57333.

Site Summary
Annual weed cutting, maintenance work, 1980.
Lowland, clay stream, rural location.
Channel: 2 metres wide at water level, depth 0.5-1 metre.
Banks: 1 to 1.5 metres high.
Channel vegetation: abundant, dominated by emergents.

Work Description
The Cary is a small clay stream in a narrow catchment that carries very low flows in summer. Plant growth is luxuriant, choking the channel every summer, a haven for insects, birds and mammals in an intensively farmed landscape. This increases the risk of both summer and winter flooding, however, so the whole length below Babcary is annually cut or treated with herbicide.
A botanical survey, carried out during 1980, funded jointly by the Somerset Trust for Nature Conservation and Wessex Water Authority, identified four locally rare aquatic plants and one nationally rare bank plant on the river. (In the herbicide treated reaches the aquatics were associated with bridges or sluices, possibly patches the sprays had missed.)
The opportunity was taken by the surveyor to point out narrow-leaved water plantain (one of the locally rare plants) to the machine operator during annual maintenance cutting with a Bradshaw bucket in September. The plant, mixed with common water plantain, is very distinct in amongst branched bur-reed. The bur-reed there formed 70-100 per cent of the plant mass filling the channel, and only small amounts of the two water plantains, flowering rush, common clubrush and other water plants were present.
After clearance, the channel was bare except for single clumps of water plantain at about 20 metre intervals (photograph right). A month later, after the first winter high flows, there was nothing to be seen: the whole channel was clear. The next summer, however, when the channel was again covered with plants, the two water plantains formed 20-30 per cent of the community, flowering rush had increased, and the bur-reed reduced to about 45 per cent.

River Cary: A clump of water plantain left in the middle of the channel, immediately after weed-cutting with a Bradshaw bucket, September 1980.

Habitat Comments
1 Leaving patches of selected plants in this reach helped to increase the abundance of less common plants, at the expense of a very common plant. This small change in established practice was a definite benefit in the conservation of local flora.
2 Invertebrate populations were not compared before and after cutting, so it is not possible to say whether they benefited from reduced vegetation clearance.
3 As bur-reed is more-or-less persistent through winter, while the water plantains die back to root stocks, it is possible that this practice actually reduced the winter flood hazard presented by the channel vegetation.
4 Leaving central patches is most effective in small, weed-filled channels such as this. Lateral patches of undisturbed plants are clearly best left in faster flowing water courses with little vegetation in the middle.

Reference
Lewis, G. 1981. Somerset Rivers Survey: a survey of the Rivers Tone, Yeo, Cary and Northmoor Main Drain, to map and describe their flora and fauna. Somerset Trust for Nature Conservation/ Wessex Water Authority unpublished report.

SPITTLE BROOK, WOOLSTON PARK, WARRINGTON
OS Map: 109. NGR: SJ 636895
Rivers Division, North West Water Authority, Box 12, New Town House, Buttermarket Street, Warrington.
Telephone: Warrington (0925) 53999

Site Summary
Maintenance works.
Lowland, urban location.
Channel: 3 metres high, slopes variable.
Substrate: clay and gravel.

Work Description
The Spittle Brook is a small stream on the edge of Warrington New Town which was enlarged and landscaped in the mid-1970s as an urban park and amenity area. Many imaginative features were incorporated in the original design, see on **256** and **261**.

Most of the stream banks are maintained and the grass is mown as short as in any urban park. The channel vegetation, however, is mechanically cut in patches over long lengths of 100 metres, on a 3 to 5 year rotation, depending on regrowth. Additional annual hand-cutting is carried out where necessary. Thus the channel has a patchwork of vegetation ranging from mature reedbed (five years old) to mixed aquatic and marsh plants (less than four years old). The whole channel was enlarged and embanked before the park was laid out so that this amount of dense vegetation in the stream bed can be tolerated (photograph below).
Aquatic plants are kept in check by hand cutting in special areas – producing attractive contrasted and blended shapes, textures and colours of natural plants. Elsewhere, plants are cut with a Bradshaw bucket mounted on a hydraulic excavator. The junction with the mown grassland on either side is uneven – probably deliberately – so that the band of natural channel vegetation varies from 2 to 4 metres from the channel centre (figure below).

Spittle Brook: Rich channel vegetation and mown upper banks in an urban park. Woolston Park, 1982.

Management of Spittle Brook, Woolston Park.

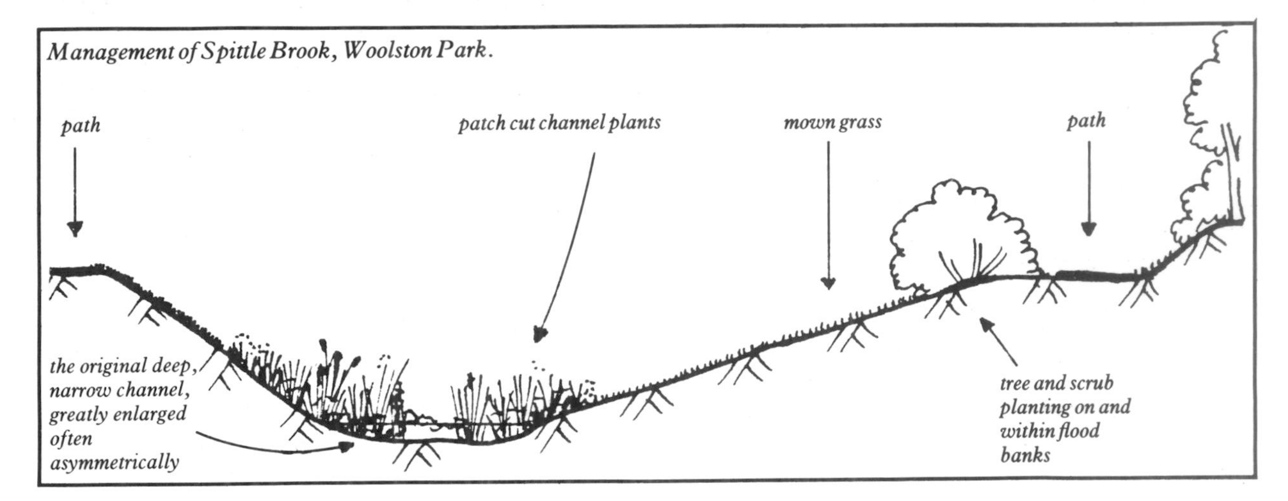

Habitat Comments

1 Fourteen species of aquatic emergent plants were noted in a short stretch of the channel – possibly some, or all, had been planted here when the park was laid out. Whether planted or not, the community is now interesting, natural-looking and varied.

2 Cutting alternate lengths on the three to five-year cycle has encouraged a more varied channel vegetation, and a more stable one, than if it was all cut every six to 10 years. Wildlife benefits from this, as there is always some mature habitat available.

3 This site has been managed in this way so as to create deliberately more wildlife interest in an urban park. Similar cutting regimes on any site, urban or rural, would benefit wildlife; cutting over longer lengths, say up to 200 or 250 metres, would be as effective, and annual hand-cutting would probably then be unnecessary.

AQUATIC AND BANKSIDE HERBICIDES

Dr C Newbold, Chief Scientist Team, Nature Conservancy Council, Huntingdon.

1. Introduction

The merits of bankside and aquatic herbicides have long been argued, but there is no ideal method to suit all management needs and all types of watercourses. In some, herbicides may be more effective, in others mechanical methods may more readily suit the management need. Thus, aquatic herbicides should be looked on as one more useful tool in a range of management methods. There are inherent disadvantages and advantages with all methods and this chapter attempts to explain the general principles of using aquatic herbicides. It does not attempt to uphold either the engineering or conservation case, to the detriment of the other: instead, the special qualities or pitfalls of using aquatic herbicides will be considered against the management aim.

2. The Management Aim

Robson (1973) identified three levels of management:

1 *Complete eradication.* Where drainage is paramount the need is sometimes for the complete eradication of all plant growth. This is only likely where there is a high flood risk.
2 *Controlled growth.* Excessive weed growth is removed at least for part of the year. This is the commonest objective and applies to both banksides and channels – where the improvement of surface drainage is the main reason for weed control but where fishing is also of importance.
3 *Occasional control.* Periodic or spot treatment is normally necessary for the management of fish and other wildlife habitats.

3. The Target Plants

Aquatic plants can only be regarded as weeds when they become a nuisance and interfere with the specific management aims of the watercourse. Aquatic plants are divided for convenience into five groups:

(1) Algae
(2) Submerged plants
(3) Floating plants
(4) Emergent plants
(5) Bankside plants

4. Choice of Herbicides

Nine years ago, only 10 herbicide formulations had been cleared for use in or by water by the Pesticide Safety Precautions Scheme (PSPS) (Newbold 1975). This compares with the present day clearance of 16 formulations.

5. Types of Herbicide and Some Nuances in Behaviour on Application

No herbicide is effective against all five plant groups. Some broad spectrum herbicides kill plants on land and in water. Others kill plants only found in the water or only on land and this broad division into aquatic and bankside herbicides will be used. Robson (1973) also split herbicides according to the spectrum of plants killed. Those killing a few species he called 'selective', those killing a wide range, 'total' herbicides. The following attempts to break down herbicides into such categories and a further distinction is made between a species selective herbicide (toxic to only one or a small number of plant species), a 'weed group selective' herbicide (toxic to a group of species) and those which can be used for 'selective' spot treatments (having properties which inhibit their wide dispersal).
All 'aquatic herbicides' except diquat alginate are designed for use in slow-flowing or standing water. (Detailed information on each formulation can be found in MAFF (1979) and Worthing (1983)).

(a) Aquatic herbicides

The species-selective herbicide dalapon has a limited number of susceptible species, leaving the non-susceptible species to take their place. It can be a valuable tool in removing problem weeds and can be used with advantage for nature conservation purposes. Dalapon has been used by the Royal Society for the Protection of Birds to remove dominant stands of *Phragmites australis*, the common reed, in selected areas of their reserves.

Table 1. The choice of herbicide formulations and their spectrum of weed control

	Terbutryne	Dichlobenil	Dichlobenil GSR	Chlorthiamid	Diquat Alginate	Diquat	Dalapon	Glyphosate	Dalapon with Paraquat	Maleic Hydrazide	Maleic Hydrazide with 2,4-D-Amine	2,4-D Amine	Maleic Hydrazide with 2,4-D-Amine/Chlorpropham mix	Asulam	Foseamine Ammonia
'Weed groups' (see section on Target Plants)															
(1) Algae	K				MR	MR									
(2) Submerged plants	K	K	K	K	K	K									
(3) Free floating plants (small leaf area)	K				K	K									
(3) Floating leaved plants (large leaf area)		K	K	K				K				MR	MR		
(4) Reeds							K	MR							
(4) Sedges							MR	K	K						
(5) Grasses/Rushes								K	K	K	K		K		
(5) Broadleaved weeds								K			K	K	K		
(5) Docks								K						K	
(5) Trees Shrub															K

Figures in parentheses refer to 'weed group', K=Kill, MR=Moderately resistant.
Where a choice of chemical exists, select the one affecting the least number of non-target groups.

The decay of the rhizomes can create open water lagoons. Such a herbicide is useful for occasional control. Similarly 2,4-D amine could be used for the control of water lilies. In water it acts in a species-selective manner whilst on land it kills broadleaved weeds (Table 1) and is a weed group selective herbicide.

Diquat, a total herbicide, can be used for selective spot treatment (Management aim 3). This herbicide is a quick acting contact herbicide so it tends to stay where applied. Equally the new formulation, a sticky diquat alginate, glues itself to plants, so it is useful for spot treatments in standing and flowing water. However, some downstream drift of the alginate can occur even in relatively slow flowing rivers before it glues itself to a plant, so the area of treatments may be *displaced* or *extended*. Diquat has been used selectively by local nature conservation trusts on the advice of the Nature Conservancy Council. However, this herbicide can be used extensively to control the growth of a large number of aquatic plant species (Management aim 2).

Other total herbicides such as dichlobenil, dichlobenil GSR (Granule Slow Release) and terbutryne kill, in turn, a larger number of species of higher aquatic plants. They are translocated through the root system to stem and leaf. This mode of action is enhanced by their formulation with a heavy granule of calcium and/or Fullers earth. The granule dissolves slowly around the root mass and some herbicide diffuses away from the site of application. This creeping effect prevents selective forms of spot treatment, but dichlobenil GSR can be used to treat a water body partially. A band of diffusion along the boundary line must be expected. Plants are only partially affected by the herbicide in the diffusion zone because its dilution lowers it beyond an effective treatment level.

Terbutryne is also prone to creep. Its effectiveness also seems to be dependent on water temperature being above 16°C (Murphy, 1982), but it is most effective against algae.

Within the terbutryne diffusion band, higher plants will be killed because of treatment levels. A level of 0.1 milligrams per litre is recommended to kill algae and 0.05 milligrams per litre for higher plants but many plants are still killed at 0.01 milligrams per litre (Barrett, R, personal communication). Partial treatment of a quarter of a lake sprayed at 0.05 milligrams per litre could effec-

tively kill all susceptible higher plants if diffusion and mixing spread the herbicide over the whole lake. The overall effective and final concentration would be 0.0125 milligrams per litre.

The only other herbicide having some effect on algae is diquat. This kills some filamentous green and blue-green algae but populations quickly recover (Balter 1963, Cassie 1966, Newbold 1975b).

All total herbicides can be used with varying success for the controlled growth of aquatic weeds (Management aim 2). Terbutryne is the only herbicide which most closely fulfils 'Management aim 1'.

(b) Bankside Herbicides

Apart from Dalapon (see paragraph 5a) asulam is the only 'species-selective bankside herbicide', being most used for bracken control. Fosamine ammonia, 2,4-D amine, Chlorpropham, 2,4-D amine+Maleic hydrazide and Maleic hydrazide tend to control specific groups of plants (Table 1). A wide number of species are found in each of these groups and so they are selective to a particular group rather than to a species (Management aim 2).

Glyphosate is a total broad-spectrum bankside and emergent plant herbicide. It is very useful for eradicating problem weeds. It does not spread on application and has been used on a County Council local nature reserve to spot treat invading *Scirpus maritimus*, the sea club rush. This chemical is almost too effective, since it tends to create bare earth and the wide scale spraying of bankside can easily result in erosion.

6. Direct Toxicity and Toxic Stress to Aquatic Animals

All PSPS-cleared aquatic herbicides have passed rigorous tests, intended to ensure that they are safe for use in waters containing fish and other animal life. However, many herbicides directly kill some invertebrates. Some species of snails, for example, are killed by diquat used at the recommended dose (Newbold 1973) and water fleas and chironomid worms seem directly affected (Newbold 1975a). But at the correct treatment levels, the direct toxic impact per unit area seems in general to be small, and most species seem to be unaffected by most herbicides.

If fish are killed directly by a herbicide then the treatment level has been far too high, but dichlobenil GSR can cause fish deaths from a series of complex interactions – the safety margin is small. Any misuse of the herbicide, such as overtreatment, can have physiological effects on fish, causing stress and manifesting themselves in severe cases by toxic lesions on the gill membranes. This damage impairs the fishes' ability to breathe at a time when the decay of target plants is depleting oxygen in the water. Ordinarily this would not affect healthy fish, but the combined effect is mortality (Wiersma *et al* 1978). For these reasons a method of partial treatment has been developed whereby only a proportion of the plant biomass is treated at any one time (Tooby *et al*, 1978) (see paragraph 5a).

7. Before Application

There is a standard procedure to follow before applying any aquatic herbicide. This is detailed in the Guidelines on the Use of Herbicides in or Near Water (MAFF 1979). For example, users must obey the laws on pollution and consult the appropriate water authority. Equally, they must take due account of the nature conservation interest and consult the Nature Conservancy Council within Sites of Special Scientific Interest.

Excellent as the MAFF guidelines are, they do not fully consider the ecological pitfalls facing the user if he chooses an inappropriate herbicide or applies them where mechanical methods should have been adopted.

A major pitfall when using aquatic or bankside herbicides is that they can be applied intensively and extensively. This gross treatment of an area can cause an ecological backlash making the treatment ineffective or, worse, resulting in a situation which reduces the future management options open to the engineer.

8. Ecological Pitfalls

(a) Time of Treatment

Aquatic herbicides are generally applied in the spring when plant biomass is low. This tends to avoid the problem of oxygen depletion, but creates problems for the aquatic fauna. Animal life is dependent on an increased plant production for its cycle of growth and reproduction. If food production is suddenly cut off, in order to survive an animal must either switch to other food or migrate: neither may be possible.

Some invertebrate species are plant specific (Mellanby 1963) and Brooker and Edwards (1974) attributed the loss of *Acentropus niveus*, a moth larva, to its host plant being destroyed by paraquat. Plants also provide a refuge against excessive predation, for both fish and invertebrates alike. Fish spawning sites may be lost.

Herbicide treatment usually occurs in spring, at the worst possible time for fauna, whereas the use of mechanical methods is not tied to any particular season.

(b) Oxygen Depletion

The rate and amount of oxygen loss during herbicide treatment is dependent on four main factors: (i) diffusion rates from the air into water; (ii) the flow rate; (iii) the plant biomass; (iv) the number of animals. The first two add oxygen to the system, while plants consume and produce oxygen and animals consume oxygen.

In slow-flowing or stagnant water the degree of

oxygen depletion depends on the biomass of the plants prior to spraying (Brooker 1974): plants left to decay take oxygen from the system (Brooker and Edwards 1973). Aerobic and anaerobic bacteria decompose plant tissues; in doing so the former use up oxygen. The greater the amount of plant material available to them, the greater their growth and oxygen demand. If the weed biomass is large, the drop in oxygen can cause fish deaths.

To reduce the severity of oxygen loss, partial treatment can be carried out by spraying a third or a quarter of the total area at a time. An interval of two to three weeks is recommended between treatments if the management aim is one of complete eradication.

An unusual side effect of one herbicide, terbutryne, is that it can lower oxygen levels beyond those expected or predicted from the biomass of the weeds present. Terbutryne seems to kill by affecting the photosynthetic side of a cell's chemistry, hence its dependence on high water temperatures (see paragraph 5a). Respiration continues for several days before the plant dies. During this time the plant acts like an animal inhaling oxygen and exhaling carbon dioxide. The carbon dioxide can only be produced from the available reserves of oxygen in the water (Robson 1974).

9. Habitat Destruction

It is probable that an efficient operator using any mechanical bucket will remove more plant and animal species per unit area than any one herbicide but mechanical buckets are relatively slow and ponderous. Areas which may take one season to clear could be treated in a matter of days with a herbicide. The mechanical bucket may be killing both plant and animal species directly by removing them but the rate of habitat destruction is slow. Herbicides can bring about a massive and rapid change in habitat. The speed or rate of change per unit area in part determines the impact on plant and animal life.

The ease of application of any herbicide is, to many users, one of its attractions. Any herbicide that is used intensively can destroy or change the aquatic flora of whole catchment areas.

Recolonisation of herbicide treated areas by plant and animal life from an unchanged or unsprayed area is less likely because of two factors. Firstly, large areas can be treated with such speed that potential recolonisation sources are sprayed and destroyed before the phytotoxic period within the first area to be sprayed has elapsed. A phytotoxic period can be defined as the time in which the chemical environment of the herbicide is toxic to the target plant species. This can last for two or three days or can be as long as three months.

Secondly, ecological factors may prevent plants similar to those sprayed from re-growing. The vacuum caused by plant death is quickly filled by non-susceptible or resistant species. If the herbicide used is one such as dalapon which kills a limited spectrum of plants, then the replacement community of plants and animals could be equally interesting (Brooker 1975). A more total herbicide such as dichlobenil could mean a replacement community of non-susceptible species such as diatoms and certain species of algae. Algae are not a favoured habitat for many invertebrate species.

10. Problems of Resistant Species and the Phytotoxic Period

Herbicides impose a constraint on the regrowth of the susceptible species as long as the phytotoxic period lasts. The selective herbicide, dalapon, and the total herbicide, diquat, persist in water for three to 12 days (Chancellor and Ripper 1960; Calderbank 1972) and appear to be phytotoxic for that period (Newbold 1975b). The total herbicides have longer phytotoxic periods; 7.5 per cent dichlobenil is phytotoxic for approximately 20 days (Newbold 1975b) but the 22.5 per cent dichlobenil GSR is designed to maintain a phytotoxic period for a longer period of time (Spencer Jones 1974).

Terbutryne has a half life of 25 days (Tyson 1974). However, Tyson also found 70 per cent of the applied dose of 0.1 milligrams per litre persisting 28 days after treatment, and Robson *et al* (1974) still detected 0.08 milligrams per litre 42 days after the original treatment level of 0.10 milligrams per litre. However, such results are variable – a phytotoxic level of 0.01 milligrams per litre was detected 40 days after treatment at 0.09 milligrams per litre (Murphy *et al*, 1981).

Although the phytotoxic period prevents the regrowth of susceptible species, resistant species can grow in their place. The longer the phytotoxic period, the greater the chance the resistant species will firmly establish themselves. To many land drainage engineers, a long phytotoxic period is considered to be a desirable property in a herbicide but it could pose future management problems and could also cause problems with irrigation and livestock watering.

The problem of the massive regrowth of resistant species, particularly algae, has long been one which has affected the efficiency of any total herbicide. Even terbutryne loses its phytotoxic period to algae after approximately 25 days but maintains a phytotoxic period to susceptible higher plants for much longer periods, allowing algae to regrow.

As there are no suitable mechanical methods for removing algae, the great danger is that a system becomes herbicide dependent. The engineer who uses herbicides in this way gains very little and he could be faced with greater expense to keep his channel clear.

11. Conclusions

Herbicides should be looked on as one effective tool

in an integrated approach to channel management. If used on a wide scale they have, however, a number of potentially harmful effects on invertebrates, fish and other river wildlife both as a direct result of habitat loss and indirectly, for example, by causing oxygen depletion or by removing food resources in early spring. They can also cause an adverse change in the plant community, in extreme cases replacing all higher plants with algae, which support little invertebrate or other life, and creating a management system which is herbicide dependent.

Management programmes which wish to maintain a fishery, nature conservation or amenity interest should consider only those herbicides which are species selective or can be used for spot treatment. Such treatments may be less damaging than some mechanical methods.

The more total an aquatic herbicide, the more it should be used with caution, with strict adherence to the MAFF Guidelines on the Use of Herbicides In or Near Water.

12. References

Brooker, M P, 1974. The risk of deoxygenation of water in herbicide applications for aquatic weed control. J Inst Water Eng, **28**, 206-210.

Brooker, M P, 1975. The ecological effects of the use of aquatic herbicides in Essex. Surveyor, **145**, 25-27.

Brooker, M P, and Edwards, R W, 1973. Effects of the herbicide paraquat on the ecology of a reservoir. I. Botanical and chemical aspects. Fresh Biol, **3**, 157-175.

Brooker, M P, and Edwards, R W, 1974. Effects of herbicide paraquat on the ecology of a reservoir. III. Fauna and general discussion. Fresh Biol, **4**, 311-335.

Butler, P A, 1963. Commercial fisheries investigations. In Pesticide Wildlife Studies, US Fish Wildlife Serv Circ 167.

Calderbank, A, 1972. Environmental considerations in the development of diquat and paraquat as aquatic herbicides. Outlook on Agric, **7**, 51-54.

Cassie, V, 1966. Effects of spraying on phytoplankton in Lake Rotoria. Proceedings Roturua Seminar on water weeds sponsored by U Ext Serv Univ Auckland New Zealand. Oct 15, 31-40.

Chancellor, R J and Ripper, W E, 1960. Control of reeds and other emergent water weeds in drainage ditches, ponds and watercourses. The effects of dalapon on fish. Weed Abstr, **9**, 696.

MAFF, 1979. Guidelines for the use of herbicides on weeds in or near watercourses and lakes. MAFF Booklet 2078. Revised September 1979. (Note: a further revision of this booklet is being undertaken, for publication during late 1984.)

Mellenby, H, 1963. Animal life in fresh water. Chapman and Hall Ltd, London.

Murphy, K J, 1982. The use of methylthiotriazine herbicides in freshwater systems: a review. Proceedings EWRS 6th Symposium on Aquatic Weeds, 263-277.

Murphy, K J, Hanbury, R G, and Eaton, J W, 1981. The ecological effects of 2-methylthiotriazine herbicides used for aquatic weed control in navigable canals. 1. Effects on aquatic flora and water chemistry. Arch Hydrobiol, **91**, 294-331.

Newbold, C, 1973. Ecological effects of the herbicides diquat and dichlobenil within a pond ecosystem. Monks Wood Experimental Station Report for 1972-1973 (The Nature Conservancy, NERC), 29.

Newbold, C, 1975a. Some ecological effects of two herbicides, dichlobenil and diquat, on pond ecosystems. PhD thesis, University of Leicester.

Newbold, C, 1975b. Herbicides in aquatic systems. Biol Conserv, **7**, 97-118.

Robson, T O, 1973. The control of aquatic weeds. Ministry of Agriculture Bulletin 194, **2nd** ed, HMSO.

Robson, T O, 1974. An account of the Weed Research Council experiment with terbutryne for aquatic weed control. Technical Symposium: the use of terbutryne as an aquatic herbicide. London, Royal Commonwealth Society.

Spencer-Jones, D H, 1974. Some recent advances in the development of dichlobenil granules in the UK for the control of aquatic weeds. Proceedings of the 4th International Symposium on Aquatic Weeds, European Weed Research Council, 192-201.

Tooby, T E, and Macey, D J, 1977. Absence of pigmentation in corixid bugs (Hemiptera) after the use of the aquatic herbicide dichlobenil. Freshwater Biology, **1**, 519-526.

Tooby, T E, and Spencer-Jones, D H, 1978. The fate of the aquatic herbicide dichlobenil in hydrosoil, water and roach (*Rutilus rutilus L.*) following treatment of three areas of a lake. Proc EWRS 5th Symp on Aquatic Weeds, Amsterdam, 323-331.

Tyson, D, 1974. The fate of terbutryne in the aquatic ecosystem and its effect on non-target organisms. Technical Symposium: the use of terbutryne as an aquatic herbicide. London. Royal Commonwealth Society.

Wiersma-Roem, W J, Vischer, L W A, Frederix Wolters, E M H, and Harmsen, E G M. Sub-acute toxicity of the herbicide dichlobenil (2,6-dichlorobenzonitrile) in rainbow trout (*Salmo gairduorii R.*). Proc EWRS 5th Symposium on aquatic weeds, Amsterdam, 261-268.

Worthing, C R (ed), 1983. The pesticide manual: a world compendium. 7th edition. British Crop Protection Council.

GRAZING

In areas of grazing marsh, the water in ditches during the summer is frequently penned at an artificially high level to provide 'wet hedges' for the enclosure of stock. Cattle will browse the marginal emergent plants, so helping to control them, and producing a patchwork of open water and vegetation – important for fauna.

Cattle will also wade into streams and the shallow edges of rivers, grazing on emergent plants, so keeping them in check. The River Piddle in Dorset illustrates this well – see Section **151** for photographs of adjacent sections fenced and unfenced against grazing cattle. Any advantage through plant control is probably outweighed, however, by the disadvantages caused by the animals trampling down the banks, so encouraging siltation and bank erosion. Section **150** illustrates banks of the River Gilpin where banks have been damaged by grazing cattle, and have been protected by fencing to exclude them. In most cases, therefore, cattle grazing does not provide a feasible means of aquatic plant control.

Another obvious wildlife group to consider is fish. Native fish graze algae rather than larger plants, or they take invertebrate foods. However, several water authorities have undertaken trials using introduced Chinese grass carp – to date only in enclosed waters. In general, although the trials have shown the grass carp to be effective in controlling weed growth in these enclosed waters, problems have been experienced. To be successful, a large number and weight of fish is required (100-250 kilograms per hectare) and, at present, difficulties are being experienced in supply. The fish do not breed in the cold British waters and artificial rearing in the UK either means that fish have to be raised from fingerlings in warm water or in extensive areas of cold water: the first is an expensive method of production, the second very slow since the carp are not adapted to growth in the cold. Most fish used in British trials have therefore been imported, and this raises the possibility of the introduction of diseased fish. From the control point of view, the weather may also present difficulties: because of their reduced appetite in cold weather, grass carp may be unable to control weed in spring. If the growth then gets underway in earnest, the fish may not be able to get the weeds under control when the warmer weather starts.

Grass carp, in any event, are unlikely to be an effective control agent in rivers, unless reaches are isolated to maintain the required stocking rate of 100-250 kilograms per hectare.

From the ecological viewpoint, the introduction of any species into an ecosystem should be viewed with caution even if it does not normally breed, as with the grass carp. Grass carp seem to select plants indiscriminately: at the end of trials in Wessex WA in a cut-off meander loop of the Axe, growth was successfully curtailed, but plant diversity was not reduced. If introduced extensively, the consequent decrease in emergent and floating vegetation could have serious implications for dependent species such as little grebe and reed warbler. Clearly, further work is required before an informed judgement can be made.

A safeguard is provided through legislation: under Section 14 of the Wildlife and Countryside Act 1981 a licence is required before grass carp can be released; the approval of the relevant authority is also required under fisheries legislation.

TREE PLANTING FOR SHADE

Alteration of the amount of light reaching a channel is the simplest site factor to change so as to reduce plant growth. Reducing available nutrients is generally not feasible, and adding chemicals specifically to kill plants is ecologically unacceptable. Changing channel depth and width provides a practical alternative but is more expensive in every way than simply planting shade belts of trees on banks.

Few shade trials have been carried out in this country, and none are mature enough yet to demonstrate the full shade effect. Many, however, have been undertaken in Holland, Denmark and Germany. There are many examples of naturally tree-shaded rivers with almost no channel vegetation in Britain, whereas adjacent treeless stretches have dense stands of emergent and submergent plants.

The conservation of rivers would not be well served by planting trees on all banks so as to eliminate channel vegetation. But the weed problem in many watercourses – particularly treeless main drains in fenland areas – could be helped by tree planting, which would also reduce the need for cutting and herbicide treatments. Wildlife would lose some aquatic plant habitat, but would benefit from less disturbance, and from the extra cover and food resources provided by trees.

The degree of shading needed

The growth of aquatic plants is slower in shade than in full sunlight. For some plants shade is intolerable, and they cannot grow at all. Others are tolerant of shade, but they produce fewer and/or smaller shoots as a result of the reduced light. Submerged plants are better adapted to reduced light conditions than emergent plants, although even the former usually only grow where full sun falls on the water surface (some mosses, lichens and encrusting algae are exceptions to this). Haslam (1978) provides the following list of comparatively shade-tolerant and shade-intolerant plants:

Shade-tolerant (in order of decreasing shade tolerance):

1 Unbranched bur-reed.
2 Starwort species, common reed, branched bur-reed.
3 Water plantain, Canadian pondweed, water forget-me-not, hornwort.
4 Fool's watercress, yellow water-lily, curly-leaved pondweed, arrowheads, narrow-leaved water parsnip.
5 Watercress, horned pondweed, water speedwell.
6 Water crowfoots, brooklimes.

Shade-intolerant:

No river plants can live under permanent heavy shade – under bridges for example. Research suggests that a 70 per cent reduction in light will inhibit nearly all growth. A 50 per cent reduction will exclude all shade-intolerant plants, and reduce the growth of others. A 50 per cent reduction is a reasonable target to achieve by tree-shading.

The siting of shade-belts

To provide weed clearing machinery with access before the trees take affect, planting can be confined to one bank. On some channels planting on both banks may be necessary, however, for effective weed control (see below).

To get maximum benefit from tree shade, they should be planted as close to the water's edge as possible. However, if the channel is deep and relatively narrow with a trapezoidal section, planting on the banktop may cast more shade and be less obstructive to flow than planting lower down. Leaving a track for machine access between the shade-belt and the water's edge will reduce the shaded area, and be less effective.

Exactly which bank is planted depends on the orientation of the watercourse. The table below suggests planting sites and their effectiveness for different channel orientations (see also figures overleaf).

The Freshwater Biological Association is preparing tables to compute the effectiveness of shading from different heights and orientations (Dawson, pers comm).

Where watercourses meander and change direction, trees will have to be planted on different banks. This gives an opportunity to improve the landscape and be more imaginative in planting. On a meander loop, for instance, a clump could be planted in the uncultivable corner instead of a single line of trees. Where tree planting changes there could be either a gap to allow a patch of plants to grow or an overlap to make a short, secluded, totally tree-lined section.

Research suggests that leaving gaps in a shade belt,

Planting for shade and channel orientation

Orientation	*Bank for shade belt*	*Effectiveness for weed control*
E—W	South bank	Maximum
SE—NW	South-east bank	Moderate to good
NE—SW	South-west bank	Moderate to good
N—S	East bank	Poor
	East and west bank	Moderate

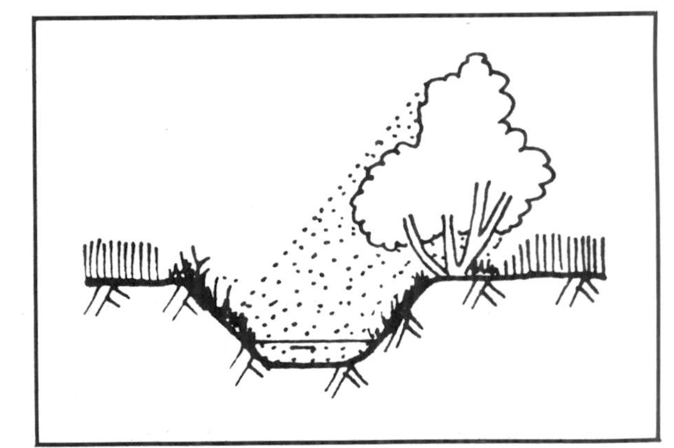

Narrow channels can be completely shaded from one side.

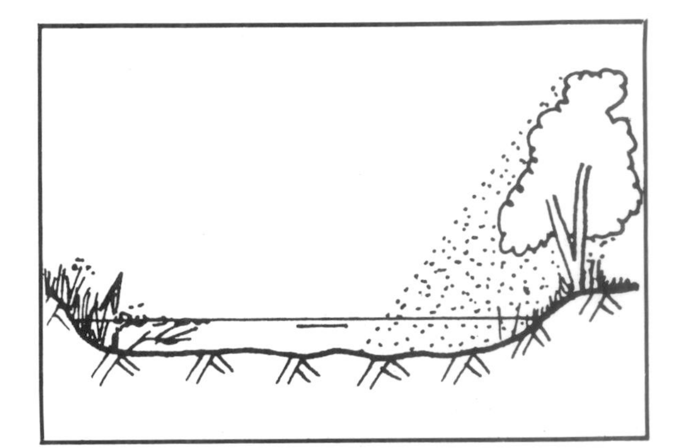

Wide channels will only be partly shaded – allowing plants to flourish on the south-facing bank.

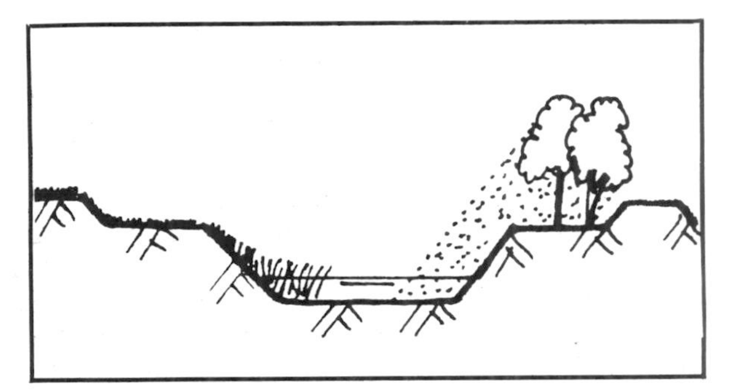

Within floodbanks, standard trees will be less hazardous in high flows.

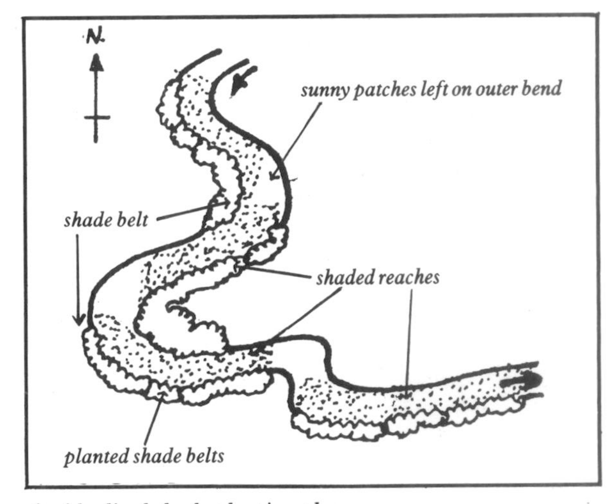

An idealised shade planting plan.

and so allowing patches of plants to grow uninhibited, maintains a better balanced ecosystem, in which the leaf litter from the trees decomposes more easily, rather than tending to form a dense, slimy, deoxygenated mass on the channel bed. Alternating tree-shaded and open stretches of river also creates the greatest variety of habitats for wildlife and plants – and a most attractive landscape for people. A survey of the River Tone in Somerset, for example, showed that the most species-rich sections were those where the natural tree cover of the river had been interrupted at 40-50 metre intervals, allowing light down to the river and permitting a rich assortment of water plants, insects, butterflies and dragonflies to flourish (Lewis, 1980).

Spacing in shade-belts

In Holland, streams have been planted up with alders set at 0.5 metre centres in a single line, or 1 metre centres set in two staggered rows. This forces rapid growth into a dense thicket which soon shades the channel. As time goes on the alder stand is self-thinning and tall individual trees grow up at 4-5 metre invervals.

A single line of trees should be sufficient, however, planted at a normal 3-5 metre spacing. Shrubs could be planted in between to form a more complete shade early on and, later, to provide an under-storey to the tall shade trees. Fencing against stock will be essential for the first five to 15 years, depending on the tree species selected.

Tree species for shade

As it is not necessary to shade rivers in winter, deciduous trees are effective. Evergreens, and especially conifers, have leaves which are resistant to decomposition, and when they finally rot they may acidify the water.

Native trees (especially deciduous species) are always preferable to non-natives: their leaf input enriches the river ecosystem; they support more invertebrates and, therefore, more mammals and birds; they fit into the landscape; finally, they may be cheaper. Most, except for willows and sallows, are relatively slow growing, but growth can be speeded by the application of a good mulch at the time of planting. The use of *quick-growing, non-native trees should be avoided* – in particular, *Leylandii* (which is also an evergreen), Italian black poplar or eucalyptus. These three add little to the river ecosystem except, possibly, cover for some creatures.

Ideal shade trees are native, deciduous, quick-growing to more than 8 metres tall, with a deep root system, and giving early leaf cover. Preferably they should be suitable for pollarding and the timber useful for timber or fuel: this may encourage landowners to accept them being planted on their land. Those trees which respond well to coppicing can also be used, although at the end of each coppicing cycle there will be a temporary loss of the shading effect. The most suitable native trees are reviewed below:

Alder – Native, quick-growing, prefers rich soil, can be encouraged by putting a high phosphorus fertiliser around each transplant. Major advantage is the deep root system, penetrating the water table, giving great stability: all other large trees have roots which avoid waterlogged soils. Reaches 8 to 15 metres within 15 years, coppices well to form a multi-stemmed tree, useful firewood. The best tree species to use by far.

Tree willows – White willow, crack willow and their hybrids. Very fast-growing and easily established from truncheons. Up to 8 metres in 10 years or less, maximum height 20-25 metres but often unstable by then. Willows coppice and pollard well, so providing stability. Will grow at water's edge or bank top.

Shrub willows (*Salix* species) – Goat willows, sallows and their hybrids. Similar to tree willows, except that they never grow taller than 5-8 metres. Bushy habit. Less suitable as shade trees, unless planted with other species.

Native black poplar – A rare tree that deserves more widespread planting. Like the willows, easily planted from truncheons. Tolerant of damp, waterlogged soils. Quick growing to 20-25 metres, but responds well to pollarding.

Sycamore – A non-native tree, well-established throughout Britain. Plant on dry bank tops only. Quick growing, casts dense shade early in year. Coppices well for fuel. Honeydew from aphids feeding on leaves enriches the water below, so increasing fish productivity. Its roots may form cavities at river level, favoured by otters as holts.

Lime, oak, beech, field maple, hawthorn – All native, relatively slow-growing, but casting good shade. Suitable for planting on dry bank tops, possibly in mixtures with quicker growing trees such as alder and willow.

Ash – although native and relatively fast-growing, it only casts a light shade and is, therefore, unsuitable for plant control purposes. It is, however, a most attractive tree for wildlife and landscape, well suited to river conditions so it should not be discriminated against on these grounds alone!

Other, smaller, native shrubs may be planted such as buckthorn, alder buckthorn, elder, guelder rose, wayfarer's tree, to fill gaps and provide a more varied landscape for people, and habitat and food sources for wildlife.

Planting techniques and aftercare are described in Section **258**.

Problems

Trees beside watercourses can cause problems. As they age, dead and diseased limbs may fall off; as years go by the channel may undercut or erode behind the mature tree until it falls into the channel (though root systems often help to resist bank erosion). Trees below flood levels will catch trash, and this may cause them to fall in severe storms.

In general, however, the hazardous trees are ones which are over-mature or have already been damaged and are growing by spatey rivers or on eroding banks. Fenland drains are seldom spatey and few have eroding banks. Proper, regular tree management will ensure that diseased and over-mature trees are pollarded or coppiced before they become a hazard. Trashing is avoided by not planting below flood level in narrow channels. After the first three years' establishment, trees should need attention only every 10 years or so, rather than annually, as weed management requires.

Land-take is a problem. When landowners can expect drainage authorities to expend considerable sums of money on annual weed-cutting free without any loss of land at the channel's edge, then they may not take kindly to being asked to give up a strip permanently as a shade-belt, so that the water authority can reduce its long-term costs. If the landowner is a beneficiary of a lowered freeboard, however, then it may be reasonable for the authority to seek some contribution in kind towards a process otherwise provided with public money. Failing persuasion, compensation, or purchase of a strip of shade belt land may be the only solutions.

References

Haslam, S M, 1978. River plants. Cambridge University Press.

Lewis, G, 1981. Somerset rivers survey: a survey of the Rivers Tone, Yeo, Cary and Northmoor Main Drain, to map and describe their flora and fauna. Somerset Trust for Nature Conservation/Wessex Water Authority unpublished report.

Three worked examples of tree planting options: based on 1982 prices, quoted from Worcestershire

1 km of shade belt, 4 m wide.

Fencing

1,008 m fencing, pig wire in 50 m rolls.	
21 rolls pig wire @ £16 a roll=	£336.00
335 fencing stakes, at 3 m intervals +10% approx	
360 stakes @ 88p each=	£316.80
Fencing materials=	£652.80

Planting Materials:
Option 1: Mixed trees at 4 m intervals
Mixed shrubs at 2 m intervals

250×2+1 transplants, trees @ 27p each	£67.50
500×2+1 transplants, shrubs @ 30p each	£150.00
	£217.50

Option 2: Single row alders at 3 m centres

330×2+1 transplant alders @ 22p each	£73.26

Option 3: Staggered row alders, at 1 m centres

2,000×2+1 transplant alders @ 22p each	£440.00

Fencing and planting materials, excluding labour:
Option 1.... £870.30/km
Option 2.... £726.06/km
Option 3...£1,092.00/km

CHANNEL ENLARGEMENT

Since the majority of bulky aquatic plants grow in shallow water of less than 1 metre deep, it follows that their growth can be inhibited by excavation of a deeper channel – provided the water-level is maintained. To permit some marginal plant growth, a shallow water berm could be cut, or alternatively a damp flood berm on one side or the other. Two-stage channels can be designed to allow plant growth in specific areas, while the main channel remains deep, swift-flowing and largely plant-free. A major advantage should be lower maintenance costs (see **89**, **131** and **178**).

Unfortunately, this may not work where flows are very slow, or reduced, such as in fen drainage systems. Even in deep water, the pond-like conditions encourage submerged plants to grow luxuriantly, unless growth is shaded out by trees. Work in the Netherlands (Pitlo, 1982) suggests that enlargement of the channel cross-section combined with the planting of floating vegetation – such as yellow water lily (*Nuphar lutea*) or floating pondweed (*Potamogeton natans*) – will retard the growth of submerged species by a combination of increased water depth and shading (the floating leaves intercept light, limiting that available to submerged species).

An alternative strategy is to design the enlargement of the channel for the required capacity and then to make an additional realistic allowance for the growth of aquatic and bankside plants. The Woolston Park Scheme (Section **208**) provides an example – a small channel was greatly enlarged for urban flood alleviation: at the same time, an allowance for vigorous plant growth in the channel was made and this has become a key park feature.

Channel design tends to consider a system of only water and substrate. In reality, there is a biological element as well, which interacts with both water and substrate to make the effective channel smaller than the design channel (figure right). The result is that rigorous control of the biological element is then required to keep as close as possible to the original design capacity.

Roughness coefficients such as Manning's 'n' are a mathematical attempt to correct the design to take

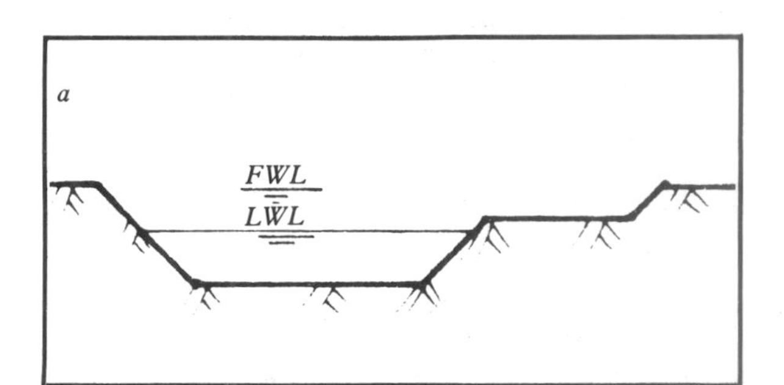

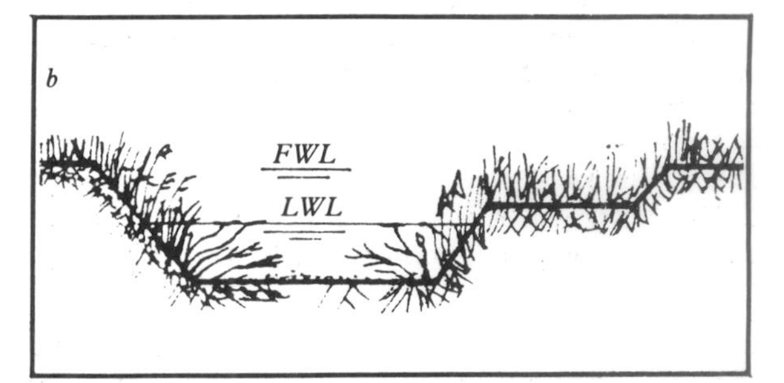

Channel design needs to take account not only of water and substrate, but the biological element as well: (a) a design drawing which considers only water and substrate, (b) reality, including the biological element as well.

this loss of efficiency due to plants into account. The choice of value is then crucial to the subsequent maintenance programme. A Manning's 'n' value of about 0.03 is commonly used in channel design, but this may underestimate by a factor of 10 the real effect of natural weed growth in British lowland rivers in mid-summer (see 'Introduction 2', pages 7-8).

More generous channel design which takes full account of aquatic plant growth is one way of cutting maintenance costs and leaving channels undisturbed for longer periods of time. The only disadvantage may be a small increase in land-take, but the significance of this will depend on individual circumstances.

Reference

Pitlo, R H, 1982. Flow resistance of aquatic vegetation. Proceedings EWRS 6th Symposium on Aquatic Weeds, 1982.

ESTABLISHING AQUATIC PLANTS

There are many reasons for planting aquatics in a watercourse. Perhaps the three key reasons are: practical – to provide bank protection; aesthetic – to add to the quality of the landscape; for conservation of a rare plant.

Newly excavated channels, in particular, require positive action such as planting to restore wildlife habitats. Although recolonisation will occur after dredging, some species take much longer to re-establish themselves than others, and changes in flow or substrate after dredging may prevent others from recolonising: the result is usually change and simplification of the structure of the community. For animal communities, the loss of plant habitats frequently reduces their variety, abundance and breeding success.

The principles of establishing most aquatic plants are straightforward:

1 Use fresh, locally abundant plants.
2 Plant mixtures of species.
3 Take plants only from the locality, preferably the same river or one of its tributaries. Note that to comply with Section 13 of the Wildlife and Countryside Act 1981, the permission of the landowner or occupier is required.
4 Plant in early spring, as the shoots first appear above ground level.
5 Dib cuttings or clumps into a hole in shallow water. Firm with the heel of your boot.
6 Protect from wave action and grazing, if necessary.

Most aquatic plants are easy to propagate from cuttings, whole plants or rhizome fragments. Common reed is the only exception (see **222**).

As well as planting by hand, transplanting can also be carried out mechanically. During dredging, patches of mixed water plants can be scooped out and stored in a pond, ditch, backwater or wet hollow until work is completed. The plants can then be returned to the dredged river.

Mixtures of species can be selected for particular bank substrates and purposes. For example, in tipped stone or cellular concrete block revetment, surface spreading plants such as reed sweetgrass, sweet flag or yellow flag would be best. On berms and in soft substrates subsurface spreading plants such as sedges, common reed or reedmace would be better. 'Biological 2 Plants' provides further details of the habitat requirements of aquatic plants and their suitability for planting.

Planting has been carried out with great success at many sites in recent years. Drainage authority staff should be able to acquire the skills required to plant aquatics rapidly. If labour is limited, however, then it may be possible to organise a group of conservation volunteers to help with the work, through the British Trust for Conservation Volunteers (Head Office), 36 St Mary's Street, Wallingford, Oxfordshire OX10 0EU, or the local Nature Conservation Trust.

RIVER STORT NAVIGATION, NEAR BISHOP'S STORTFORD, HERTFORDSHIRE
OS Map: 167. NGR: TL 495193 to 493203
Eastern Division, Thames Water Authority, The Grange, Crossbrook Street, Waltham Cross, Hertfordshire.
Telephone: Waltham Cross (0992) 23611.

Site Summary
Flood alleviation scheme, capital works, 1978-80.
Urban fringe, lowland location.
Channel: pounded navigation 10-15 metres wide.
Berms: graded 1 in 3 to 1 in 4.5; 1.5 metres wide.
Substrate: clay.
Research Student: D Kite.

Work Description
See Section **132** for details of the site and construction of shallow-water berms 1.5 metres wide, on a gradient of approximately 1 in 4.

In 1980, a research student was appointed to study, amongst other topics, the success of planting various marginal plants (Kite, in prep). The techniques adopted are briefly described below:

Most plants were taken from wetlands and channels within 3 kilometres of the planting site, from patches where they were already abundant. All the sources happened to be on land already owned or managed by Thames WA or British Waterways Board (otherwise the landowner's permission would have had to be sought to uproot the plants). The species used were perennial, narrow-leaved, emergent water plants, many commonly found in permanently wet soils or shallow water. Some were propagated by shoot cuttings, others from clumps of rhizome and shoot material, or from individual plants. All were planted in water up to 16 centimetres deep (relative to NWL), the actual planting depth for each species depending on the water depth in which it was observed growing elsewhere in the Lee catchment. Single species were planted in plots 5 metres or 10 metres in length, early in the growing season in March, April and May.

Planting Methods
A *Shoot cuttings:* 1-2 centimetres of rhizome attached to a sturdy young shoot, or a shoot section of shoot-tip only (depending on growth from the species) cut out of a healthy patch with a knife (figures below and right). 'Pioneer' rhizomes provide the best cuttings. Planted by hand in shallow water, two per site, 25 centimetres apart in 5 metre long plots. Gently but securely firmed in by hand; some cuttings are extremely fragile.
B *Rhizome and shoot clumps, and individual plants:* 10-20 centimetre diameter clumps were dug out of healthy patches, using a spade. Old growth was cut back to prevent 'flopping' that would lead to the plant washing out (figure below right). Planted by hand in shallow water, 1 metre apart in 10 metre long plots. Firmed in securely by hand, or for tougher plants, with the heel of a boot.

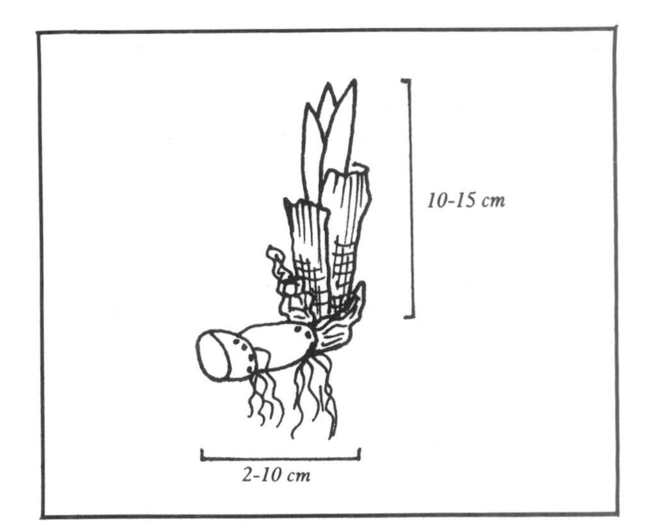

Shoot cutting of yellow flag.

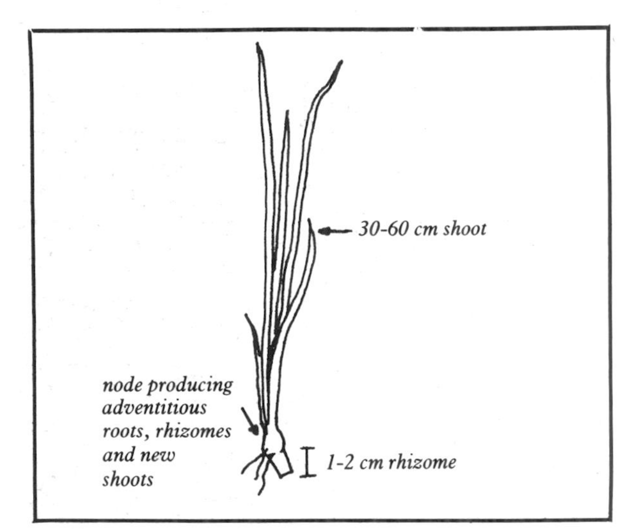

Shoot cutting of greater pond sedge.

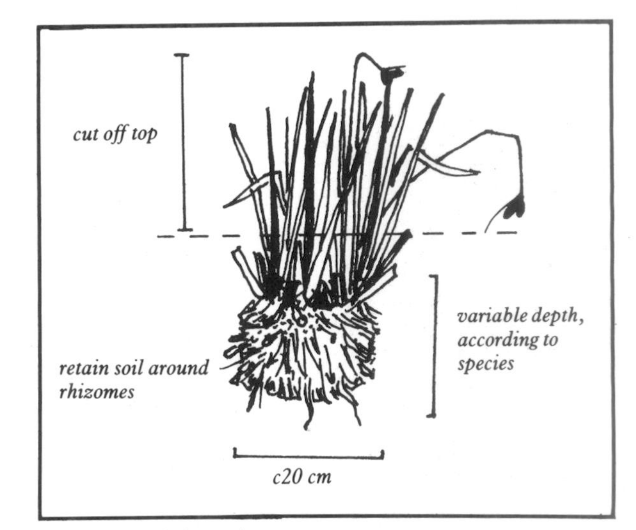

Rhizome and shoot clump.

Plants	Planting Method	Growth
Reed sweet-grass	Rhizome & shoot clumps	Excellent, but heavily grazed*
Greater pond-sedge	Rhizome & shoot clumps	Excellent
	Shoot cuttings	Excellent
Lesser pond-sedge	Rhizome & shoot clumps	Very good
	Shoot cuttings	Very good
Slender tufted sedge	Rhizome & shoot clumps	Good
	Shoot cuttings	Poor+
Common reed	Rhizome & shoot clumps	Poor*
	Shoot cuttings	Poor
Common clubrush	Rhizome & shoot clumps	Moderate*
Galingale	Shoot cuttings	Very good*[1]
Yellow iris	Rhizome & shoot clumps	Good*
Sweet-flag	Rhizome & shoot clumps	Good
Hard rush	2-year-old plants	Moderate
Branched bur-reed	Rhizome & shoot clumps	Moderate
Reed canary-grass	2-year-old plants	Moderate*
Bulrush	Rhizome & shoot clumps	Excellent

+=smothered by overhanging bank vegetation.
*=grazed by birds or water voles, but not killed.
[1]=winter die back.

After two summers the cover of most species had increased from 10 per cent to more than 50 per cent of the length of the plot, and some to more than 90 per cent (photographs below and right). ('Cover' was measured by the amount of ground occupied by the clump and its side-shoots, at soil level.)
Losses were due to vandalism (1 per cent), trampling (1 per cent), damage during transplanting (2 per cent), insect attack (2 per cent) and grazing by swans and Canada geese (7 per cent). Many species were grazed by water vole, a few had more than half the shoots grazed, but none so severely that the plant was killed.
The unplanted banks, graded to 1:1.5 or steeper, were showing signs of wave wash scour and subsidence (from boat traffic) after two summers. In contrast the berms were showing signs of sedimentation behind most of the more vigorous species within one year of planting.

River Stort: Bulrush partially dies back in winter, but regrows vigorously in early spring.

River Stort: The towpath and bank protected by a dense growth of greater pond-sedge, planted two growing seasons before in 1980 (March 1982).

Habitat Comments
1 Planting stands of different local plants in sites which would otherwise be bare is an obvious benefit to wildlife, in particular invertebrates and fish. If a wide band is planted, away from human disturbance, some nesting water birds would benefit too. Careful planting can be used to perpetuate rare or local plant communities.
2 Because there were no other reedbeds nearby, the planting attracted swans and Canada geese from adjacent gravel pits, which grazed many of the most palatable species. This demonstrates that new plantings in bare channels should be over long lengths, with large patches of each species if they are to have a chance to grow on. It also shows how beneficial such planting may be to herbivorous species such as swans and water voles.
3 Not all sites are suitable for this type of planting: be guided by the conditions existing before work starts – provided it has not been dredged, cut or sprayed in recent years.
Sites where plants are absent or sparse because of water pollution (especially sewage and industrial effluents), will not benefit from aquatic planting until water quality has been improved, although *marginal* planting at the water's edge and just above should survive.

Reference
Kite, D (in prep). Land drainage, its influence on river bank vegetation and associated waterbirds along pounded watercourses in the Lee catchment. PhD thesis, University College, London.

ATTENBOROUGH GRAVEL PITS, NOTTINGHAMSHIRE

OS Map: 129. NGR: SK 528357

Norman Lewis, Conservation Officer,
Nottinghamshire Trust for Nature Conservation,
10 Darley Avenue, Toton, Beeston, Nottingham.
Telephone: Long Eaton (060 76) 60926.

Work Description

The Trust manages part of the gravel pits as a nature reserve. They have successfully developed beds of common reed on sand and mud banks formed from gravel washings. The common reed is notoriously difficult to establish by planting, but the Trust here has had success with several methods.

1 *From clumps:* Large, 20 square centimetre clumps of rhizome with as many terminal buds as possible are cut with a spade from a healthy reed-bed, and planted in the same sized holes *above* the mean water level (figure below). Rhizomes planted below water level will usually rot. Once established, the reeds will gradually colonise downslope into the water. The best season for using this method is October to March, and it has usually proved successful. Great care should be taken not to damage the new swollen terminal stems when firming the clump in. Care also needs to be taken to minimise trampling of the reedbed when extracting the clump in the first place; damage to emergent shoots will be caused otherwise.

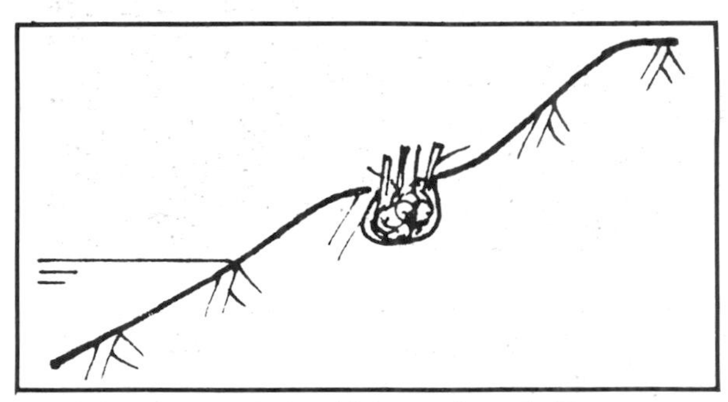

Rhizome clump, with the odd shoots trimmed off.

2 *From cuttings:* Non-flowering green shoots are cut when about 1 metre high (May or June), and planted a handful at a time, in angled slits made with a spade (figure top right). They must be planted at water level, and firmed so that at least three leaf nodes are buried. This method is usually successful. If the substrate is shallow, horizontal insertion will ensure that the maximum number of nodes are buried – at least one-third of the stem should be left exposed, however.

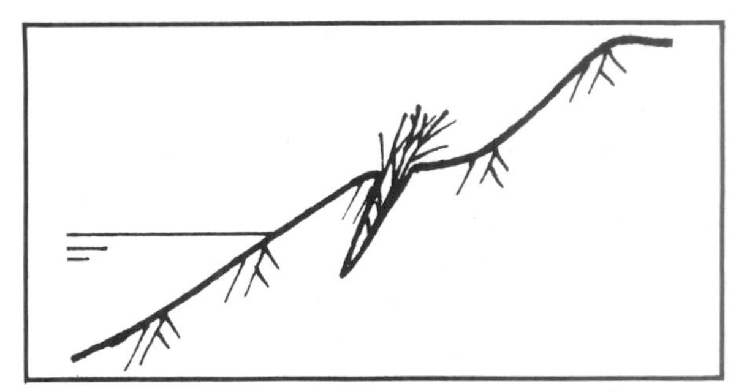

Stem cuttings, planted into a spaded slit.

3 *By layering:* This can only be done at the edge of an already established reedbed to help colonisation of water, or lower bank. Mature non-flowering shoots are laid out horizontally from the parent plant and pegged down or pressed into a spaded slot, with the tip *lower* than the parent stock (figure above). They soon root from each node. Best done in May or June. Usually successful.

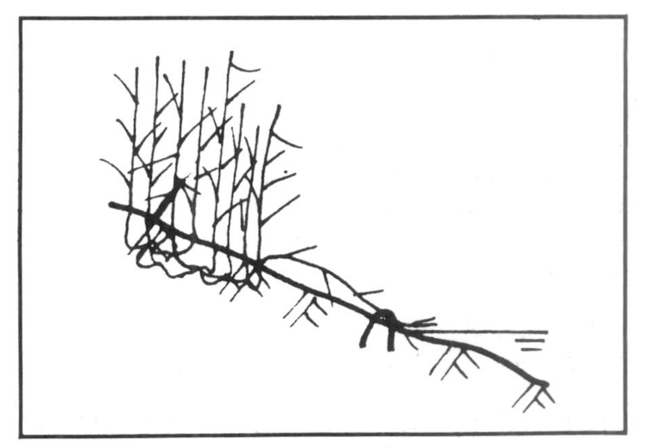

Non-flowering shoots layered downhill.

4 *By seed:* Although the common reed very rarely has fertile seed, some clones do, so this is a method worth trying. The best germination conditions are in the mulch of tide-line detritus that accumulates on lakeshores and some river edges. Mature seed heads are pegged down in this mulch, and, if fertile, they will readily germinate. Since the seed is late ripening, this is best done in December: the success of this technique is, however, variable.

In Holland, fertile seed is grown in peat blocks and individually planted out, like bedding plants.

Habitat Comments

1 Stands of common reed are becoming scarcer, yet it is an extremely valuable habitat for invertebrates, otter and birds; as well as species such as reed warbler, which breed in reedbeds, several other birds find the habitat of great value when gathering for migration – these include swallows, house and sand martins, and yellow wagtails. Planting reed on lakeshores and riversides will almost always be a welcome addition.

2 Common reed can be established on riversides, as well as lakes, using the methods described here, and either on its own or with cellular or mesh revetment will protect the bank from erosion (see **171** and **173**).

MEECE BROOK, NORTON BRIDGE, STAFFORDSHIRE
OS Map: 127. NGR: SJ 868306
Upper Trent Division, Severn Trent Water Authority, Trinity Square, Horninglow Street, Burton-on-Trent DE14 1BL.
Telephone: Burton-on-Trent (0283) 44511.
Regional Architects' Department, Severn Trent Water Authority, Abelson House, 2297 Coventry Road, Sheldon, Birmingham B26 3PU.
Telephone: 021-743 4222.

Site Summary
Land drainage scheme, capital works, 1981.
Lowland, rural location.
Channel: 3-4 metres wide.
Banks: up to 2 metres, irregular slopes.
Substrate: gravel, clay, sandy alluvium.
Engineers: S Powers, D Pinnegar.
Landscape Architect: M Ericsson.

Work Description
See Section on 223 for a fuller description of this scheme.
A small shelf was excavated on a short stretch of the Meece during land drainage work deepening the river by up to 1 metre, so recreating that lost in dredging. The shelf is on the inner bank, downstream of a meander, and was cut 20 metres long by about 2 metres wide, the bank behind graded to 1 in 1.5. It was designed to be 15 centimetres above normal water level, at the channel edge, so that soils are always either waterlogged or damp.

Meece Brook: The shelf on completion in May 1981. Clumps of plants have been transplanted at the water's edge. Note the opposite bank is untouched. ▶

Meece Brook: The berm, on the left, well grown with grasses and transplanted bankside plants, in September 1982. ▼

Before work started, the shelving channel edge had a mixed community of brooklime, fool's watercress and water forget-me-not; whole plants were dug out in spade-deep chunks, by hand, and left in a nearby damp hollow while dredging was carried out. The clumps were then replanted in holes in the shelf, which was fenced off from stock. The work was completed by mid-May, and all the plants grew and spread in that summer's growing season. By summer 1982 the area was well vegetated and naturalised (photograph on previous page).
The work was carried out by the Division's direct labour staff.

Habitat Comments
1 This berm and wetland planting is in a remote situation – on a small river, in pasture land, with no footpath for public access. The work has been done solely for habitat improvement following dredging, and not for recreation or amenity. Such sites are as important for conservation as sites on larger rivers in public places – and because of their general lack of disturbance, make an important contribution.
2 The mixed replanting of species already growing on the site is excellent, as it conserves local types of plants, and their associated invertebrates. Introducing plants from elsewhere, in particular from another catchment, can change the distribution of aquatic species and is not necessarily good conservation practice.
3 Although stock-fenced initially, cattle were allowed access after the first winter. They have grazed down plants and prevented many plants from flowering so that the value of the site to insects, nesting birds and small mammals has been reduced. Grazing may have been useful, however, by preventing colonisation by tall herb species, such as nettles and willow herbs.

RIVER ALNE, HENLEY-IN-ARDEN, WARWICKSHIRE
OS Map: 151. NGR: SP 153659 and 153663
Avon Division, Severn Trent Water Authority, Finham Reclamation Works, St Martins Road, Finham, Coventry CV3 6PR.
Telephone: Coventry (0203) 415115.
Regional Architects' Department, Severn Trent Water Authority, Abelson House, 2297 Coventry Road, Sheldon, Birmingham B26 3PU
Telephone: 021-743 4222.

Site Summary
Flood alleviation scheme, capital work, 1980/81.
Lowland, urban location.
Channel: 2 metres wide at low water level, shallow.
Banks: 2 metres high, variable slopes, 1 in 1 to 1 in 3.
Substrate: sandy clay, gravel, introduced peat and clay.
Engineer: B Tinley.
Landscape Architect: J Purseglove.

Work Description
As part of a flood alleviation scheme for the town, carried out in 1980/81, a new flood by-pass channel was cut across a sharp bend (see **87**). The new channel was managed so as to create a 'natural', diverse habitat and landscape as quickly as possible. Bank slopes were varied by the excavator, between 1 in 1 and 1 in 3. The channel was deliberately cut slightly wide. Berms were then created on each side of the channel, by dumping soil and associated plant material (mainly meadowsweet) dredged from a nearby wetland, which was being excavated for a small riverside pond (figure below). Volunteers, arranged through the British Trust for Conservation Volunteers, transplanted additional species from a site in Staffordshire. Meadowsweet was flowering abundantly on the new berm within a few months; common spotted orchid even survived transplanting to flower two summers later (photograph top right).

River Alne: The bypass channel and associated pond.

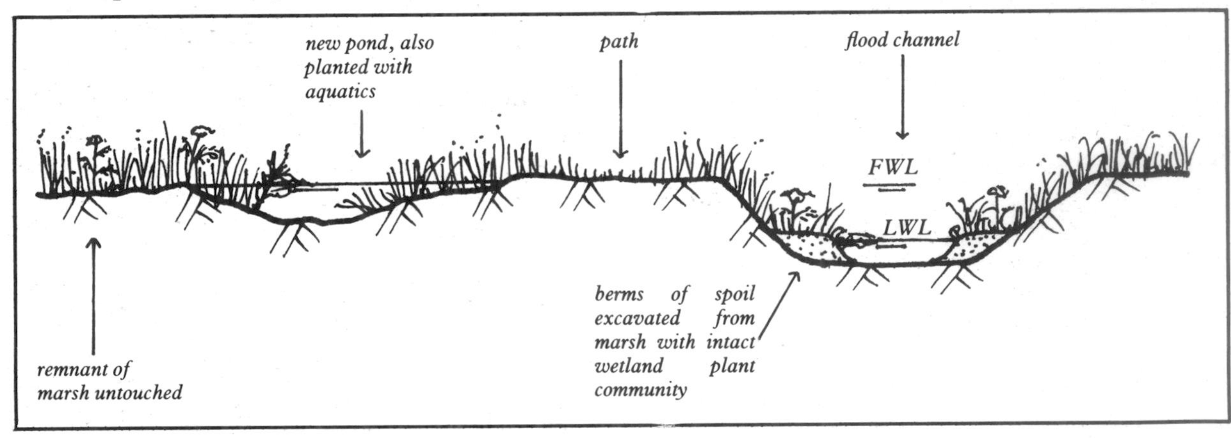

A second flood channel (at 153663) was constructed without a permanent flow (see on **87**). It was sown with a grass mix, but in addition, wetland plants were transplanted into it by British Trust for Conservation Volunteers. Marsh marigold, figwort, meadowsweet and rushes were included. The channel is grazed by horses (photograph below).

Habitat Comments

1 This planting method has clearly worked very well; the channel now looks attractive, and supports a good variety of plants, providing food and cover for wildlife.

2 Careful choice of seed mixtures for the graded banks, followed by no cutting and no grazing, has allowed the transplanted materials to flourish without competition or set-back.

3 The circumstances of this planting scheme are rather unusual. The marshy area was quite large, yet poor in species. It did not support any rarities. The landscape architect judged that excavating part of it as a pond would increase the variety of local habitats and provide material for streamside planting at the same time. Although the decision made was correct here, this may not always be the case. If in doubt, seek advice from an ecologist.

River Alne: The bypass channel with all-year flow, in November 1982.

River Alne: A flood bypass channel without all-year flow, in November 1982.

GREAT LINFORD GRAVEL PITS, NEWPORT PAGNELL
OS Map: 152. NGR: SP 849425.
Game Conservancy, Fordingbridge, Hampshire.
Telephone: Fordingbridge (0425) 52387.

Work Description

The Game Conservancy has planted up and managed Great Linford gravel pits over the past decade to improve the habitat for breeding and wintering wildfowl. Without planting, gravel pits usually remain very poor in cover and variety of water plants for many years, and hence support smaller wildfowl populations than well-established waters of comparable size. The duck population of a pit is governed more by the length and suitability of its shoreline than by the area of water.

Clearly, in encouraging wildfowl, the productivity of the whole aquatic community will be increased, since they depend on both water plants and invertebrates at some stage in their life.

At Great Linford, the shoreline was prepared by excavating shallow bays and pushing out spoil from shallow-water berms up to a metre deep (photograph below top).

Water plants were brought on site, either selected from nearby natural water bodies, or taken, by arrangement with Anglian Water Authority, from river dredging. The latter were dumped on the bank and then sorted out for planting by hand.

Planting used the same techniques as described in **219** (photograph below bottom).

The most successful planting was done early in the growing season, when new shoots are still small.

Great Linford: Forming a shallow edge and berm, in preparation for planting.

Great Linford: Volunteers planting rhizomes and clumps of aquatic plants, selected from river dredgings.

Autumn plantings worked, but had to be held down with stone and protected with an arch of wire netting, to prevent washing out and pulling out by coots or swans.

On exposed lake shores, floating timber baffles were fixed temporarily until the young plants were firmly established (six to 12 months) (photograph below top). For river plantings, such protection is usually unnecessary but, where wash from boat traffic along river navigation occurs, protection may be important. Within three months a dense stand of plants had grown up (photograph below bottom).

Plant species are selected carefully to ensure that aggressive quick-growing plants do not suppress slow-growing ones, and so that there is a variety of food sources for duck. To establish a complete aquatic plant community the Game Conservancy recommends planting submerged species (such as stonewort, fennel-leaved pondweed, and, in streams, water crowfoot), floating leaved plants (such as broad-leaved pondweed and amphibious bistort), emergent plants (such as arrowhead, bur-reed, sea clubrush and common bulrush) as well as wetland plants for the bank edge (such as water-cress, starwort, brooklime, great water dock and marsh marigold). These are all duck food plants; others could be recommended for cover and shelter. The wetland plants should be put in slightly later, in May or June when growing vigorously, but before flowering. Whole plants with a good ball of undisturbed roots should be transplanted.

Great Linford: On exposed shores, especially on lakes, gravel pits and river navigations, new planting may need protection from waves. Here, floating, flexible booms of logs, posts and wire protect bur-reed and reed-mace plantings.

Great Linford: The same site as below left, three months later.

Habitat Comments

1 Habitat management for game obviously benefits other groups of wildlife. Many landowners may be prepared to accept habitat conservation measures if sporting, as well as wildlife, interests are benefited.

Reference

Game Conservancy, 1981. Wildfowl management on inland waters. 2nd edition. The Game Conservancy, Fordingbridge.

TECHNICAL 5: GRASS AND HERBS

A key part of the river-bank plant community is the terrestrial ground vegetation – grass and tall herb species. The range of species present depends on a wide variety of factors, some natural, some not. Natural influences include the degree of shading from trees and scrub; the bank profile, the flood régime of the river. Land-use practices are important, especially whether the bank is grazed by stock and whether the bankside vegetation has been affected by spray drift, if the adjacent land is arable. The river manager also has considerable influence over bankside vegetation both directly – through, for example, mowing, re-seeding and herbicide spraying practices, and indirectly – through dredging operations, tree removal (affecting shading) and altering the bank profile.

Bankside grassland communities are often important: as conditions change from wet to dry up the bank slope so different plants find suitable habitat. Many have bright flowers attracting insects in summer and seed-eating birds and mammals in the autumn – teasel, hogweed, water mint, purple loosestrife, thistles, willowherbs and mallows. Under this tall cover live many invertebrates, food for small mammals which in turn are hunted by other predators – barn owl, fox and kestrel. Bank-nesting birds such as mallard, reed bunting and sedge warbler use tall herbs for nest-cover. With the widespread loss of old grasslands, banksides are often the remaining stronghold of meadowland flowers, harbouring cowslip, greater burnet, orchids and other scarce plants.

Short grass cover is also frequently required for engineering reasons – particularly on the flood-banks of lowland rivers. Grass roots bind and protect the soil; short grass has a low roughness coefficient, crucial where it is important to maintain channel capacity; short grass aids the inspection of floodbanks for subsidence, seepage, cracks and rodent burrows, and the control of woody vegetation reduces cover for burrowing animals.

In managing bankside grassland areas, there are two problems to be addressed: first, how to manage existing grassland areas to maintain or develop a varied plant community and second, how to establish new grassland areas (such as floodbanks) to create varied plant communities. At most locations. it should be possible to achieve both without unreasonably affecting engineering requirements.

The first part of this section, **229-33**, examines the influence of key management practices on grassland plant communities: grazing, mowing, burning and herbicide use are considered. The second part, **234-40**, looks at the techniques available for recreating natural plant communities after engineering operations have been carried out, including natural recolonisation, the use of seed mixtures and transplanting turf.

The management of grassland plant communities must be seen against the background of Section 13 and Schedule 8 of the Wildlife and Countryside Act 1981. It is an offence for any unauthorised person to intentionally uproot any wild plant or to pick, uproot or destroy intentionally any wild plant in Schedule 8, unless the action was done under and in accordance with the terms of a licence, or if the damaging action was an incidental result of a lawful operation and could not *reasonably* have been avoided. In practice, this means that before uprooting any wild plant authorisation from the landowner or occupier is required. If a plant is listed on Schedule 8, a licence should be obtained from the Nature Conservancy Council, which will normally permit transplantation for conservation purposes.

GRAZING

One of the most important influences in determining the nature of bankside vegetation is grazing. In the pasture areas of western and northern Britain, tall bankside vegetation may be absent and tree regeneration poor for this reason. In areas where bankside cover is low, the fencing of short lengths of bank (say 10 metres or so) may be a useful technique to provide additional shelter and food for wildlife.

Grazing is also frequently used by drainage authorities to maintain floodbanks and to keep the sward short, for the reasons outlined in the introduction to this section. Sheep are usually preferred, as their grazing results in the production of a tight, even sward and their hooves cause little poaching. Cattle and horses are occasionally used, but are operationally less desirable for the sward they produce tends to be more tussocky and they may cause poaching.

From the wildlife conservation viewpoint, grazing provides a useful management tool. Grazing pressure reduces the influence of the taller grass and herbaceous species, so preventing them from out-competing the less vigorous species. This tends to maintain, and perhaps increase, species richness as long as grazing is not too heavy. Because sheep, cattle and horses all have different grazing effects their consequences for wildlife are different too. Thus the tussocky structure produced by cattle may produce nest sites for breeding birds, while sheep produce a close sward with little suitable

cover.
In some areas such as the arable regions of eastern England, stock may not be readily available; elsewhere the physical characteristics of the structure to be maintained may make it unsuitable for grazing. In these situations other methods of management such as mowing may be required.

THE TIMING OF MOWING

Cutting can produce major changes in the plant community, the nature of which will vary according to the time of cut, the dominant species present and the interval between successive cuts.

The timing, frequency and pattern (see **231**) of cutting should be selective and based on the engineering objectives to be attained, eg floodbank inspection; the need to maximise channel capacity; the control of woody vegetation; or the suppression or encouragement of target plant species.

In areas dominated by tall, vigorous herbaceous species (such as nettles and dock) pre-August cutting may be desirable to reduce their dominance and to encourage less competitive species, although it must be recognised that such communities are frequently of value to invertebrates, small mammals and birds and may be at a premium in pasture areas where most banksides are likely to be grazed.

In areas dominated by grass swards the conservation of bankside grassland communities is best served by mowing as late in the year as possible – although this may conflict with labour deployment requirements.

Mowing after the end of July:

– permits seed to ripen, aiding herb survival, especially those short-lived herb species which cannot maintain themselves by vegetative growth.
– maintains the abundance of many tall herbaceous species, since they do not have to draw on their remaining vegetative reserves to produce new top growth.
– maintains insect populations, by retaining shelter and food plants.
– avoids the bird breeding season.

There are also engineering advantages, in that cutting during the growing season promotes grass growth. Banks should therefore be mown as late as possible, unless the risk of summer flooding is very great. If possible a proportion each year should also be left uncut (see **231**).

Many river banks are already mown late in the year – although this is usually for operational convenience rather than conservation reasons. The photograph on the right shows a floodbank with herbage cut annually to 10 centimetres in autumn. Sited along the River Thrushel, Devon, it was seeded 15 years ago with a standard 'agricultural' seed mix. It now has been colonised by a variety of pasture herbs, including meadow cranesbill, plantains, hogweed and yarrow. The nature of the cutting régime (both in terms of timing of cut and height of cut) have no doubt helped this process. Cutting to only 10 centimetres has probably aided tall herb survival by doing less damage to the ground-level overwintering buds of herbs, than had the cut been closer.

The régime to be adopted will depend upon the individual site: the Nature Conservancy Council or local Nature Conservation Trust should be able to give site specific advice.

River Thrushel: Floodbank left ungrazed and cut annually to 10 centimetres each autumn. Photographed August 1982.

PATCH CUTTING

As with the management of aquatic plant growth for wildlife conservation, a 100 per cent cut of bankside vegetation should not be the sole aim. Leaving areas uncut will provide structural diversity to the river channel – refuges for plants and animals.

Patch cutting can be done in many patterns. Leaving a strip from water's edge to banktop provides a good start, so that a range of plants from aquatic to wet meadow to dry meadow is retained. Developing this basic principle – the pattern of uncut patches, the size of each uncut patch and the siting of uncut patches – depends on the individual circumstances of each site. Small patches at close intervals on alternate banks may suit one site; long stretches on one bank another. A minimum of 10 per cent should be left uncut on most channels (figure below).

If grass banks are cut annually, then leaving uncut patches will allow biennial and perennial plants to flower and seed. If the same areas are left uncut every year, then woody plants will grow, which would probably be undesirable. Varying the cutting pattern each year would avoid this, so that no patch remains uncut for more than two or three years.

Patch cutting.

Patch-cutting grass banks will benefit tall herb plants, as their seeds will have the opportunity to mature and be dispersed, rather than just depending on vegetative spread. Insects will benefit: tall herb vegetation provides shelter, with flowers, seeds and shoots as food. Butterflies, moths, grasshoppers, beetles and other smaller invertebrates require the varied microclimates found amongst tall plants – absent in short, cut vegetation. Seed-eating birds, such as goldfinches, gain some food from uncut areas and the dense cover is valuable for small mammals such as bank vole and water shrew.

Patch cutting should not present engineering difficulties: it should be possible to tolerate a certain amount of natural growth in patches, even along low-gradient channels. Such channels are usually in intensive arable areas, where wildlife habitats are at a premium. Leaving isolated small patches of tall vegetation is unlikely to have a significant effect on overall channel roughness in channels of more than 2 metres in width at low water level. If cutting is carried out on a rotation, and different areas are left uncut each year, then there will be no risk of woody plants colonising. Neither should plant debris accumulate to cause channel blockages: woody debris is the principal cause of blockages. Herbaceous material decays very quickly, and is easily removed by minor annual floods.

Despite the advantages to wildlife conservation of this slight change to standard bank maintenance practice, it has not yet been generally adopted by drainage authorities. Some sections of the River Lee Navigation have been patch cut by Thames Water Authority's Eastern Division since 1976; Northumbrian Water Authority cut a small trial section of Baydale Beck in this manner in 1982. The latter is described below.

BAYDALE BECK, DARLINGTON, DURHAM

OS Map: 93. NGR: NZ 262156
Tees Division, Northumbrian Water Authority, Trenchard Avenue, Thornaby, Stockton-on-Tees.
Telephone: Stockton-on-Tees (0642) 760216.

Site Summary
Maintenance work, 1982.
Lowland, urban edge location.
Channel: 1 metre wide at low water level, shallow.
Banks: 1.5 metres high, slope 1 in 2, low embankments set back.
Substrate: clay and gravel.
Land Drainage Co-ordinator: D Burnley.

Work Description
The Beck is a small embanked stream on the edge of Darlington. Channel and bank vegetation is annually cut, above the road bridge, with a Bradshaw bucket to maintain capacity for carrying winter high flows. The top of the bank is normally hand-scythed at the same time.

Present vegetation is dominated by grasses, to 50 centimetres high, with some short herbs, and fool's watercress in the channel edge.

In July 1982, the operator of the Bradshaw cutter was asked to leave 2 metre lengths uncut, at about 25 metre intervals, on alternating sides. The adjacent aquatic vegetation in the channel of the Beck was also left uncut. There was no operational

difficulty in making this change of practice. Instructions were given verbally, on site, and the reasons for it explained.

Habitat Comments

1 The plant community of the Beck was not particularly important but leaving a proportion undisturbed should initiate a gradual change to a more varied habitat if this practice is continued.

Baydale Beck: The channel before cutting.

Baydale Beck: The channel after cutting: note the patch of bank and aquatic plants left uncut on the right. The low road bridge, behind, limits capacity.

BURNING

Burning is only rarely used for grassland management along river banks. It is more frequently used for the disposal of brashings and, if done in situ, may cause grass and other herbage to be burnt as well.

On riversides burning is an undesirable practice. It is indiscriminate, and if not properly supervised may cause damage to trees, scrub, crops and property. Burning alters the structure of the plant community. If carried out between early March and late July, the invertebrate community, breeding birds and their young may be incinerated. For these reasons, amongst others, burning of grass and heather is controlled by Regulations laid down by Parliament. (Statutory Instrument 1983 No 425.) It is always illegal to burn without sufficient people to control the blaze: notice has to be given to adjoining landowners of intention to burn not less than 24 and not more than 72 hours beforehand, and all reasonable precautions must be taken to avoid damage to neighbouring property. If burning of grass or heather is to be carried out between 1 April and 31 October in lowland areas, and 16 April and 30 September in upland areas, a licence must be obtained from the Ministry of Agriculture, Fisheries and Food.

Burning is also undesirable operationally. It removes the cover of surface vegetation which may, in the short-term, leave the bank open to erosion. After burning, a flush of nutrients is released, encouraging the more competitive, less desirable species which are able to colonise rapidly disturbed ground – which may require further management. Burning of the bankside vegetation may also release nutrients to the watercourse, encouraging the growth of marginal and aquatic vegetation – again posing further management problems.

If burning is to be used for the disposal of brashings or other woody material, it should be cut, collected and burnt in bonfires situated in a safe location and well supervised. Burning of brashings in situ should not be carried out because of the incidental indiscriminate damage which will be caused, whatever the season.

References

Statutory Instrument No 425, 1983. The Heather and Grass Burning (England and Wales) Regulations 1983. HMSO.

Ministry of Agriculture, Fisheries and Food, 1984. Heather and Grass Burning – Summary of Good Burning Practice. MAFF.

Ministry of Agriculture, Fisheries and Food, 1984. The Heather and Grass Burning Code; advice on the burning of heather and grass. MAFF.

HERBICIDES

The use of herbicides, particularly broad-spectrum chemicals, is not compatible with the maintenance and establishment of flower-rich grasslands. Herbicides used against nettles, hemlock or docks will also take out other more desirable herbaceous species. The key brushwood herbicides – 2,4,5-T or 2,4-D – are also toxic to broad-leaved herbaceous species.

This is not to say, however, that herbicides do not have a role if used in a specific and controlled manner. The use of a selective herbicide to kill undesirable tall herb species such as dock prior to seeding an area with a conservation seed mixture; or using a wipe to kill undesirable plants individually is acceptable and may even help towards conservation objectives.

Only a restricted range of chemicals are approved for use in or near watercourses, and then only in accordance with MAFF guidelines. Further information about the use of herbicides on banksides is given in section **209**.

References

Ministry of Agriculture, Fisheries and Food, 1979. Guidelines for the use of herbicides on weeds in or near watercourses and lakes. ADAS. Ministry of Agriculture, Fisheries and Food Booklet 2078, revised 1979.

Ministry of Agriculture, Fisheries and Food, 1981. Weed control in grassland, herbage legumes and grass seed crops 1981-1982. ADAS. Ministry of Agriculture, Fisheries and Food. Grassland Practice 16. Booklet 2056 (81).

Ministry of Agriculture, Fisheries and Food, 1983. 1983 list of approved products and their uses for farmers and growers. Agricultural Chemicals Approval Scheme. Ministry of Agriculture, Fisheries and Food Reference Book 380 (83). HMSO.

NATURAL RECOLONISATION

After engineering operations have been completed, drainage authorities usually sow the disturbed ground with a seed-mixture to stabilise the soil and bind it against erosion. Frequently, seeding is carried out to establish a flush of green to try to make the new works look natural as rapidly as possible. As explained on **235**, however, this course of action is disastrous ecologically, since the productive agricultural seed-mixes which are used retard or prevent the establishment of a native mixed plant community.

In many locations, it should be possible to leave the area bare to allow self-sown grasses and herbs to grow, although leaving a bank to regenerate its own natural plant community will take time. The first plants to take advantage of the site will probably be invasive – docks, thistles and nettles. Many of these early colonisers produce large quantities of seed: food for small birds and mammals. If left, this group of species will probably remain dominant for a period of some years. Regular cutting will reduce their competitiveness, however, gradually others will become established and a species-rich community of grasses and herbaceous plants will develop. The final mix depends on soil type, bank morphology, temperature, altitude, adjacent plant community types and degree of wetness (both in terms of soil saturation and flooding). Mowing, grazing and other influences such as herbicide use or burning will greatly affect the developing plant community.

Most sites could be left to recolonise naturally. Exceptions are floodbanks and berms, grazing land, the immediate vicinity of structures, and other areas liable to rapid scour.

Natural recolonisation will be aided if, before engineering works are carried out, about 10 centimetres of top-soil are skimmed from the area to be disturbed by operations and stored. Top-soil should be stored well away from the area of operations, so it does not become compacted by (for example) vehicles and the soil structure is not damaged. Once spread after completion of works, regeneration will occur from the seeds, roots, rhizomes and other plant material in the soil.

Imported top-soil should not be used. Frequently it is spread on newly-graded banks to improve fertility and provide a friable medium into which productive seed-mixes can be sown. This again, however, militates against the establishment of a natural plant community, since the native plants are unable to compete with the more productive agricultural grasses.

RIVER WEAVER, BRADNINCH, DEVON

OS Map: 192. NGR: ST 028033
Environmental Services (East Area), South West Water Authority, Manley House, Kestrel Way, Sowton Industrial Estate, Exeter.
Telephone: Exeter (0392) 76201.

Site Summary

Land drainage scheme capital works, 1982.
Rural location, upland/lowland transition zone.
Channel: 2 metres wide at low water, depth 0.5-1 metre.
Banks: 1.5 metres average, slope 1 in 1.5 on graded bank.
Substrate: clay and shale.

Work Description

The Weaver is a small clay catchment river, deepened and slightly widened in 1982 to improve land drainage. Work was carried out mostly from one bank; the existing trees, grassy vegetation and irregular bank-form were largely untouched on the non-working bank. The regraded bank was pulled back to about 1 in 1.5, left without topsoil and not seeded.

Before work, the adjacent field was pasture and the banktop was fenced. After work, the fence was

River Weaver: Natural regeneration in a non-seeded or top-soiled bank two months after regrading, in September 1982. Although initially patchy, 100 per cent cover should be attained within another 12 months, with a mixture of plants which benefit wildlife.

replaced, but since the farmer has now turned the field over to rootcrops, the river bank will not be grazed in any case (photograph left).

Habitat Comments

1 Not spreading topsoil and not seeding was probably done for economy reasons rather than as a conservation measure. The effect, however, has been to allow a variety of wild plants to recolonise this site which otherwise may have been excluded.

2 It is possible that leaving the opposite bank untouched has and will help in re-establishing a natural community on the graded bank, since it will provide a source of seed.

3 As the land drainage scheme has encouraged conversion to arable, the wild land on the river margin becomes even more important as a refuge for wildlife. Allowing the disturbed river banks to develop a wild plant cover as quickly as possible is no compensation for the loss of mixed plant communities of the pasture land, but at least it ensures that habitat loss along the riverside is only temporary.

SEED MIXTURES

Drainage authorities frequently re-seed areas disturbed by engineering operations to stabilise and bind the soil surface against erosion. The standard seed-mixes used are generally productive agricultural mixes, which will take rapidly and grow lushly and evenly. Most are based on perennial ryegrasses (such as S23, S101 and S321) and white clover: the plants are long-lived, wide-spreading and can dominate a site for years before letting other plants establish. They also grow rapidly, are responsive to fertiliser use (especially nitrogen) and are resistant to damage from grazing, trampling and mowing. Such seed-mixes are also disastrous ecologically, for they delay for many years the development of a native mixed plant community.

A 'conservation' seed-mix is one which will permit the re-establishment of native plants. To be acceptable operationally, it also has to stabilise the soil surface quickly, but other criteria are that the non-native species in the mix should be short-lived and have low competitiveness, to allow native plant species to colonise from surrounding areas, whenever possible.

Westerwold ryegrass, for example, generally behaves as an annual and gives a quick cover after sowing. If this growth is cut back and removed, this will prevent seeding of the ryegrass in the following year and also assist establishment of the sown flora.

Rye, oats and barley have also been used on riverbanks as nurse crops. As long as they are cut before their seed ripens, so that they do not persist after the first year, they provide wild plants with excellent cover in which to become established. Their seed is relatively cheap but they grow upright rather than prostrate over the soil and this may provide the bank with insufficient plant protection.

Wild-flower seeds can be mixed in with low-productivity native grasses or short-lived nurse crops (as described above) to establish a varied plant community more quickly. Several commercial firms offer wild-flower seeds, either in mixes or as separate species.

Choosing the correct species for a particular site requires practical botanical knowledge. A standard wild-flower mix for southern England would not be correct for northern England and, within a region, soil type and geology would influence seed selection. The Nature Conservancy Council, local Nature Conservation Trust or possibly the seed firm should be able to give advice. Wells, Bell and Frost (1981) provides detailed written information on the composition of seed mixes, the use of nurse crops, and the sowing and management of mixed grass and herb communities. It suggests lists of species for sowing on various soil types, with sowing rates, and these are reproduced in the table overleaf.

Because of the expense and difficulty of obtaining adequate supplies of seed from native British wild flowers, a number of commercial firms use seeds of foreign origin in their mixtures. We cannot endorse the use of such seed which often contains cultivars, strains of species unlike our native forms, or are not adapted to our local conditions. This may appear a minor point, but some of our most serious weeds are 'foreigners' closely related to British plant species, eg Japanese knotweed, Himalayan balsam and giant hogweed.

Seed firms which supply native British wild-flower and grass seed include (in alphabetical order):

British Seed Houses Ltd, Bewsey Industrial Estate, Pitt Street, Warrington, Cheshire.

J Chambers, 15 Westleigh Road, Barton Seagrave, Kettering, Northamptonshire.

Emorsgate Seeds, Emorsgate, Terrington St Clements, Norfolk.

Fothergill's Seeds, Regal Lodge, Grazely Road, Kentford, Newmarket, Suffolk.

Naturescape, St Peter's Cottage, Colston Bassett, Nottingham.

Suffolk Herbs, Sawyers Farm, Little Cornard, Sudbury, Suffolk.

Key points to the establishment of mixed native plants from seed are:
– establish a fine, firm seed-bed, free of weeds and with satisfactory drainage. This is best achieved through repeated harrowing and rolling, although the timing of these operations with respect to weather conditions is crucial.
– grass and wild-flower seeds should be thoroughly mixed before sowing. Especial care should be taken because, typically, there is a great disparity in seed sizes. The addition of small quantities of sand may ensure more even distribution.
– if there is time before sowing the seed-mix, allow undesirable tall herb species (such as docks, nettles, thistles) to germinate naturally and then kill with a specific contact herbicide (eg Razol). Without treatment they may dominate the site and set back the development of a more mixed community.
– after the seed is sown, a light raking or harrowing followed by a flat roller, will encourage rapid germination and establishment, by helping to attain good contact between seed and soil.
– fence from stock. Prevent grazing for at least a year.
– to encourage low soil fertility, do not spread imported top-soil or add fertilisers, as this will only encourage more vigorous grasses and undesirable tall herb species such as docks, thistles and nettles.
– to reduce competition from the nurse crop (if sown) and weeds, plants sown in spring and mid-summer should be cut with a rotary cutter or Allen scythe at a height of 8-10 centimetres, six to eight weeks after sowing – the precise time of cutting should be judged by the growth the weeds and/or nurse crop have made. The cut material should be raked off and disposed of. Cutting should then be continued at about two-monthly intervals (depending on soil fertility and soil conditions) until late October.
– in the second year, the grassland will probably only require cutting once or twice – the timing depending on growth.
– a low (5 centimetre) cut in April, followed by a second October cut, when most species will have set seed, should be sufficient. The cuttings can be left.

On steeper banks, hydroseeding may be a useful method of sowing seed. A mixture of seeds, bitumen (or similar binding agent) and mulch are sprayed over the soil. The bitumen holds the soil and the mulch aids seed germination. There is no reason why 'conservation' seed-mixes should not be established in this way, although a mulch without fertiliser would have to be made up. For further information, contact Hydraseeders Ltd, Coxbeach, Derby DE2 5BH.

An alternative, and possibly cheaper, way of establishing flower-rich grasslands is to spread hay cut from an unimproved meadow that is rich in flowers. The hay should be cut, by arrangement with the owner, during August or September. Before spreading, the area to be treated should either be rotovated and the hay spread over the bare ground, or the hay spread over a nurse crop (such as Westerwold rye-grass). Note that because rates of flower development are usually temperature dependent, the ideal hay cutting date varies by more than a month between different areas of the country; some species also ripen earlier than others. The seed of most species should be ripe by August/September: the Nature Conservancy Council or local Nature Conservation Trust may be able to provide specific advice for particular localities.

No examples of establishing flower-rich grasslands from seed are given here. It is an area of habitat creation which appears to have been largely neglected. The only drainage authority which attempted to use wild-flower seed mixes reported failure. Clearly, more use of the technique is required on an experimental basis to establish its relevance and value to river conservation.

Reference

Wells, T, Bell, S and Frost, A, 1981. Creating attractive grasslands using native plant species. Nature Conservancy Council.

Lists of species recommended for sowing on various soil types. From Wells, Bell and Frost (1982)

1. Seed mixtures for sowing on heavy clay soils

(a) Grass/short herb mixture

		Sowing rate (kg/ha)
Alopecurus pratensis	Meadow foxtail	5.0
Briza media	Common quaking grass	0.5
Festuca rubra 'Highlight'	Red fescue	10.0
F rubra 'Rapid'	Red fescue	8.0
Hordeum secalinum	Meadow barley	1.0
Trisetum flavescens	Yellow oat grass	1.0
Anthyllis vulneraria	Kidney vetch	3.0
Chrysanthemum leucanthemum	Ox-eye daisy	0.2
Galium verum	Lady's bedstraw	0.3
Leontodon hispidus	Rough hawkbit	0.5

Lotus corniculatus	Bird's foot trefoil	1.0
Medicago lupulina	Black medick	2.0
Plantago media	Hoary plantain	0.2
Primula veris	Cowslip	0.5
Prunella vulgaris	Self-heal	0.5
Rhinanthus minor	Hay rattle	2.0

(b) Grass/tall herb mixture

Alopecurus pratensis	Meadow foxtail	5.0
Briza media	Common quaking grass	0.5
Cynosurus cristatus	Crested dog's tail	5.0
Festuca rubra 'Cascade'	Red fescue	10.0
F rubra 'Highlight'	Red fescue	10.0
Hordeum secalinum	Meadow barley	1.0
Trisetum flavescens	Yellow oat grass	1.0
Centaurea nigra	Knapweed	1.0
C scabiosa	Great knapweed	1.0
Chrysanthemum leucanthemum	Ox-eye daisy	0.5
Daucus carota	Wild carrot	0.9
Filipendula vulgaris	Dropwort	1.0
Geranium pratense	Meadow cranesbill	2.5
Hypochoeris radicata	Common cat's ear	0.3
Lotus corniculatus	Bird's foot trefoil	1.0
Plantago lanceolata	Ribwort plantain	2.0
Poterium sanguisorba	Salad burnet	0.3
Ranunculus acris	Common meadow buttercup	1.0
Silene alba	White campion	0.5

2. Seed mixtures for sowing on chalk and other limestone soils

(a) Grass/short herb mixture

		Sowing rate (kg/ha)
Briza media	Common quaking grass	0.5
Cynosurus cristatus	Crested dog's tail	5.0
Festuca rubra 'Highlight'	Red fescue	10.0
F rubra 'Rapid'	Red fescue	8.0
Koeleria cristata	Crested hair grass	0.1
Trisetum flavescens	Yellow oat grass	1.0
Anthyllis vulneraria	Kidney vetch	3.0
Campanula glomerata	Clustered bell-flower	0.01
C rotundifolia	Harebell	0.01
Chrysanthemum leucanthemum	Ox-eye daisy	0.2
Galium verum	Lady's bedstraw	0.3
Hippocrepis comosa	Horseshoe vetch	0.1
Medicago lupulina	Black medick	2.0
Plantago media	Hoary plantain	0.2
Primula veris	Cowslip	0.5
Prunella vulgaris	Self-heal	0.5
Scabiosa columbaria	Small scabious	0.5
Thymus drucei or T pulegioides	Common or larger wild thyme	0.1
Veronica chamaedrys	Germander speedwell	0.1

(b) Grass/tall herb mixture

Bromus erectus	Upright brome	2.0
Cynosurus cristatus	Crested dog's tail	5.0
Festuca longifolia	Hard fescue	10.0
F ovina	Sheep's fescue	4.0
F rubra 'Highlight'	Red fescue	10.0
F rubra 'Rapid'	Red fescue	8.0
Centaurea nigra	Knapweed	1.0
C scabiosa	Great knapweed	1.0
Chrysanthemum leucanthemum	Ox-eye daisy	0.2
Clinopodium vulgare	Wild basil	0.1
Daucus carota	Wild carrot	0.5
Galium verum	Lady's bedstraw	0.3
Lotus corniculatus	Bird's foot trefoil	1.0

Onobrychis viciifolia	Sainfoin	3.0
Reseda lutea	Wild mignonette	0.03
R luteola	Dyer's rocket	0.01
Scabiosa columbaria	Small scabious	0.5
Tragopogon pratensis	Goat's beard	1.0

3. Seed mixtures for sowing on alluvial soils

(a) Grass/short herb mixture		*Sowing rate (kg/ha)*
Agrostis tenuis	Common bent	1.0
Alopecurus pratensis	Meadow foxtail	5.0
Briza media	Common quaking grass	0.5
Cynosurus cristatus	Crested dog's tail	5.0
Festuca rubra 'Dawson'	Red fescue	10.0
F rubra 'Cascade'	Red fescue	10.0
Poa pratensis 'Baron'	Meadow grass	3.0
Chrysanthemum leucanthemum	Ox-eye daisy	0.2
Conopodium majus	Pignut	1.0
Daucus carota	Wild carrot	0.9
Galium verum	Lady's bedstraw	0.3
Hypochoeris radicata	Common cat's ear	0.3
Lychnis flos-cuculi	Ragged robin	0.005
Medicago lupulina	Black medick	2.0
Plantago media	Hoary plantain	0.2
Poterium sanguisorba	Salad burnet	0.3
Primula veris	Cowslip	0.5
Prunella vulgaris	Self-heal	0.5
Rhinanthus minor	Hay rattle	2.0
(b) Grass/tall herb mixture		
Agrostis tenuis	Common bent	1.0
Alopecurus pratensis	Meadow foxtail	5.0
Cynosurus cristatus	Crested dog's tail	5.0
Festuca rubra 'Dawson'	Red fescue	10.0
F rubra 'Cascade'	Red fescue	10.0
Poa pratensis 'Baron'	Meadow grass	3.0
Chrysanthemum leucanthemum	Ox-eye daisy	0.2
Daucus carota	Wild carrot	0.9
Lotus corniculatus	Bird's foot trefoil	1.0
Lychnis flos-cuculi	Ragged robin	0.005
Plantago lanceolata	Ribwort plantain	2.0
Poterium sanguisorba	Salad burnet	0.3
Primula veris	Cowslip	0.5
Rhinanthus minor	Hayrattle	2.0
Sanguisorba officinalis	Great burnet	0.5
Silaum silaus	Pepper saxifrage	1.0
Silene alba	White campion	0.5

TRANSPLANTING TURF

Meadow turf can be laid to give a rapid scour-resistant surface to banksides, flood berms and floodbanks where a short 'grass' cover is wanted. It also introduces a variety of appropriate plants – and their associated invertebrates. The benefits for conservation are obvious.

In special locations – such as wild areas within a riverside park – blocks of turf with attractive species like primroses can be introduced which, if the rest of the site is managed correctly, will act as a nucleus for a colony of the plants.

If an old pasture is to be 'lost' through under-drainage and conversion to arable, a landowner may be willing to allow turf to be stripped for transplanting into appropriate sites, on floodbanks, for example, so that the plant community has a chance of survival.

If flood berms for a two-stage channel are being cut in pasture, the top layer could be cut as turf, stacked on one side and relaid on the same site once the berm has been excavated.

Before turves are cut, unless they are on drainage authority land, permission from the landowner or occupier will be required to comply with Section 13 of the Wildlife and Countryside Act 1981 (see **229**).

A survey of the cutting site should be carried out and the plants present listed, to ensure totally protected species are not present – in which case it would be illegal to remove them except under licence from the Nature Conservancy Council. The survey is also required to ensure the turves are suitable for transplanting to the intended new location. The Nature Conservancy Council or local Nature Conservation Trust should be able to help with this survey work.

Laying meadow turf on banks is easiest in damp or dry locations. The turves hold together well; they can be cut and stacked, and once relaid, mat together well. Turves of wet marsh plants, however, tend to break up and in many cases it may be easier to transplant individual plants or to use an alternative method (see section **219**).

Turf is best cut with a commercial turf-cutting machine – it is quicker, cheaper in the end, and less wasteful than trying to use shovels and spades. It can be stored for up to a month in stacks, not more than 1 metre high (or those turves at the bottom will be damaged by compaction), but must be kept moist in hot weather. Cutting and relaying can be done at any time between October and March, but is best carried out when growth is near-dormant in winter or early spring. Even if there is a dry spell, the weather is not hot enough then to dry out and scorch the roots. Fertilisers should not be applied to encourage growth – as with native seed mixtures, reduced fertility promotes a varied plant community.

If turf is only laid in patches – say to act as a nucleus of plants to colonise the rest of the site – weed growth such as docks or grasses around them must be cut back, as shade will gradually kill off delicate meadow plants. If the area around is sown with a seed mix then species should be chosen which will not creep and invade the turves: wild white clover and perennial rye-grass in particular should not be sown around meadow turf patches.

Commercial turf can be used in the same way, but is expensive, likely to have different plants in it from those found on local river banksides and be grass dominated so that wildlife conservation is not properly served.

Once turves are established they can be left unmanaged or managed as any other grassland, by mowing or grazing as required.

RIVER AVON, BARTON, WARWICKSHIRE

OS Map: 150. NGR: SP 109512

Avon Division, Severn Trent Water Authority, Finham Reclamation Works, St Martins Road, Coventry CV3 6PR.
Telephone: Coventry (0203) 415115.
Regional Architects' Department, Severn Trent Water Authority, Abelson House, 2297 Coventry Road, Sheldon, Birmingham.
Telephone: 021-743 4222.

Site Summary

Flood alleviation scheme, capital works, 1981.
Lowland, edge of village location.
Channel: a navigation
Floodbank: up to 2.5 metres high, slope 1 in 1.5 to 1 in 3.
Engineer: G Lane.
Landscape architect: J Purseglove.

Work Description

A floodbank was constructed in 1981 to protect the village of Barton. Throughout the scheme attention was given to retaining as far as possible existing river vegetation and to encouraging the new floodbank to naturalise. Thus, material for the floodbank was imported and not dredged from the river, and tall beds of emergent sedges were left untouched along the channel edge.

In a section within a small caravan park, turves were transplanted from an adjacent unimproved horse-grazed meadow to form the nucleus of a flower-rich plant community. The meadow had cowslip, ox-eye daisy, lady's bedstraw, quaking grass and scabious. Horse grazing is not ideal for that type of community, tending to make it rank, so that removal of the turves was saving plants which might otherwise have been lost. The landowner agreed to the turves being taken (figure overleaf).

Turf-cutting and laying was done by conservation volunteers, by hand, in March. The turves were relaid in a chequer-board pattern – to spread them over a wider area – on the river side of the floodbank. Two irregular patches, each about 25 metres long were laid; the rest of the area was sown with Mommersteeg International's fine grass mixture.

The floodbank is not grazed, but mown during late July or September and the grass cuttings removed. This enables the plants to flower and seed before they are cut. Cutting is essential to reduce the influence of the more competitive dominant species, so that succession to a lusher, taller plant community (which would exclude the cowslips) does not take place. Removal of mowings, by helping to reduce fertility, also helps to prevent succession. (Photograph overleaf.)

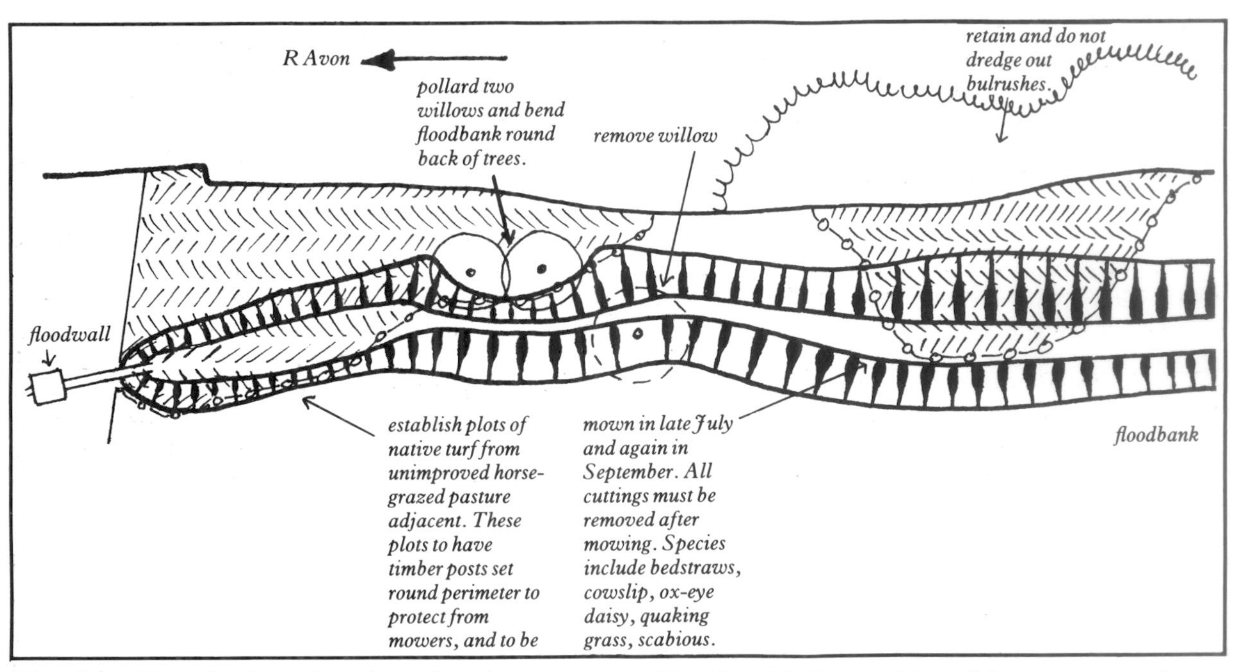

River Avon: Transplanting turf – re-drawn from the architect's drawings for the Barton Flood Alleviation Scheme, 1981. Scale about 1:500.

River Avon: A close-up of the turfed area, two years after laying, showing the proportion of herbs to grasses in this short turf.

Habitat Comments

1 Two years after the work, the bank is well covered with a mixture of short grass and herbs which are spreading into the non-turfed areas. It is not possible to distinguish the chequer-board now as the two treatments have blended, as was intended.

2 Turves provide a way of establishing a diverse plant community quickly which will support a richer insect population than newly-sown grass. The bedstraws growing in these turves, for example, are food plants for moths.

3 A regular cutting régime may be difficult to maintain using water authority labour, unless the floodbank is especially important for flood alleviation reasons. In such circumstances, it may be possible to arrange for interested local people to take over the regular management that meadow turf like this requires. The landowner or occupier may be able to undertake this work; the local Nature Conservation Trust may be able to help if not.

TECHNICAL 6: TREES AND SCRUB

Just as discharge is a major factor determining the characteristics of a river, so the presence of trees and scrub is a major factor determining the wildlife and plants of its banks. In turn, the key factor determining whether trees are on the river bank is man!

The importance of woody plants along rivers has been emphasised throughout this handbook and is summarised here:

LIVING SPACE – the bark, branches, leaves, buds and roots of trees and scrub each provide micro-habitats for many creatures which cannot inhabit a treeless site (figure below). Algae, mosses, ferns, lichens and the invertebrates which live and feed among them are examples. Many birds require trees or scrub for nesting: every type of tree cover has some bird species adapted to make use of it. Mature and old trees are amongst the most valuable 'living space' – their size and structure makes it possible for them to support a great diversity of other organisms; not least they tend to develop large holes which are used by owls, goosanders, bats and otters.
COVER – for all animals, simply so that they can move about and feed unseen by man and predators. Bramble, rose, blackthorn and hawthorn scrub and hedges are particularly useful.
SHELTER – from extremes of climate. Trees modify humidity, temperature, wind speed and sunlight. In extremes, such as the winter of 1981/82 or the summer of 1976, tree and scrub cover provides a vital refuge for wildlife. In 1976, for example, anglers reported that the only successful hatches of mayfly were in the shelter of trees. The denser the trees, the greater the shelter. In particular, dense woodland cover over a river can shelter delicate ferns, mosses, lichens and invertebrates. Opening up tree cover may destroy the balanced, sheltered climate and hence the woodland community. Particularly rich river-woodland sites containing many uncommon species are found in south-west and north-west England, and Wales.
PRODUCTIVITY – flowers, fruits, leaves, bark and roots are a direct and abundant food source for many insects, birds and mammals – and thus an indirect source for the other insects, birds and mammals that eat the first group. Trees also contribute directly to the productivity of the river system below – leaves and insects fall into the water to become the detritus on which the majority of

Trees and scrub increase habitat diversity – the living-space for wildlife.

The River Okement, North Devon.

stream organisms depend. Trout take insects floating on the surface – many of which will have dropped from trees on the river bank. Sugars wash off the leaves of trees (sycamore and lime in particular) to boost the production of plankton. Alders have nitrogen-fixing bacterial nodules on their roots, and directly improve the nutrient supply of base-poor waters.

STABILITY – mature trees and scrub, with young growth coming on to replace them, indicate that conditions have remained stable for decades, possibly centuries. This is a most valuable attribute in plant and animal communities. The trees are the longest-lived component, and within the habitats they provide, succeeding generations of other organisms are able to interact and the complex process of soil development and nutrient accumulation takes place. Sites that are stable usually have a greater variety of tree species and hence of animals and plants than new or unstable sites.

This is not to say that all rivers should be lined by trees. Surveys have shown an overall greater variety of plants, insects and birds occurs on rivers where the tree cover is interrupted by open patches which allow sunlight to reach the ground and the water, allowing light-loving wildflowers and aquatic plants to flourish.

Tree and scrub management on rivers is a major part of the revenue works programme of drainage authorities. It is assigned many names – 'pioneer tree clearance', 'uprighting', 'detimbering' and 'tree maintenance'. In addition, trees are often lopped or removed as an incidental result of weed-cutting, dredging and capital works, because they hinder machine access. The net result has been an overall decrease in the numbers of trees on river banks, and in the amount of bramble and thorn scrub. Combined with hedgerow clearance by farmers over the last 30 years, there has been a dramatic loss of wildlife cover in the countryside.

Tree cover may be of direct benefit to drainage authorities. This was recognised as early as 1954 when Johnson commented 'unfortunately some of this (tree clearance) work was done without a proper appreciation of the fact that the presence of tree growth, and the shade it gave, prevented or at least discouraged the growth of water weeds'.

All 10 water authorities have now accepted their responsibility to limit further losses, and have instructed their staff to remove as few trees as possible. Many have a good record for replanting young trees. Tree management is clearly improving in many areas – though not all – but more skills could yet be learned and more effort expended to conserve the tree cover that is left and to reinstate tree and scrub cover which will be of value to wildlife.

Landowners and occupiers, too, are becoming more aware of the value of trees, and many are now making a positive contribution towards tree management and new planting.

Improvement in the quality of tree management requires an input at all levels of drainage authority structure:

TRAINING – the chainsaw operator and his supervisor, as the people responsible for lopping, coppicing and pollarding, should be fully trained in the tree management techniques involved. Brooks, 1980a, provides an excellent practical guide. As the team in the field is the group directly responsible for carrying out the drainage body's policy on tree conservation, they should also be trained in conservation aims and methods, and be aware of its importance.

WORK SCHEDULES – trees have been removed so that excavators can work more quickly, instead of going round or between them. This is inexcusable. The work schedule should be altered so that speed is not the only criterion by which a bonus can be earned. Contracts – when work is put out to tender, management practices for tree and scrub conservation should be stipulated – and checked on as work proceeds. Penalty clauses could be included for damage to trees.

SUPERVISION – for any scheme, designers, managers and/or supervisors must walk the river bank to decide and note down the tree management that is required. Supervision and follow-up visits are then needed to check that the programme is being carried out correctly. The conservation of habitats on rivers must be promoted by supervisors as an important part of the job, worth spending time on. The 'feature mapping' suggested in the introduction to this part provides the best opportunity to start this process.

These practical steps towards tree and scrub conservation cannot be illustrated in the same way as those that follow. Many divisions are already making sure that training and supervision of direct and contract labour includes tree conservation. Such care needs to be extended to *all* work that water authorities undertake, whether revenue or capital, in remote rural or busy urban areas – trees matter in all of these situations.

The question of how frequently tree management work should be done is relevant. For the continuity of wildlife habitat 'little and often' is the best policy, but realistically this cannot be expected with current manpower limitations. As a result, restraint and tolerance must be exercised so that all the dead, leaning and overhanging branches are not taken out at one time 'just in case' they become a hazard before the next maintenance period.

Of all the natural features of a river system, its tree cover is the most vulnerable, the most fragile, the most difficult to reinstate. This may seem strange when trees are such large, solid things – surely dragonflies and water plants are more fragile? But dragonfly populations and water plants have great powers of recovery and soon reach maturity: riffles and pools, steep banks and shallows can all be created in a matter of a year or two. Replanting a tree, even of the right species in the right place, is not recreating the tree cover that was lost. That needs time, maybe a century or more, before landscape and wildlife habitat is restored. Tree planting should be seen as an *addition*, it can never be a replacement for trees lost. Hence, the rest of this section concentrates on tree conservation practices (**243-58**) and planting is a relatively minor addition at the end (**258-67**).

References mentioned in text

Brooks, A, 1980a. Woodlands. A practical conservation handbook. British Trust for Conservation Volunteers.

Johnson, E A G, 1954. Land drainage in England and Wales. Proceedings of the Institution of Civil Engineers, **3**, 601-651.

WORKING THROUGH SCRUB

'Scrub' is woody growth with multiple stems, often thorny, between 1 and 5 metres high. Bramble, rose, blackthorn, hawthorn and gorse thickets, and tangles of sallow and willow are all 'scrub'. It may be considered untidy and may be blamed by farmers for harbouring 'vermin', but it is vital for many of our commonest species – especially invertebrates, birds and mammals.

The easiest way to conserve scrub is to ignore it. Where access to the river is needed, for cutting or dredging, caterpillar-tracked vehicles can simply drive through scrub patches (Photograph below). In pasture areas, once work has ceased the patch must be temporarily fenced to prevent grazing. It should then be left to regrow – which it will do, vigorously.

Any large woody stems can be treated as small

Tracking through bramble scrub, Laugherne Brook, Worcestershire (Lower Severn Division, Severn Trent WA, 64 Albert Road North, Great Malvern, Worcestershire).

trees, that is, coppiced, and then fenced temporarily if stock is likely to have access.

If possible, the bird breeding season should be avoided (March to late July) since scrub provides some of the most valuable nesting habitat for small birds.

If hedges are over 2 metres tall and 'unkempt', they can be either laid (figure opposite), following traditional practice for the district (Brooks 1980b provides all the practical guidance required), or coppiced down to stumps, fenced and allowed to regrow once work is finished (see **249**).

If hedges have been kept trim, and are 2 metres in height or less, then machinery can simply work over the top.

When hedges have to be removed – for example where a channel is widened, or when floodbank construction cuts hedges at right angles to the river, then a mixed-species hedge should be replanted, and not a post-and-wire fence put in its place (figure opposite). Again, Brooks, 1980b, contains advice on planting and maintenance.

Reference

Brooks, A, 1980b. Hedging. A practical conservation handbook. Revised edition. British Trust for Conservation Volunteers.

Nature Conservancy Council, 1979. Hedges and shelterbelts. NCC Nature Conservation Guides Series.

Pollard, E, Hooper, M D and Moore, N W, 1974. Hedges. Collins.

HEDGES

Hedges are quite distinct from other types of woody cover, as a result of their often long history of management. Unlike thickets and scrub, an old hedge usually has a rich and varied ground-flora – violets and primroses are perhaps the most widely appreciated of 'typical' hedgerow flowers. In general, the older the hedge, the greater will be the variety of trees and shrubs represented within it.

Added to their significance for plants and wildlife, hedges have a strong historical interest, going back many centuries. They have been planted to mark county, parish or ownership boundaries, although the oldest hedges were not planted; they were simply the remains of woodland after clearance. This is why they contain such a diversity of trees, shrubs and herbs: their ground-flora is so often of woodland origin (photograph below).

For wildlife, historical and landscape reasons, hedges are important. Thousands of miles have been lost in recent years – the old county of Huntingdonshire has lost more than 90 per cent of its hedges since the early 1960s, and, at present, hedge-clearance in the West Country is causing concern. In general, hedge-removal along rivers and streams serves no good purpose, and drainage authority staff should try to conserve hedges as much as other types of bankside cover. Indeed, a positive attitude might help to influence a landowner away from grubbing out his riverside hedge – or at least not help him to do it.

Bibliography

Farming and Wildlife Advisory Group, 1983. A hedgerow code of practice. FWAG information leaflet.

A mixed hedge by Laddon Brook, Avon.

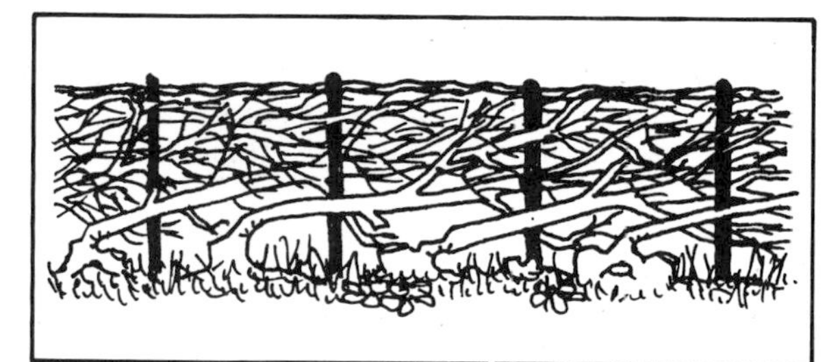

Hedge laying.

A typical hedge planting plan for the Midlands (provided by J Purseglove, Severn Trent WA).

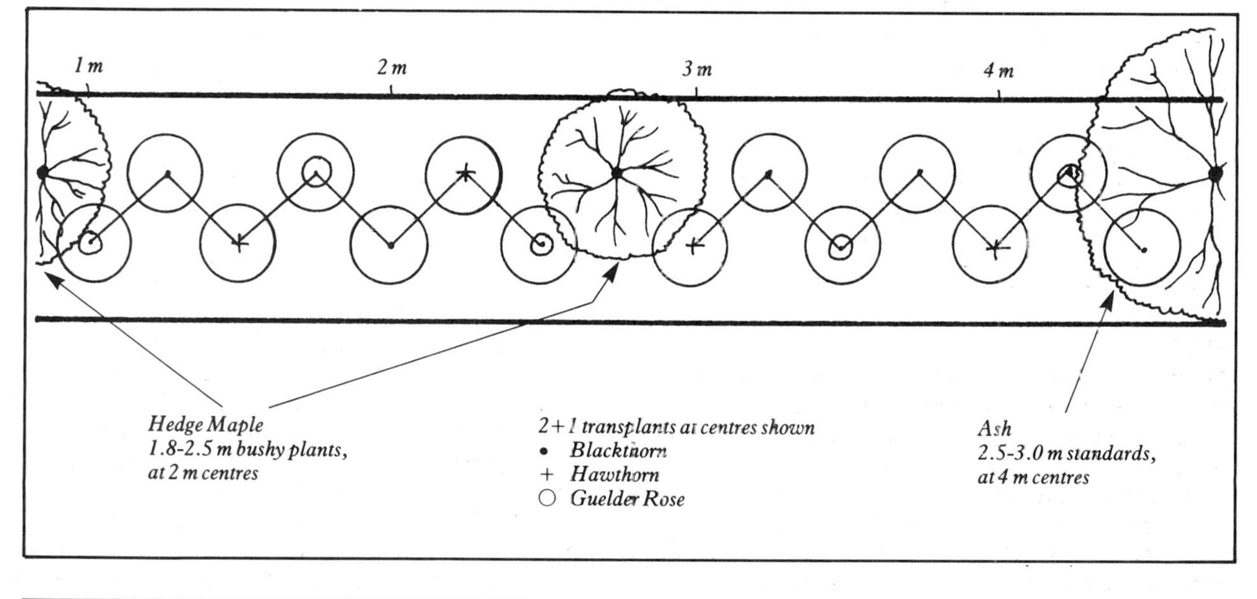

LADDON BROOK, IRON ACTON, AVON
OS MAP: 172. NGR: ST 671844
Bristol Avon Division, Wessex Water Authority, Box 95, The Ambury, Bath, Avon.
Telephone: Bath (0225) 313500.

Site Summary
Land drainage scheme, capital works, 1979.
Lowland, rural location.
Channel: 2 metres wide at low water level, depth

Laddon Brook: The hedge in the foreground and on the right was trimmed to about 1.5 metres, and the channel dredged over the top of it.

1.5 metres.
Banks: 1-1.5 metres high, 1 in 1 slope, or steeper.
Substrate: clay.

Work Description
The Brook was dredged in 1979, to increase depth by 1 metre.
As there are hedges on both sides of the channel, one side was trimmed to fence-top height, and the dredger worked from that side only, over the top, without difficulty. Trees in the hedge were retained (photograph on previous page).

Habitat Comments
1 Although the hedge over which the dredger operated is clearly more battered and disturbed than the opposite hedge (perhaps it was before anyway?) it has survived well, and provides good cover. Working over a hedge is bound to damage it slightly in some way, but recovery will be rapid.
2 Having two hedges alongside a brook is unusual, but gives an enclosure and 'separateness' to the riverine habitat which is valuable in this intensively farmed landscape. The care taken to conserve both hedges is excellent.
3 The opposite hedge – on quick examination – had a richer variety of woody plants than the one that was trimmed, and may therefore be older. The water authority here chose the most convenient side to work on, and by luck chose the botanically poorer side. If there is an operational choice, then a survey should be carried out to decide the best working bank from the wildlife viewpoint.

MARK TREES TO BE TREATED

Marking trees is frequently done during pioneer tree clearance, for operational reasons, to calculate the amount of work to be done by the labour gang. Tree marking, however, can also have an important role in nature conservation, to ensure trees are treated sympathetically and as intended. Points to consider are:
1 A code should be used to show exactly what is to be done to each tree –
'L' for lopping branches
'C' for stems to be coppiced
'P' for trunks to be pollarded
'F' for trees to be felled
– and the marks should be put on the branch to be lopped and the stems to be coppiced, so the chance of mistakes is reduced.
2 Trees that must not be disturbed in any way – perhaps because they have an otter holt in the roots, a bat colony in a hollow branch or a woodpecker nest – should be distinctively marked in a different colour. A coloured spot instead of a white letter is the best system. As these trees are likely to be old it is worth marking them as 'not to be cut down' – if there is no mark the man with the chainsaw might make his own decision thinking the supervisor has missed it!
3 Whether brush-on or spray-on paints are used, they wear off bark within a few months (even car spray-paints), so marking should be done as work proceeds or a few weeks before each reach will be worked on.
In deciding which trees are to be lopped, pollarded or coppiced, the aim should not be 100 per cent efficiency. There is no doubt that rivers densely overhung with low branches may be a flood hazard – but clearing all of them devastates wildlife habitat. Leaving 10-20 per cent significantly reduces the flood risk to the point where it is negligible, and leaves wildlife a refuge. Ideally, a rotational system of tree management should be developed so that only a small proportion are worked on at any one time.
Similarly, when considering the clearance of overmature or leaning trees to prevent them from falling into the river, remember that while a large number on a reach may well present a flood hazard, the retention of a few makes a significant difference to wildlife habitat but may pose only a negligible flood hazard.

WORKING BETWEEN OR AROUND TREES

If blocks of trees on the riverbank are not more than 20 metres across, then excavators and draglines should be able to work from either side to clear the channel in front of them.
With care, machinery can operate between trees that are 3-4 metres apart, so that they need not be felled, or a few smaller trees can be coppiced to allow access between larger trees.
Lower branches that are in the way of machinery can be lopped – that is better than losing a whole, mature tree. Proper tree surgery methods should be used – ie careful sawing so that a splinter does not rip off with the falling branch, and the wound should be sealed.
Lopping branches that are either in the way of machinery, or are dead, broken or dangerous

should be one of the most frequent operations in tree management on rivers. Coppicing, pollarding and felling are all much more drastic measures and consequently should be needed less often (photograph right). Lopping can be dangerous, especially when a chainsaw is used for high branches. It is essential for safety that men who do this work are trained and equipped properly and that the correct number of people work as a team. In one instance, a mature tree with a high overhanging dead branch was felled, rather than the one branch being lopped, because the gang of men assigned to detimbering work did not have anyone properly trained to use a chainsaw off the ground. The proper training of men assigned to tree management is as important for the conservation of trees as it is for the safety of the men.

Finally, working round trees, to preserve them, may slow down weed cutting or dredging work – if this is the case, this should be taken account of in the preparation of bonus schemes and work programmes, so that operators are not tempted to 'cut corners'. Trees on river banks are too important to be lost for short-term gain.

In addition to the two schemes described here, see **102**, Treddington-on-Stour (STWA), **141**, River Alne (STWA) and **200**, Sandwell Valley (STWA).

An oak branch ripped off during maintenance work. It should have been lopped before work started, if it was essential to get that close to the tree.

UPPER LUGG, LEOMINSTER, HEREFORDSHIRE
OS Map: 149. NGR: SO 450620-480607
Wye Division, Welsh Water Authority,
St Nicholas House, St Nicholas Street,
Hereford HR4 0BB.
Telephone: Hereford (0432) 57411.

Site Summary
Flood alleviation scheme, capital works, 1980/81.
Upland/lowland transition zone, rural location.
Channel: 10-12 metres wide, 1-2 metres deep.
Banks: variable height and gradient.
Substrate: alluvial and glacial sands, clay, gravel.
Engineer: R Vivash.

Work Description
The plans for a capital flood alleviation scheme in 1980/81 (described in more detail on **75**) stated 'as many trees as possible to be left', and the resultant hydraulic inefficiencies were accommodated in the scheme design. The channel was deepened, in some places widened, large stone weirs were built, floodbanks were constructed and for two summers according to its designer 'the place looked like a motorway'. Despite this a large percentage of mature tree cover remains:

A Mature alders were retained on the bank top, though draglines and excavators worked between them. Some work was completed by machines working within the channel (photograph overleaf).
B Willow scrub and poplars were retained, although well within the flood channel.
C A wet alder copse was fenced off and retained untouched.
D Ancient pollard oaks were retained within the floodbanks.
E Hedge lines were replanted on the new floodbanks, to replace sections of old hedge lost in construction.
F No tree planting has had to be done to 'replace' lost tree cover; the only planting has been of willow stumps and stakes for bank protection (**168**).

Habitat Comments
1 The amount of mature tree cover on the banks is quite striking, and prevents the scheme having the 'raw', bare look of so many rivers after major work.

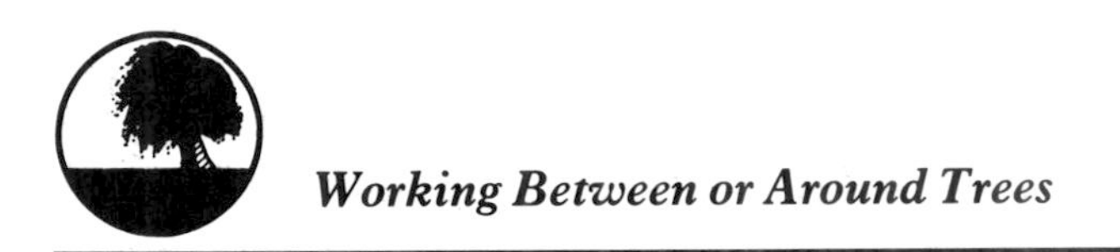

A great variety of types of tree cover has been retained, and wildlife must benefit from this.

2 Under the alders (see photograph on right) the bramble scrub and rough grass that might be expected to have been lost will, given time, regenerate from roots and fragments. The important aspect is that the trees, which are the major structural element of the habitat and the hardest to replace, remain.

3 There are very few scrub patches or tree branches overhanging the water, as cover for moorhen, coot or otters, but this may develop from the woody growth left on the banks. Meanwhile the willow scrub, wet alder woodland and 'reed' beds left in wider parts of the channel act as a refuge.

River Lugg: Excavators worked between these mature alders to dredge the channel beyond.

MEECE BROOK, NORTON BRIDGE, STAFFORDSHIRE

OS Map: 127. NGR: SJ 868306

Upper Trent Division, Severn Trent Water Authority, Trinity Square, Horninglow Street, Burton-on-Trent DE14 1BL.
Telephone: Burton-on-Trent (0283) 44511.
Regional Architects' Department, Severn Trent Water Authority, Abelson House, 2297 Coventry Road, Sheldon, Birmingham.
Telephone: 021-743 4222

Site Summary

Land drainage scheme, capital works, 1981.
Lowland, rural location.
Channel: 3 to 4 metres wide, depth variable.
Banks: now about 2 metres high; irregular slopes.
Substrate: gravel, clay, sandy alluvium.
Engineers: S Powers, D Pinnegar.
Landscape Architect: M Ericson.

Work Description

The Meece Brook is a small attractive river, which was lowered and regraded in 1981, to improve local land drainage. With advice from the Regional Architects' department, care was taken throughout

Meece Brook: A mature alder, before trimming, May 1981.

the scheme to conserve as many of the natural features as possible.

Dredging was carried out from one side, changing sides as necessary to avoid damaging habitat features. Although the trees are scattered along the river, one or two were in the way of the excavator's access to the river. These were mature, single-stemmed alders. The lower branches were trimmed off, up to about 3 metres above the ground, and they need no other treatment (photographs on left).

Habitat Comments

1 Trimming lower branches has allowed river work to proceed as planned, but with the retention of trees – an excellent compromise.

2 An alternative to trimming would have been to coppice the tree – alders regrow easily from coppice (see below). Care would then have been needed to ensure the stool was not damaged by machinery running over it, and it would have had to be securely fenced to prevent stock grazing the coppice shoots.

Meece Brook: The same alder with lower branches lopped, August 1982. Note the new side shoots sprouting from each cut.

COPPICING

Coppicing is a traditional method of managing trees so that the stump (known as the stool) and roots remain alive and provide a basis for periodic harvesting of the stems that grow from the stool. The principle of coppicing is based on the naturally vigorous regrowth produced from cut stumps of most broad-leaved trees.

In the past, many riverside trees were managed in this way. Alders were grown for clogs and firewood, willows for basket-making and ash for firewood, poles and small tools. It was the decline of such management by landowners that meant that by the 1930s, many rivers were liable to flooding as a result of blockages from fallen over-mature trees. If landowners could be persuaded to look after and harvest their own trees on proper coppice-cycles again, many river management and conservation problems would be solved.

Coppicing. Alder, willow, poplars, birch and ash coppice easily. Oak, elm, beech, chestnuts and sycamore require a little more care.

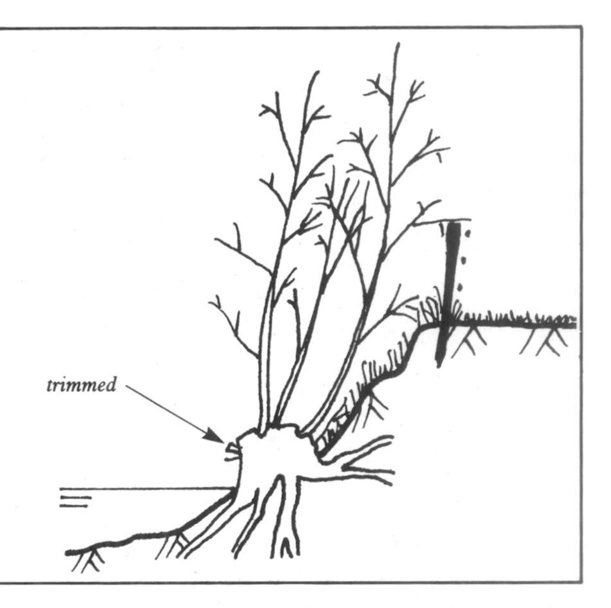

The need for fencing. Browsing restricts the growth of vertical shoots, so outward curving shoots become the main growth, perhaps causing instability in later years. Fenced from browsing, the main growth is upright.

Coppicing is simple, but does require some skill. Brooks, 1980a, provides clear instructions on tools and methods. Large trees can be coppiced with a chainsaw; a billhook is suitable for smaller stems, say less than 10 cm diameter. The tree – single or multiple stemmed – is cut just above ground level, or at the top of the old stool if it has been coppiced before. The cut faces should be inclined slightly, to shed water so that the stool does not rot (figure on **249**). Coppicing is a winter job, and should not be done when there are leaves on the tree, or it may die.

Secure fencing is vital to ensure that the cut stools regrow to form trees, otherwise cattle, sheep and horses will eagerly eat every shoot that appears. Fencing should be at least 1½ metres from the stool to prevent animals reaching the shoots. When the new tree is above browse height (two to three years for willows, five to ten years for other species) the fencing can be removed.

Fencing may also be needed to prevent young trees growing outwards from the bank and becoming obstructions in the future. When animals are allowed to browse the tops off the shoots which are growing inwards from a stool at the water's edge, the shoots growing away from the bank will become the major trunk. Fencing the banktop next to the young tree, and trimming the outward growing shoots, will allow a vertical bole to develop (figure above).

Coppicing for riverside tree management

i Where trunks and stems curve out from the base over the river and present an unacceptable hazard, they can be cut away, leaving only the upright stems; these will make a spurt of growth, and new shoots will grow from the cut bases. Such partial coppicing may shift the tree's centre of gravity, making the tree unstable, especially if the roots are undercut; to compensate, therefore, heavy branches leaning away from the river may also have to be cut.

ii Trees that have been coppiced and then allowed to grow large are liable to split at the base, so that the entire stem falls. Crack willows in particular get into this state. Re-coppicing ensures that trees do not *become* dangerous, and prolongs their life. Once split and fallen, wood rots invade, eventually resulting in the death of the tree.

iii Willows and sallows planted for bank protection grow rapidly and should be coppiced on a 6-12 year cycle, whenever they get so tall and bushy that they would impede flow (see **158, 165, 166**).

iv On wider rivers (say more than 10 metres wide), the bushy regrowth from coppiced alders and willows provides useful bank protection: coppicing on a short cycle of three to six years keeps the trees as bushes, and encourages root growth which also binds and protects the bank (see on **154, 158, 165, 166**).

Coppicing is already practised by water authorities for river management, in more or less skilful or deliberate ways. The following examples simply illustrate the response of alders to coppicing.

On the River Okement, South West Water Authority carried out tree clearance work for the first time in 1982. In narrow gorge-like sections, trees below flood level were coppiced. In wider sections (as shown in photograph on **251**), only the trunks leaning out into the channel were cut (partial coppicing). These alders were partially cut about four months before the photograph was taken; regrowth from the cut stems has been very rapid. The mass of young shoots will deflect high flows away from the mature trunks and protect the bank somewhat. These shoots will not be coppiced again for at least

20 years – and should be fully grown trees within 10 years.

In the times of horse-drawn barge traffic on the Severn, tree growth was kept constantly short by coppicing. Although tow ropes are not used now, the riverside trees are still periodically coppiced, to maintain a close, vigorous bank-protecting cover which will not be a flood hazard in high flows. For the most part, the trees are a mixture of alder, willows and ash (photograph below). Maintenance is on a 10-15 year cycle.

River Okement. Coppicing.

The River Severn, upstream of Tewkesbury.

Habitat Comments

1 The technique of coppicing and partial coppicing helps to maintain trees on river banks, and can be regarded as good conservation practice.

2 Coppicing does still cause a drastic reduction in tree cover, even if only temporarily. Coppicing all the trees along a stretch at one time would cause severe disturbance. As with all other clearance methods, some patches should be left untouched to provide a refuge and cover for wildlife until conditions have returned to normal.

3 Coppicing short stretches of riverbank at one time will benefit ground flora for a season or two. Many woodland plants are adapted to survive without flowering when shade is dense and will come into bloom if the canopy is opened up. Primroses, wood anemones, bluebells and other flowers may be a reward for the rejuvenation of old coppice.

River Teme at Leintwardine: Pollard crack willow.

POLLARDING

In pollarding the tree is cut 2 metres or more above the ground and so develops a crown from which branches grow (photographs above), to be cropped repeatedly when they reach the required size.

Pollarding was generally used to produce larger timbers than coppicing but poles grown from pollards can also be harvested for small timber or firewood. Withies and rods from the various pollarded or coppiced basket willows are a specialised product. The period between repollarding depends on the type of tree, and the product wanted – if any. Willows can be harvested annually for withies, every three to five years for rods, or every 15-20 years as longs (for enclosed wood stoves). Ash might be cut every 10-20 years for firewood or poles. Repeated pollarding seems to increase the lifespan of the tree – the rejuvenated crown may be relatively young, but the boll (that is, the trunk) and roots could be centuries older. For this latter reason, pollards are often of historical importance.

Since the crown of the pollard is above the reach of browsing animals, it does not have to be fenced while the regrowth gets away – hence the abundance of pollards along rivers with grazing meadows beside them. Although typical of Somerset and the Midlands, they are found in nearly all English counties. The distinctive shape of pollards and their longevity meant that they were often grown as boundary markers.

For wildlife, pollards are a unique habitat. The crown of mature pollards accumulate leaf litter, a soil develops and other plants grow in them – bramble, honeysuckle, rose and hawthorn. For a wide variety of animals, old pollard crowns provide breeding and resting places. Owls frequently use holes in rotten pollard willows; mallard may nest in the crowns, or foxes lie up during the day. Willows, in particular, are pollarded. Alder is almost never pollarded – always coppiced. Ash, elm and oak are other frequently pollarded trees.

Repollarding: to repollard trees that have been pollarded before, the stems are simply cut as close to the callus as possible, and the crown cleaned of debris to discourage rot. Because the cutting has to be done by a man standing on a ladder or in the crown, only an adequately trained and equipped team should do the work. A contractor in the Midlands quoted various prices (1982, excluding VAT) for repollarding 13 large and four small old

willows, from £136 for simply pollarding and leaving all trimmings for disposal by others, to £368 for pollarding, burning brashings and cutting poles into logs left on one site. As he also quoted £217 for pollarding, burning brashings and then taking poles away for his own disposal, the poles were clearly worth at least £151 to him – more than the basic cost of pollarding.

For wildlife conservation there is a difficulty – the older a pollard the more valuable it becomes, as more animals and plants inhabit it. At some point, however, the crown must be repollarded, or it will split the boll with its weight, rot may get in and eventually kill it – although willow pollards are amazingly resilient to damage and can shoot new growth when the boll is no more than a hollow shell. Each tree should be judged on its merits – repollarding every 20-40 years should balance the tree's safety and development of the rich crown community.

Leaning pollards should never be half trimmed. This is likely to unbalance them and encourage splitting of the bole: the whole crown should be repollarded at one time.

Pollarding: trees that have not been pollarded before can be done by cutting horizontally at the required height – usually 3-5 metres. New pollards are best started when the stem is 10-15 centimetres in diameter: although pollarding can be successfuly carried out on trees with trunks up to 30 centimetres in diameter, this is a job for experienced workers. Assuming the tree is not to be fenced, the height at which the pollard is to be started will depend on the stock kept, if any – 2.1 metres plus will be required for cattle, 3 metres plus for horses.

On banks, especially below flood level, pollarded trees may be preferred to multi-stemmed coppice as they collect less trash – although water swirling round the boll may scour the bank behind. Pollarding may also prevent a top-heavy crown from developing, which could destabilise the tree – but once pollarded, repollarding must be carried out regularly.

RIVER STOUR, TREDDINGTON-ON-STOUR, WORCESTERSHIRE

OS Map: 151. NGR: SP 260434

Avon Division, Severn Trent Water Authority, Finham Reclamation Works, St Martins Road, Finham, Coventry.
Telephone: Coventry (0203) 415115.
Regional Architects' Department, Severn Trent Water Authority, Abelson House, 2297 Coventry Road, Sheldon, Birmingham.
Telephone: 021-743 4222.

Site Summary

Maintenance dredging, 1981.
Lowland, rural village-edge location.
Channel: 3-5 metres wide.
Banks: 2-3 metres high, batter 1 in 2, variable.
Substrate: clay and gravel.
Tree: crack willows.
Engineers: D Alcott and W Garrad.
Landscape Architects: J Purseglove and M Ericson.

Work Description

The programme for maintenance dredging of the Stour in 1981 included provision for tree maintenance and tree planting. With the advice from the landscape architects a number of overmature pollard willows on the bank top were repollarded at the same time as the area around was planted up (photograph right) (see also **262**).

Pollarding was carried out by a contractor. The costs fell within the 1.5 per cent of the whole scheme costs assigned to the landscaping budget (including tree planting and fencing).

River Stour: The line of pollard willows, with two seasons' growth in the crown. The bankside – left rough – has been planted with mixed native species of trees and scrub.

Habitat Comments

1 Repollarding these willows ensures that they continue both as wildlife habitat and landscape features, which is preferable to leaving them to decay to the point where they become dangerous and have to be removed.

2 Along the Stour valley, pollarded willows are a characteristic feature, and they are – or have been until recently – maintained by owners. Few other areas are so fortunate. As the water authority would have to clear them if they decayed to become potential flood hazards, it makes sense for the water authority to take steps to maintain them – or else to persuade landowners to maintain them by harvesting poles and firewood from them once more.

LONGDON BROOK, MARSH END, WORCESTERSHIRE
OS Map: 150. NGR: SO 825355
Lower Severn Division, Severn Trent Water Authority, 64 Albert Road North, Great Malvern, Worcestershire.
Telephone: Malvern (06845) 61511.

Site Summary

Maintenance work, 1981.
Lowland/fenland, rural location.
Channel: 1.5 metres wide at low water level, shallow.
Banks: 2 metres high, graded 1 in 1.5
Substrate: clay.
Adjacent land-use: arable on bank with pollards (the left bank in photographs below and right), pasture on the other.
Area Engineer: D Shuker.

Work Description

Main drainage channels in this area are frequently lined on one side with pollard willows of varying age. During maintenance dredging of the Brook in early 1981 the willows along a 200 yard stretch were uniformly repollarded (photograph below). Within two years there was a dense regrowth on all the trees (photograph right). Adjacent willows pollarded just before the severe cold of winter 1981/82 have regrown very patchily.

The pollards are close spaced, with crowns at 2-3 metres above the ground. All the work was carried out by direct labour.

Longdon Brook: Pollarding in progress in early 1981.

Habitat Comments

1 Pollard willows make an important contribution to the landscape quality of open, flat areas such as Longdon Marsh. They also support an abundance of insects and provide many birds with nest sites.

2 Pollarding has ensured that the willows are maintained at this site, preventing them from becoming decrepit to the point where they might present a flood hazard beside the Brook, and so have to be removed.

3 In these 'traditional' willow areas, local hybrids may have survived. Poles and whips taken from the pollards can be used to propagate willows elsewhere in the locality, for various river management purposes. This will help to ensure the survival of local varieties, rather than importing standard varieties from nurseries.

Longdon Brook: The same pollards at the end of two summers' growth.

MYTHE POOLS, RIVER SEVERN, TEWKESBURY, GLOUCESTERSHIRE
OS Map: 150. NGR: SO 882346
Lower Severn Division, Severn Trent Water Authority, 64 Albert Road North, Great Malvern, Worcesteshire.
Telephone: Malvern (06845) 61511.

Site Summary
Flood bank maintenance, 1981.
Lowland, rural location.
Tree: native black poplar.
Area Engineer: D Shuker.

Work Description
Work is being carried out over five years to raise the flood banks of the Severn. At Mythe Pools, clay was dredged out of old clay pits, left to dewater for a year, and then used to raise the adjacent banks. (Incidentally, this also improved wildlife habitat and angling on the claypits – clay was dredged so that shallow water was left for reedbeds to grow as isolated islands in the middle of the pit, and the sludge was left to dewater just above the pit's edge, producing a soft, marshy margin where waders could feed in winter.)
Throughout the work, care was taken to disturb tree cover as little as possible: excavators worked over the top of bankside scrub and small trees. Native black poplars growing on the floodbank which were old and leaning were retained by new pollarding. They were pollarded at about 3 metres above ground level. Native black poplar is closely related to willows and responds to pollarding in the same way. Two years later, the trees are regrowing well (photograph right).

River Severn: Native black poplar, a year after being pollarded, starting to sprout profusely. As it matures the branches will be self-thinning, but the tree will grow a rounded bushy crown, similar to a pollard willow.

Habitat Comments

1 Native black poplar is now a very rare tree, and worth conserving wherever it grows. It has a natural habit of leaning when full grown, although this does not necessarily mean that it is unstable. In this situation it obviously was a risk to the floodbank, and pollarding it is an excellent step towards conserving the tree, yet reducing the risk of it toppling.

2 When pollarding a native black poplar it is worth taking poles and two-year-old branches to plant (just as willows – see **265**) in suitable river and ditchside sites in the same locality, to propagate this rare tree.

RETAINING TREES WITHIN FLOODBANKS

Many designers and river managers have demonstrated that it is feasible to retain trees *within* embanked channels (see, for example, **72**, **74** and **75**), even winding an embankment between the trees so as to cut down as few as possible. If a realistic assumption of the roughness coefficient of the trees within the banks is used in design calculations, and the trees are subsequently well maintained, there is no reason for them to be a hazard. Because of the extra cost of constructing sinuous banks between trees, this has, on the whole, only been carried out in parks, gardens or large estates where individual trees and the landscape details are especially important. In rural areas, siting floodbanks well back from the river provides a more feasible solution (eg the Upper Lugg, **75**).

Trees located in the actual path of floodbank construction or channel excavation are usually lost. The two following examples demonstrate how they might be preserved. The trees have been retained for their landscape value but, as a remnant of the former plant community which has been almost totally obliterated, the trees are also a refuge for at least some wild plants and invertebrates, and their conservation will help to start the recolonisation of disturbed areas. They would be better wildlife and plant refuges if a few square metres of natural scrub or grassland were left around the bases.

SPITTLE BROOK, WOOLSTON PARK, WARRINGTON

OS Map: 109. NGR: SJ 636895

Rivers Division, North West Water Authority, Box 12, New Town House, Buttermarket Street, Warrington WA1 2QG.

Telephone: Warrington (0925) 53999.

Site Summary

Flood alleviation scheme, capital works, mid-1970s.

Lowland, urban location.

Channel: 2 metres wide at low water level, shallow.

Banks: 3 metres high, slopes variable, 1 in 2 at this location.

Substrate: sand and clay.

Work Description

The Brook was widened and embanked for urban flood alleviation, at the same time as the narrow riverside park was landscaped, during the mid-1970's (see **208**, and **261** for other details of the work).

The channel before work was done was narrow and steep-sided, with coarse grass, tree and scrub cover in patches along the banks. In the scheme, the banks were excavated to varying angles, and the bed lowered, so that all original plant cover was lost. However, two trees on the bankside were conserved even though they were within the excavated area.

Tanalised stakes were driven in side by side, 2 to 3 metres from the trees' bases to support the soil around the roots. The slope was then excavated around and below the trees. Heavy gauge wire was bound around the stake 'palisade', strained and the ends buried securely in the bank behind (figures below and right; photograph on right).

Habitat Comments

1 The two trees maintained here give 'maturity' to the landscape and the habitat, while new tree planting was becoming established, and provide food sources for insect and berry-eating birds in the meantime. The patch preserved may have acted as a refuge for invertebrates, which then spread out to

Spittle Brook: Retention of a sycamore and hawthorn.

Spittle Brook: Retention of a sycamore and hawthorn, a sectional view.

recolonise the disturbed areas – but a 'refuge' as small as this is probably insignificant.

2 The channel works have resulted in the trees being distanced from the brook, and cannot contribute cover or shelter to the river's wildlife.

3 That said, the scheme does demonstrate a practical method of retaining trees within the river channel.

A sycamore and a hawthorn retained below the bank top of Spittle Brook, Woolston Park.

RIVER AVON, BARTON, WARWICKSHIRE

OS Map: 150. NGR: SP 109512

Avon Division, Severn Trent Water Authority, Finham Reclamation Works, St Martin's Road, Finham, Coventry CU3 6PR.
Telephone: Coventry (0203) 415115.
Regional Architects' Department, Severn Trent Water Authority, Abelson House, 2297 Coventry Road, Sheldon, Birmingham.
Telephone: 021-743 4222.

Site Summary

Flood alleviation scheme, capital works, 1981.
Lowland, edge of village location.
Channel: a navigation.
Flood bank: Up to 2.5 metres high, slope 1 in 1.5 to 1 in 3.
Engineer: G Lane.
Landscape architect: J Purseglove.

Work Description

A floodbank was constructed in 1981 to protect the hamlet of Barton (see **239** for other aspects of the

scheme). The embankment had to be built close to the river bank, and a number of willows and other trees had to be felled. However, because of the village situation, every effort was made to retain as many trees as possible, by slightly altering the embankment's line, or width.

A large ash tree growing about 1 metre within the planned path of the embankment has been conserved by creating an alcove in the bank slope around it. The walls of the alcove are steep, 1 in 1 or less, and this potential weakness in the embankment was protected by drystone revetment (figure right; and photograph below).

Habitat Comments

1 Saving any mature tree is worthwhile, especially a native such as this ash. The retention of this tree, whilst making only a small contribution to wildlife and landscape in itself, is part of a scheme in which many other natural features were retained, and new features created.

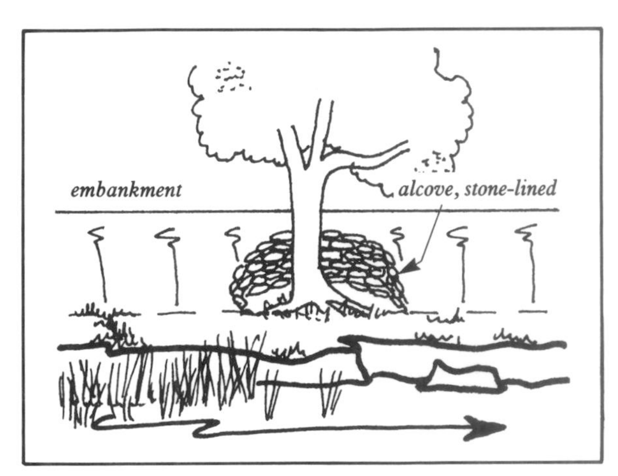

River Avon: 'Alcove' for retaining an ash tree.

River Avon: The ash tree on the river side of the flood embankment, now in an 'alcove' with the sides protected with stone revetment.

TREE AND SCRUB PLANTING

Because reinstating tree and scrub cover is such a long process, replanting must always be a secondary option to conserving the existing woody vegetation. However, apart from replacing trees unavoidably lost during capital or maintenance works, the following might be reasons for planting, by the water authority or landowners:

- for shade, to reduce weed growth (**214**).
- for bank protection (**154, 158, 165, 166**).
- to improve the landscape, or screen buildings.
- as shelter for stock or a windbreak for crops.
- for timber and firewood.
- as cover for wildlife and game.
- to improve existing derelict or species-poor woodland.

Co-operation between the landowner and water authority is necessary in tree planting (as in all other river management work). As the trees will become the landowner's property, it may be possible to persuade him that it is in his own interests to maintain the planting – and even contribute to planting costs! – and of course to play a part in deciding the species of tree to be planted and where. The local Farming and Wildlife Advisory Group (FWAG) may be able to help. Grant-aid may be available for material costs from the Ministry of Agriculture, the Countryside Commission, the local authority or the Forestry Commission for various types of planting, from shelter belts to amenity planting and small woods.

Tree and scrub planting will almost always be a benefit to wildlife, provided that the majority of trees planted are native species. However, treeless sites already valuable for nature conservation, and where trees would irrevocably change the habitat, *should never* be planted up. These might be: existing wetlands, unimproved chalk grassland, unimproved meadowland, rivers with rich and varied plant and insect life. The Nature Conservancy Council or local Nature Conservation Trust will be able to advise, in case of doubt.

The choice of what to plant and where to plant depends on the purpose of the scheme and local soil conditions. Many publications give detailed advice on this and planting techniques (see bibliography at end of this section). The following is a general guide for planting beside rivers:

i In general, plant native trees and shrubs, even in urban settings. These support far more native butterflies, moths, other insects, and birds, and blend in more easily with the natural landscape.

ii In your choice of species, be guided first by the trees and shrubs already growing nearby – but there is no harm in adding other species which might be expected to occur naturally in that area and habitat type, especially if they offer some particular benefit – berry-bearers such as guelder rose or bird cherry, for example.

iii In general, plant mixtures of trees and shrubs, to create 'semi-natural' woodland with tall trees and understorey (but see exceptions, below).

iv Clumps and clusters of woody cover are more useful to wildlife than long, narrow lines of trees. Even where a line of trees is planted for shade or shelter, take the opportunity to 'thicken up' the planting in field corners, next to hedges, or on the inside of meander loops. Also leave gaps of, say, 20 metres in every 200 metres to allow a patch of aquatic plants to develop in summer (figure below).

Tree planting for shade.

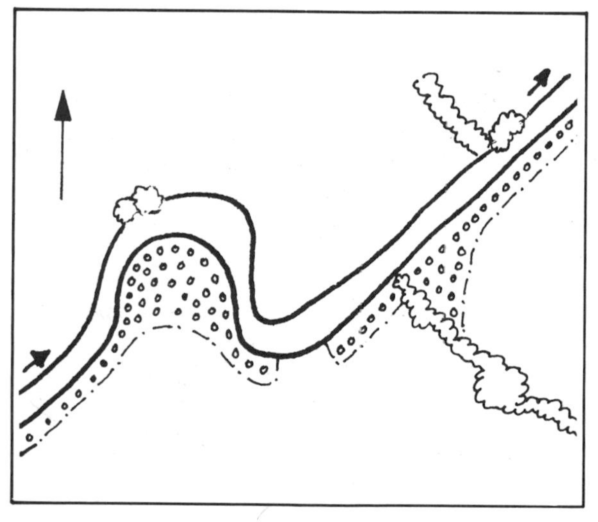

Although tree and scrub planting is simple, care is needed to keep down costs *and* to achieve a good success-rate. The most common avoidable causes of failure are listed below.

i Poor planting technique – roots not spread out carefully, soil not firmed hard enough so that frost and/or drought is able to get to the roots and wind battering is able to loosen them.

ii Inadequate fencing – so sheep, cattle or horses are able to get through fencing, or can lean over the top to eat the young trees. Fencing may collapse after collecting trash in floods. Netting must be used where there are sheep, and a 1.5-2 metre space left between the fence and nearest shrub where there are cattle or horses. Beside steep banks, the fence-end, illustrated in figure below, will keep out most stock and collect trash less frequently.

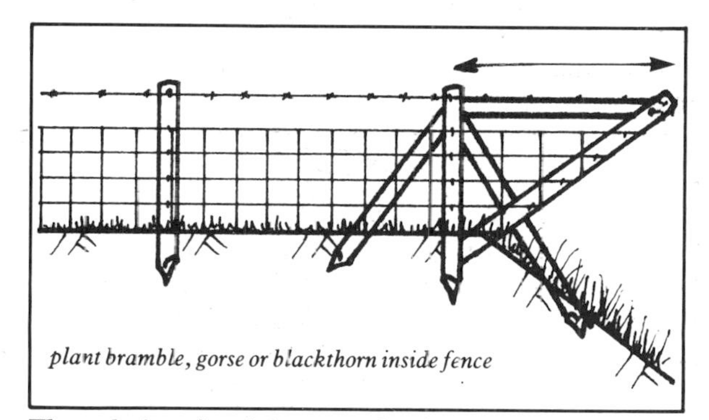

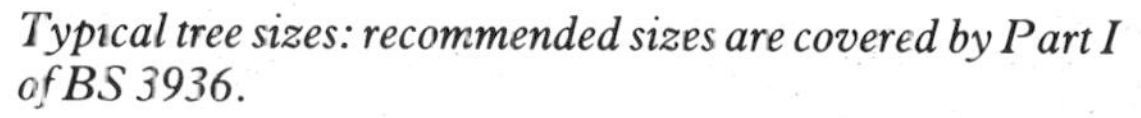
The exclusion of stock from tree planting areas.

iii Inadequate maintenance – tall grass and weeds can kill young trees by shading and root competition. Annual weed slashing or spraying around young trees is essential in mid to late summer for the first 3 to 5 years.

Typical tree sizes: recommended sizes are covered by Part I of BS 3936.

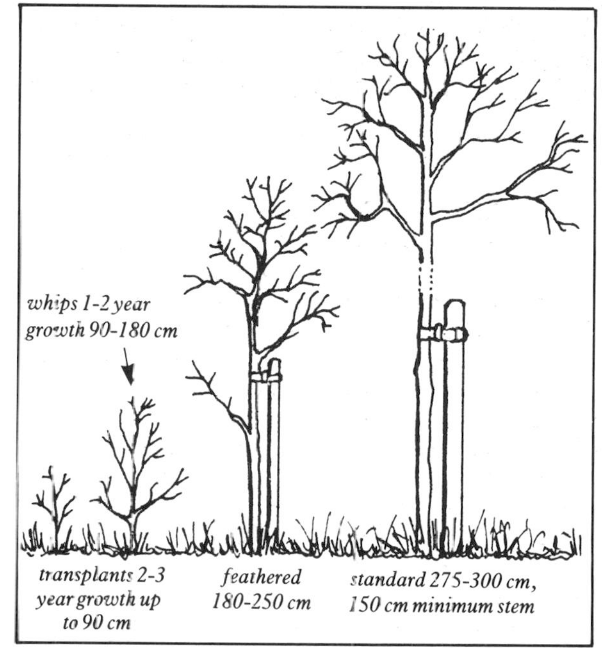

iv Poor planting stock – avoid job-lots of sickly transplants; take care not to damage stock during transit and do not let the roots dry out between delivery and planting. Always order well in advance (three months or more) from a reputable local nursery if the stock is being purchased; plant as soon as possible, or heel into a trench if planting has to be delayed.
v Natural predators – use hare guards or rabbit netting to prevent damage. Little can be done about damage by voles, or human vandals.
The following specific suggestions may be useful in planning different types of tree planting:
Willow and sallow – the surest method of getting 'instant trees', with shoots growing up to 2 metres in the first year. For bank protection, willow and sallow can be very easily planted as short stakes (see **158** and **165**) at the water's edge or on the bank, at 2-3 m centres and maintained as bushy coppice. Willows are excellent for insects and birds, even when planted alone. Mixtures of different types of willow are attractive from the landscape viewpoint: osier, goat willow, and bay-leafed willow, of which there are many local variants, have colourful young shoots, and some are rare and worth conserving in their own right.
For shade, landscape and wildlife, or firewood, crack willow or white willow can be planted as long stakes, at 8-10 metres centres and maintained as pollards, on the banktop.
Alder – for bank protection and/or shade, alders can be planted in lines and clusters along the bank. One to two years transplants at ½ metre centres in a single line, 1-metre centres in a double line, from 0.5-1.5 metres above low water level are recommended to give very dense shade. Planting at 3 metre centres, and later thinning to 6 metre centres gives a light shade, and more natural landscape. Alders are excellent 'habitat improvers' for aquatic and terrestrial wildlife, even when planted alone. In large planting schemes, other trees can occasionally be planted for variety – *eg* ash, sycamore, native poplars, birch or field maple.
Native poplars – aspen, white, grey and black poplar are all very beautiful trees that deserve more widespread planting. They are the food plants of many insects, thrive in damp places, grow rapidly and propagate easily. *They should not be confused with hybrid poplars, which are planted for pulpwood.* Best planted amongst mixtures of other tall trees, eg oak and ash, or in single-species clusters. Black poplar does not throw suckers, but the other species do, which may present problems in some circumstances.
Semi-natural group planting – mixtures of two or three tall tree species, planted with three or four smaller tree or shrub species, in the ratio of about 1 to 3. The species mix depends on site conditions and locality, for example –
alkaline clay: ash and oak, with hazel, field maple, guelder rose and wayfarer's tree;
more acidic clays: oak and small-leaved lime, with hazel, crab-apple and Midland hawthorn;
dry sandy soil: oak and beech, with holly, birch and hazel;
upland rivers: oak and ash, with rowan, bird cherry, birch, holly and hazel.
Scrub – either planted alone, or to form the edge of a tree planted area. Usually only one or two species are planted together, with occasional others on the edge for variety. Again, the mix depends on local conditions; for example –
dry, acidic soils: gorse with birch;
damp clays: buckthorn or alder buckthorn, with sallows;
limey soils: hawthorn, dog-rose, guelder rose and spindle tree;
almost anywhere: hawthorn and blackthorn, with a few ash or oak, or bramble and dog-rose.
When planting trees or scrub along rivers, it is important to have some trees very close to the water – otherwise their contribution to the river's wildlife is negligible. Low branches over the water provide perches for kingfisher, they shelter coot and moorhen, shade fish pools, and from them drop insects and leaves, which becomes food for fish and invertebrates. Roots exposed by scour may form holts for otter, and provide shelter for other mammals. Obviously, not all watercourses could enjoy the benefits to wildlife of this type of planting. However, where realistic allowances are made in designs for the roughness of trees or shrubs below flood level, and the extra land-take is seen as essential for the functioning of the *whole* watercourse, not just the passage of water, then new tree planting can take place. On existing watercourses, a revolution in outlook will be needed – on the part of drainage authorities and landowners – before tree planting can begin to restore the wildlife cover that once existed on rivers and has been lost in recent years.

Recommended information on tree planting
Beckett, K and Beckett, G, 1979. Planting native trees and shrubs. Jarrold. (Well illustrated guide with photographs and maps of distribution, site guide, and lists of suppliers.)
Brooks, A, 1980. Woodlands. A practical conservation handbook. British Trust for Conservation Volunteers. (An excellent guide to the choice of trees, planting methods, aftercare and tree management.)
Carter, E, 1982. A guide to planting trees and shrubs for wildlife and the landscape. Farming and Wildlife Advisory Group.
Countryside Commission. Countryside conservation handbook. Countryside Commission, jointly with the Forestry Commission, Ministry of Agriculture, Fisheries and Food and Nature Conservancy Council. Including:

Leaflet 1: A guide to grant-aid and other assistance for farmers and landowners in England and Wales (1979).
Leaflet 2: Dutch elm disease – dealing with the aftermath (1979).
Leaflet 3: The planting and after-care of trees and shrubs (1979).
Leaflet 6: Managing small woodlands (1980).
Countryside Commission for Scotland, 1981. Plants and planting methods in the countryside. CC for Scotland. (Handbook of information sheets, periodically updated and expanded relevant to upland areas of Britain.)

SPITTLE BROOK, WOOLSTON PARK, WARRINGTON
OS Map: 109. NGR: SJ 636895
Warrington New Town Development Corporation. Rivers Division, North West Water Authority, Box 12, New Town House, Buttermarket Street, Warrington WA1 2QG.
Telephone: Warrington (0925) 53999.

Site Summary
Flood alleviation scheme, capital works, mid-1970s.
Lowland, urban location.
Channel: 2 metres wide at low water level, shallow.
Banks: 3 metres high, slopes variable.
Substrate: sand and clay.

Work Description
The Brook is the core of a linear urban park laid out in the mid-1970s. The channel and banks were excavated and reshaped, so creating a broad, shallow flood basin on one side of the stream – forming a central 'wetland' area. Spoil was built up as irregular floodbanks on either side. Almost all the original vegetation of the stream was lost (but see **256**). The main theme of replanting was to create thickets and screens of native shrubs and trees. The whole park layout demonstrates superbly what can be done to bring wildlife into urban situations (photographs below and right).

Spittle Brook: Standard cherry with a ground cover of common gorse, established on the dry upper bank.

Spittle Brook: Common osier, established from stakes and maintained as coppice, in a planting that screens the path from the stream.

The main features are –
i Trees and shrubs are nearly all native, with an emphasis on berry-bearing species and contrasting foliage. Almost all are deciduous;
ii All planting is in large and small clusters, concentrated on the flood banks and, in places, as screens between the pathway and the brook – such as close to the wetland area;
iii Standard willows were planted within the flood storage basin, on the upstream side; elsewhere various types of willows have grown from short stakes or coppiced stumps;
iv Although there are no trees close to the channel itself, bankside and marsh plants are allowed to grow freely, and are only cut back intermittently in patches, so providing cover for wildlife and making an attractive park feature (see **208**).

Habitat Comments
1 The trees and shrubs make an attractive landscape. Through planting it makes the best use of native species to bring as much wildlife as possible to the area for people to enjoy. The berry-bearing species, in particular, should attract many birds to feed in the park during winter.
2 The list of trees and shrubs planted is impressive and includes –

Gorse	Berberis	Redcurrant
Broom	Cotoneaster	Blackcurrant

Rose – various scrambling varieties – often used as 'kid-deterrents' beside bridges.

Laurel	Dogwood	Guelder rose
Hawthorn	Snowberry	Field Maple
White poplar	White willow	Crack willow (red twigged)
Common osier	Goat willow	Sycamore
Whitebeam	Rowan	Birch
Wild cherry	Horse chestnut	

3 The inclusion of evergreen species such as laurel or holly is good in principle, because they provide shelter for roosting birds in winter, when protection from wind and rain can be vital. Natural, unmanaged woodlands contain much evergreen cover, especially ivy, which is valuable for invertebrates as well as birds. Care must be taken with the selection of species, however. Laurel and rhododendron are particularly invasive and will shade out other vegetation.

RIVER STOUR,
TREDDINGTON-ON-STOUR,
WARWICKSHIRE
OS Map: 151. NGR: SP 260434
Avon Division, Severn Trent Water Authority,
Finham Reclamation Works, St Martin's Road,
Finham, Coventry.
Telephone: Coventry (0203) 415115.
Regional Architects' Department,
Severn Trent Water Authority,
Abelson House, 2297 Coventry Road, Sheldon,
Birmingham.
Telephone: 021-743 4222.

Site Summary
Maintenance dredging 1981.
Lowland, rural village-edge location.
Channel: 2 to 5 metres wide.
Banks: 2 to 3 metres high, batter 1 in 2 , variable.
Substrate: clay and gravel.
Engineers: D Alcott and W Garrad.
Landscape architects: J Purseglove,
M Ericson.

Work Description
Maintenance dredging of the Stour in 1981 dropped bed levels by up to 1 metre. Throughout the work, care was taken to maintain and improve the landscape and wildlife habitats of the river corridor. Five hundred pounds a mile was set aside for tree planting and fencing. The landscape architect undertook planning and organisation of the planting scheme, including negotiations with landowners.

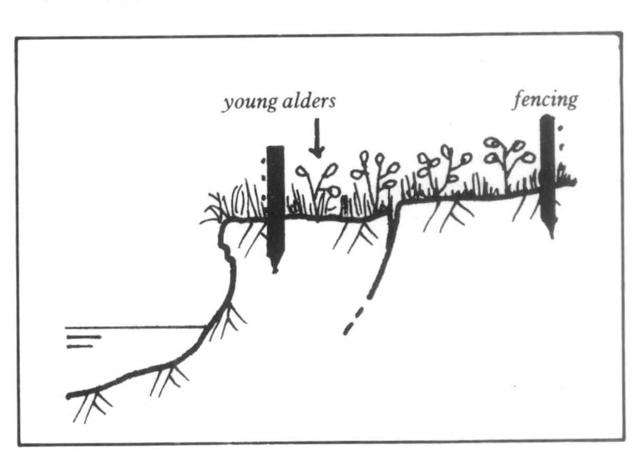

River Stour: The use of alder planting to help stabilise slippage in steep clay banks.

Planting was used to thicken up existing hedge lines, to improve the landscape and to stabilise slippage areas in steep clay banks (figure above). The plan of part of the scheme (figure right) shows the general pattern of planting, that is –
small, fenced plots at irregular intervals usually on one side of the river only, but not always (E), often linked to field corners (A), existing trees (B), on the inner side of a bend (C), or at a confluence (D). All plots contained a mixture of trees and shrubs. With the exception of seven feathers of alder and white willow, which had to be staked, all trees and shrubs were planted as two plus one transplants, with hare guards, but without stakes. All transplants were put in at 1.2 metres centres, and feathers at 3-metre centres. The fencing used consisted of pig-wire, 4-inch round tanalised larch poles, and

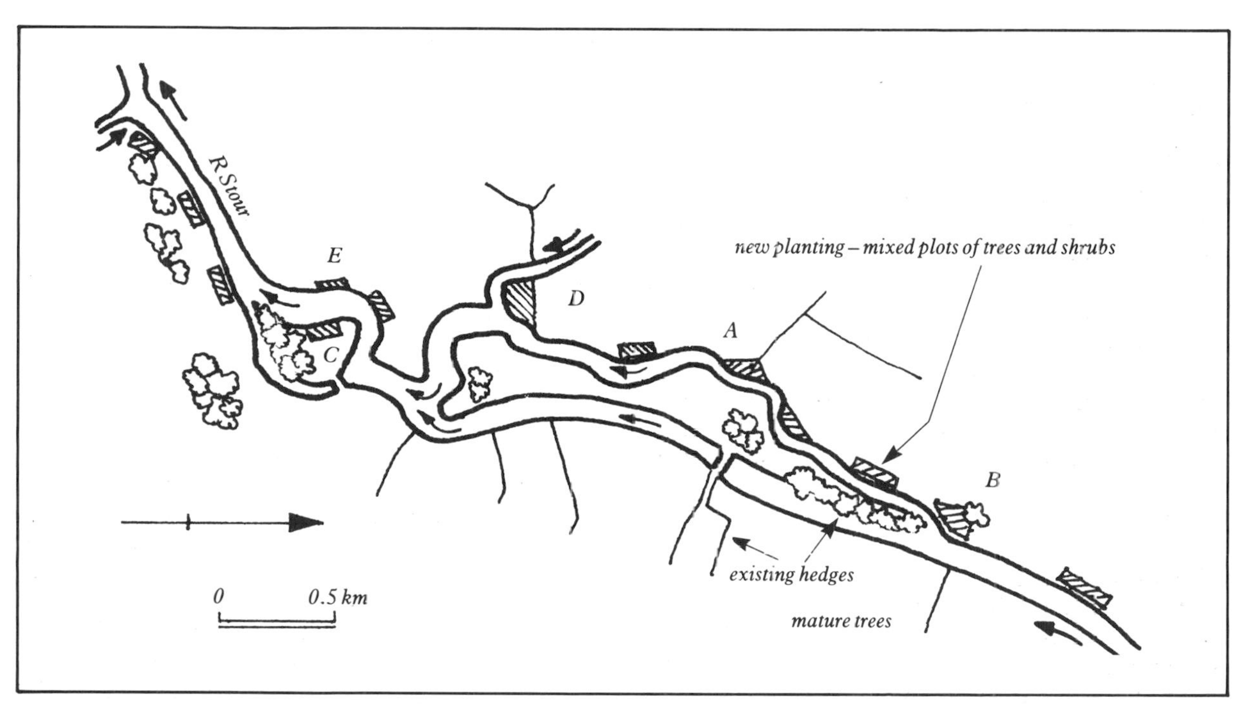

River Stour: Part of the Treddington-on-Stour planting scheme, 1981 (after STWA drawings).

barbed wire (photograph below). A summary of costs for planting in the whole scheme appears below.

1128 trees and 689 shrubs	£668.00
753 linear metres fencing	£494.48
materials, delivery etc	£72.00
13 days for two-man gang (incl transport & tractor)	£1976.00
Total	£3210.48 (1981 prices)

Since the aim was to create semi-natural copses, the species planted were all native, and appropriate to the Midland lowlands.

Trees	**Shrubs**
Field maple	Hazel
Horse chestnut	Hawthorn
Alder	Dog rose
Beech	Goat willow
Ash	Guelder rose
Bird cherry	
Pedunculate oak	
White willow	
Whitebeam	
Rowan	

The planting scheme was partially grant-aided by the Countryside Commission.

Habitat Comments

1 The planting scheme promises to form excellent habitat for wildlife: a good addition to the existing cover of hawthorn, sycamore, privet, oak, ash and willow, almost none of which was lost during dredging.

River Stour: Tree planting well fenced, and maintained in the first year so that grass and weed growth was checked.

2 The planting pattern of scattered, small plots maximises cover for small mammals and birds. Trees planted at a confluence or on a bend maximise the edge-effect of tree cover on the riverside, for the benefit of riverine wildlife – and minimises the effect on adjacent fields.
3 Because STWA was using direct works staff on a limited budget to carry out the planting, minimum maintenace was carried out in the first year. As a result, heavy weed growth – mainly hemlock from the dredgings – smothered a lot of the smaller stock (photograph right). STWA have now learnt from this experience: in the winter of 1982/83 replanting with standard sized trees has been carried out, which should prove to be more robust. It is hoped that maintenance can also be improved for the next two seasons.

River Stour: New tree planting overwhelmed by hemlock, because there was no maintenance in the first year.

RIVER ALNE, HENLEY-IN-ARDEN, WARWICKSHIRE
OS Map: 151. NGR: SP 154665
Avon Division, Severn Trent Water Authority, Finham Reclamation Works, St Martins Road, Finham, Coventry.
Telephone: Coventry (0203) 415115.
Regional Architects' Department, Severn Trent Water Authority, Abelson House, 2297 Coventry Road, Sheldon, Birmingham.
Telephone: 021-743 4222.

Site Summary
Flood alleviation scheme, capital works, 1979/80.
Lowland, urban location.
Channel: 4 to 5 metres wide, depth variable.
Banks: variable slopes, 1 in 3 to 1 in 1, some stone revetment.
Substrate: sand, clay, gravel.
Engineer: B Tinley.
Landscape architect: J Purseglove.

Work Description
Flood alleviation works for Henley-in-Arden deepened the Alne by up to 1 metre in 1979/80. Throughout the work, care was taken to conserve and improve the landscape, for the sake of wildlife as well as amenity (see also **87**, **182** and **224**).
Tree planting was planned and some of it was carried out during the winter *before* dredging work started (ie 1977/78). The channel was dredged from one bank only, leaving all trees and rough cover on the opposite bank, and all individual mature trees on the worked bank. Varied slopes were left on the worked bank, with stone revetment where necessary.

The aim of the tree planting was to improve the landscape and increase the wildlife resource within the town. Small plots of mixed trees and shrubs were planted in field corners, around existing mature trees, and along one of the newly cut flood bypass channels and pond. The footpath along the riverside was already fenced off from the adjacent field and, with the informal agreement of the landowner, path and fence were diverted by up to 3 metres into the field in places and scrub species planted in the crescent this created. Short posts help to separate the new path from the planting plots (figure right and photograph right).
To reduce the requirement for aftercare, faster-growing shrubs and small trees were planted densely, at about 1-metre centres, to grow up and smother weeds within three seasons. 'Roundup' was sprayed around tree bases during the first two years. The trees, at wider spacing, should now be able to grow up through the thickening scrub canopy – as they would in a natural situation. Trees and shrubs used are listed below:

Trees	**Shrubs**
Pedunculate oak	Alder buckthorn
Ash	Blackthorn
White willow*	Guelder rose
(red twigged)	Goat willow
Birch†	*Rosa longicuspes*‡
Elder†	

*some to be coppiced.
†small trees, fast growing.
‡only in town sites, eg on gabions, and then only adjacent to obvious urban structures.
See **87** for details of planting around the flood bypass channel.

River Alne: Three year old riverbank planting around an existing bush. The path goes around it, to the right (November 1982).

Habitat Comments

1 This is an important scheme, for the planting was carried out so that some stretches of the river would become established with tree and scrub growth on both sides of the river. The planting plots, on the working bank, were small enough blocks to permit future machine access. Existing vegetation on the opposite bank was retained.

2 The use of native species increases the value of the sites for wildlife, providing a variety of food plants and types of cover. Alder buckthorn is a shrub well worth planting; it thrives in damp, slightly acid conditions, is not very common, is a food plant for the brimstone butterfly, and has attractive bright autumn colours. Buckthorn is similar, spiny, prefers damp limy or fen peat conditions and also is a brimstone food plant.

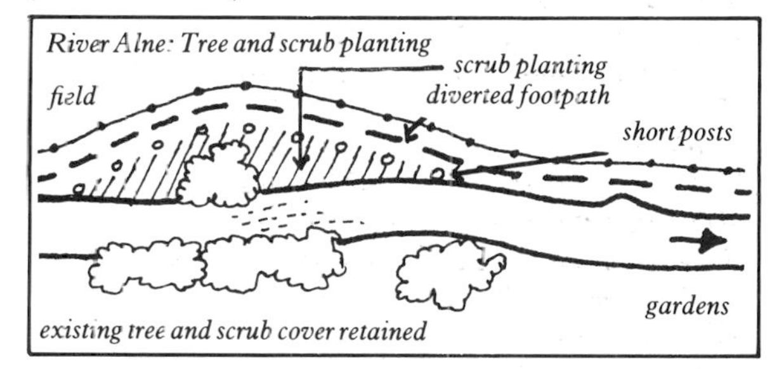

3 Elder and willows planted amongst the shrubs creates dense cover very rapidly – benefiting wildlife as well as reducing the need for weed management. The elder provides flowers and berries for birds, badgers and foxes as well as for wine-makers.

ATTENBOROUGH GRAVEL PITS, NOTTINGHAMSHIRE

OS Map: 129. NGR: SK 528357

Nottinghamshire Trust for Nature Conservation, 10 Darley Avenue, Toton, Beeston, Nottingham NG9 6JP.

Telephone: Long Eaton (060 76) 60926.

Site Summary

Maintenance works, 1982.
Lowland, rural edge location.
Substrate: clay, gravel, fen peat.
Field Officer: Norman Lewis.

Work Description

Although the gravel pits are still being worked, part is managed as a nature reserve by NTNC. Reinstatement of good wildlife habitat is a major part of reserve work – to provide cover and feeding sites for wildlife in general, and to partially screen the lakes from people so that waterfowl are less disturbed. At this site, the majority of trees planted were willow and alder.

When contractors were working in the reserve, access for their vehicles was demarcated by stakes and tape, as normal practice. The stakes used, though, were live willow and were left in place after the work was finished. They had sprouted within a few months and will rapidly establish as trees.

Stakes were cut from old pollards or mature willows nearby between the end of October and late March, and used within a week at most; the most common is a hybrid crack x white willow. Straight branches about 10 centimetres in diameter, and 2 to 3 metres long, were selected, sharpened with a billhook, and driven in with a mallet or post-thumper, the hole

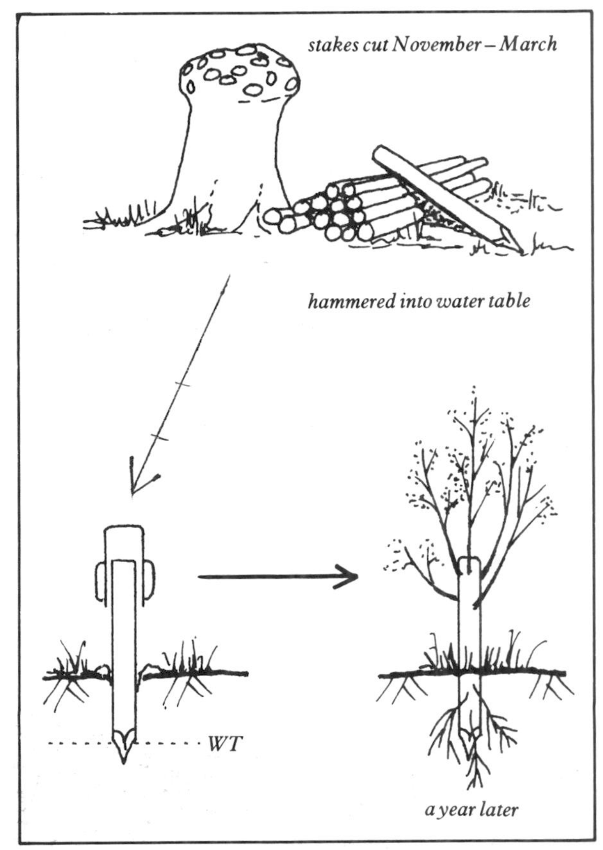

Attenborough Gravel Pits: Willow staking.

first being driven with a crowbar (although not essential, rags wrapped around the top of the stake, will help to protect the bark). Chances of them 'taking' is increased if they are driven down so the base is at the water-table. By August, shoots 1 to 2 metres long had sprouted – giving 'instant trees' (figure and photograph above).

This way of propagating willows is the simplest, surest and probably cheapest of all tree planting methods: it also gives the quickest results. Any type of willow or sallow is suitable. The length of stake is unimportant, but a diameter of about 10 centimetres is best to ensure success – it also makes the new planted 'tree' easy to see, so it is not accidentally damaged by machinery or maintenance crews. Tall stakes, over 2 metres above ground level, do not need fencing from stock, (but should be very firm, as cows will rub against them) and may be pollarded after two years. Short stakes, 1 metre or so, are ideal for establishing coppice, or scrub.

Attenborough Gravel Pits: A stake, 'planted' in January, seen here in June.

Habitat Comments

1 Willows of all types are excellent 'habitat improvers' for wildlife. Their many forms, sizes, foliage patterns and twig colours make them suitable for any situation, urban or countryside. Their rapid establishment, durability and flexible response to various management practices make them extremely useful in many river situations (see **155**, **158**, **165**, **166**, and **176**).

2 Sallows, or any willows kept coppiced to sprout from the base, form dense cover for all types of wildlife – otters may use patches for day-time resting places; reedbed adjoining or mixed with willow scrub supports more breeding warblers than either habitat alone. Mature tree willows or pollards provide nesting cover for little owls, mallards and otters.

RIVER TEME, LEINTWARDINE, HEREFORDSHIRE

OS Map: 137. NGR: SO 412734

Lower Severn Division, Severn Trent Water Authority, 64 Albert Road North, Great Malvern, Worcestershire.

Telephone: Malvern (068 45) 61511.

Site Summary

Maintenance work,
1981.
Rural location.

Upland/lowland transition zone.
Channel: up to 15 metres wide, depth variable.
Banks: 0.5-2.5 metres high.
Substrate: cobbles, gravel, sand, alluvial and boulder clays.
Supervision: B Draper.

Work Description
During maintenance work (described in **110**, **128** and **152**) in 1981, trees and scrub were planted on the banks, for habitat improvement. The Teme is known to be used by otters at least occasionally, but this stretch below Leintwardine has little cover.

Four-metre square plots were sited on the dry bank top, about 5 to 10 metres from the edge. A single standard of ash or lime was planted in each, with hawthorn transplants at approximately 1 metre centres around it.
Fencing is crucial in this site, which is grazed. Two strands of barbed wire are sufficient in the cattle-grazed fields, but inadequate protection in the sheep fields – the bark was eaten and the standard and hawthorn killed. The sheep-netted plots were fine and the trees are growing well (photographs below).

River Teme: Small leaved lime, planted as a standard, with hawthorn transplants around it. Sheep netting is successfully protecting the young trees.

Habitat Comments
1 The planting pattern and mixture promises to give good wildlife cover along this reach in years to come – as well as berries, sweet flowers and honey-dew as food-sources for birds, small mammals and insects.
2 If the plots were *on* the river's edge, instead of some distance away, the trees could contribute more to the river's wildlife. The ash trees will only be potential otter holt sites if hollows and tunnels are washed under their roots. The lime can enrich the river water – and hence algae, invertebrate and fish productivity – but only if its branches actually overhang the water. It may well be, however, that in the 150-200 year lifespan of these trees, the river will shift so that they are right on its brink.

River Teme: The same type of planting, in the same field, but without sheep netting – the trees are dead.

TECHNICAL 7: INVERTEBRATES

The habitat requirements of riverine invertebrates and the impact of river management operations upon invertebrate communities have been discussed in detail in 'Biological 2: Invertebrates'. The adverse effects of routine management and engineering operations on aquatic and riparian invertebrates may be summarised as follows:

1 **Disturbance** by, for instance, removal of part of the invertebrate community from the river bed during dredging. Although invertebrate communities are often able to recover fairly rapidly, if such treatment is extensive or repeated it can eliminate less tolerant species.
2 **Alteration of the physical or chemical characteristics of the water,** for instance by a reduction in dissolved oxygen concentration or an increase in temperature, silt loading or plant nutrient concentrations. Such alterations may render the environment unsuitable for sensitive species and produce a distorted invertebrate community.
3 **Reduction in habitat diversity** within the river channel and on the banks, for example, by the removal of water plants and trees, the elimination of riffles and pools, or eroding vertical banks and gravel islands. This makes for a uniform habitat with an impoverished invertebrate fauna.
4 **Loss of wet river valley habitats** such as flushes and fens, due to the lowering of the water table or a reduction in flooding, with subsequent intensification of agriculture. Whole communities of wetland invertebrates disappear with the demise of these habitats, often an indirect result of river improvement schemes.

If arterial river engineering works lead to agricultural intensification there may be no means of avoiding some deterioration of water quality or the loss of certain peripheral habitats. However, disturbance and reduction in habitat diversity can often be avoided or minimised by adopting sympathetic management techniques or reinstating features of the habitat which have previously been destroyed.

Disturbance of aquatic invertebrate communities may be avoided by carrying out options **71-98**, leaving the channel untouched, and disturbance of riparian invertebrates is likewise avoidable by using options **145-54**, leaving the banks untouched. Disturbance can be kept to a relatively low level by employing option **98**, dredging two-thirds or less of the channel, and by conserving riffles, pools and meanders (**101, 103**). Patch cutting plants (**204, 229**) is obviously preferable to more extensive removal of aquatic or bankside vegetation.

An increase in silt loading of the water after channel works can be minimised by stabilising the bank using stumps, logs, faggots, willow stakes, hurdles, reeds, stone or artificial materials (**155-96**). However, some of these techniques may be so effective that habitat diversity is reduced for riparian invertebrates, and groups such as crane-flies and solitary bees, which need muddy margins or eroding banks, may suffer. Tree planting (**154**), minimal tree removal (**258, 256**) and sympathetic management of trees and shrubs (**243-56**) will maintain shaded sections, so preventing an increase in water temperatures and maintaining the supply of leaf litter which contributes substantially to the food supply of aquatic invertebrates.

Conservation of aquatic and riparian invertebrate communities relies heavily on maintaining habitat diversity. The adoption of the following options will preserve or enhance habitat diversity or minimise habitat destruction:

71-89 – leaving channel and banks untouched.
89 – constructing a multi-stage channel (this benefits aquatic communities but may damage riparian ones).
98 – dredging two-thirds or less of channel.
101, 103 – conserving riffles, pools and meanders.
111 – recreating riffles and pools.
118 – constructing low stone weirs.
131, 137 – creating shallow-water berms and bays.
142 – whole channel re-alignment.
146 – working from one bank only.
152 – conserving vertical banks.
154 – conserving islands.
154 – planting alders for bank protection.
171 – reed planting on berms.
197, 202 – disposal of spoil away from river banks.
204 – patch cutting and dredging of aquatic plants.
218 – over-deepening and over-widening.
219 – establishing aquatic vegetation.
229 – patch-mowing bank vegetation.
230 – late mowing bank vegetation.
235, 238 – sowing native seed mixtures or laying old meadow turf on disturbed banks.
243, 244 – working through scrub and over hedges.
246, 256 – retaining trees.
246, 249, 252 – lopping branches, coppicing and pollarding trees and shrubs rather than removing them.
258 – tree planting.

TECHNICAL 8: FISH

Fish are the most sought after of all riverine wildlife, with a vast following of interested, knowledgeable and expert fishermen – and yet, habitat management is giving way to 'put-and-take' methods to maintain populations. This may be a response to the numbers of people who want the experience of catching fish, but it is also, partly, a response to modern river engineering operations which have impoverished natural fish habitats. Different types of fish community are vulnerable to different types of disturbance and change. In the same way as other groups of wildlife, however, they respond to the loss of habitat diversity by a reduction in biomass, number of species or number of individuals – or all three. There may also be a change in community types. This can be serious whether the river is managed for game or coarse fishing, or not. Native communities of fish need conservation as much as other forms of British wildlife.

Habitat requirements for various types of fish differ (see 'Biological 4: Fish'), but in general the requirements are:

i. food supply – aquatic plants, algae on stones and plants, aquatic invertebrates, insects falling into the river from overhanging vegetation and organic matter on the surface;
ii shelter – from the fastest currents. Even fish of turbulent streams such as trout tend to congregate where there is an obstruction providing slack water;
iii. breeding sites – either clean, well-oxygenated gravels, or rooted water plants, or plants on an inundated floodplain;
iv. nursery sites – for young fish. That is, plants to shelter amongst, and/or shallows to escape from larger predatory fish such as pike;
v. suitable temperatures, oxygen concentration, and dissolved salt concentration;
vi. appropriate fluctuations in discharge – since for many fish, from trout and salmon to minnows, rising discharge triggers migration for spawning;

– and for migratory species –

vii. free passage up and downstream – even species which spend all their lives in freshwater may migrate upstream to breed or to deeper water to overwinter.

General options which help to conserve fish habitat are:

71-98 – leaving the channel completely untouched, as well as at least 50 per cent of the bankside vegetation.
98-103 – partial conservation of a significant percentage of the channel, in particular shallow riffles, deep pools, and a complete range of emergent and submerged plants, as breeding and feeding sites.
103 – retaining meanders linked to the main channel, providing a vital refuge for breeding fish stocks, particularly if the main channel is made uniform.
146 – working from one bank, so retaining the overhanging vegetation and physical irregularities of the opposite bank.
149 – fencing to keep stock from breaking down the banks and thus silting fish holes; since this also conserves overhanging vegetation, provision of cover and food for fish is also maintained.
154 – retaining islands, which diversify the flow giving downstream shelter. Also, the banks may have irregularities and holes as fish-lies.
154 – planting alders behind eroding banks to act as a 'stop' to future erosion, so that the undercuts and holes will persist as fish shelters.
197-202 – careful dumping so as not to infill marshy or low-lying areas next to the river which may be fish spawning grounds in summer floods.
204-14 – leaving significant patches of untouched weed when dredging, spraying or weed-cutting, as refuges for fish and their invertebrate or plant foods.
214-18 – using weed control techniques which cause least disturbance to the channel community. Shade belts of trees both control weed growth and contribute organic matter and insects as a food resource.
229-30, 243-58 – retaining overhanging, native bankside grasses, herbs, trees and scrub, as cover and a major food resource.

A combination of these options is necessary to ensure that fish populations are protected. Of those above, the most important are retaining riffles and pools, patches of aquatic plants and overhanging bankside vegetation. Recent work in the Midlands has shown that coarse fish populations fall drastically following dredging (Swales 1982a) and weed-cutting (Swales 1982b) and that recovery is slow. Refuges of untouched aquatic plants and overhanging trees and plants appeared to protect some of the population during channel work, so that sections not totally cut retained more and larger fish than other sections. Territorial species such as chub may be more severely affected than shoaling species such as dace.
The timing of weed-cutting can be crucial. Cutting early in summer can remove plants on which perch, pike or roach have laid their eggs; as water levels drop, eggs laid on remaining plants may dry out. (This is in addition to the harmful effects of weed-cutting on aquatic invertebrate larvae and hatching adults – see section 7). Water

authority fisheries staff are in the best position to advise on the least damaging times for weed-cutting.

Options which reinstate fish habitat are:

111-44 – all techniques which vary the physical habitat, create pools and shallows, patches of slack water and faster water, and give shelter. Current deflectors and low stone weirs are classic fish habitat improvement structures. Bays and shallow water berms recreate the water's edge conditions which many fry require.
155-96 – creating, to a greater or lesser extent, uneven banks below water level, and encouraging aquatic or overhanging vegetation to redevelop.
219, **234-40**, **258** – planting aquatic and bankside plants where and as appropriate, for shelter, cover, breeding and as food resources. Sycamore and lime, which secrete honeydew on their leaves which washes off into the water below, have been shown to increase the organic production of a stream, with effects on the food chain right up to increased trout populations. Other trees have a similar, but less dramatic effect.

Two good examples of creating fish habitat in enlarged channels are described elsewhere in the handbook:
On a rocky upland river, the Afon Gwyrfai, Gwynedd Division of Welsh Water Authority reconstructed salmonid gravel spawning beds (**113**), built stone weirs (**119**), current deflectors (**127**), used natural stone revetment (**176**), placed boulders as shelters in uniform reaches, and planted alders and sallows on both banks, including between stones in the revetment.
On a lowland clay river, the Roding, Eastern Division of Thames Water Authority rehabilitated a straight canalised reach with a gabion weir (**124**) and gabion current deflectors (**129**) which had the effect of increasing velocities in some areas and decreasing it in others. As a result, there were more large fish in the reach after the works than before, and of more species.
In addition, fish passes may be needed in new weirs and sluices. Their construction is normal practice on game fishing rivers. The standard text for the design of fish passes is Pryce-Tannatt (1938).
Apart from the weirs, groynes and current deflectors already described, various types of fish shelters can be constructed which serve no other purpose; some of these are described below.

REFERENCES

Pryce-Tannatt, T E, 1938. Fish passes in connection with obstructions in salmonid rivers. Edward Arnold.

Swales, S, 1982a. A before and after study of the effects of land drainage work on fish stocks. Fish Management **13**: 105-14.

Swales, S, 1982b. Impact of weed-cutting on fisheries: an experimental study in a small lowland river. Fish Management **13**: 125-137.

FISH SHELTERS

American work – carried out with the intention of mitigating the damage done to natural game fisheries by arterial drainage works – has shown that current deflectors, small dams and artificial shelter can significantly increase the numbers and biomass of fish in an improved channel. This is supported by work in Britain on both upland and lowland rivers (see Section **113**, **119** and **127**, the Afon Gwyrfai; also **124**, **129** and **273** the River Roding).
Current deflectors and low dams create shelter by diversifying flow conditions. Structures specifically designed as fish shelters provide shade as well, and possibly give protection from predators. Such shelters can be fixed above or below water level and be floating or built onto the bank (figures on right). One of the simplest methods is to tie brushwood to a stake at the river's edge. Clearly all, except cavities in the bank, will obstruct flow to a certain extent, and so will be in conflict with the

Cross-section of a fish-shelter, redrawn from Mills, 1980.

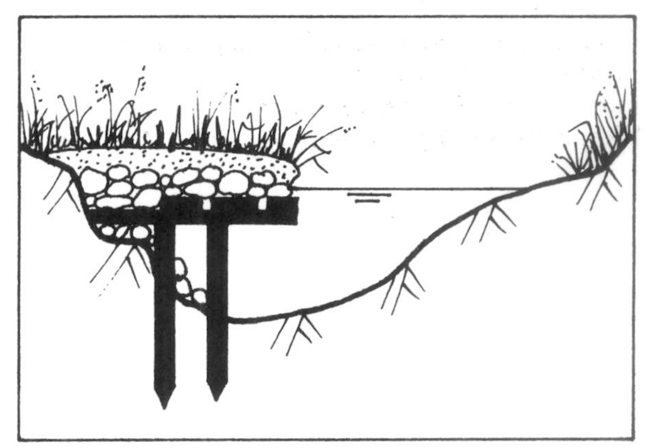

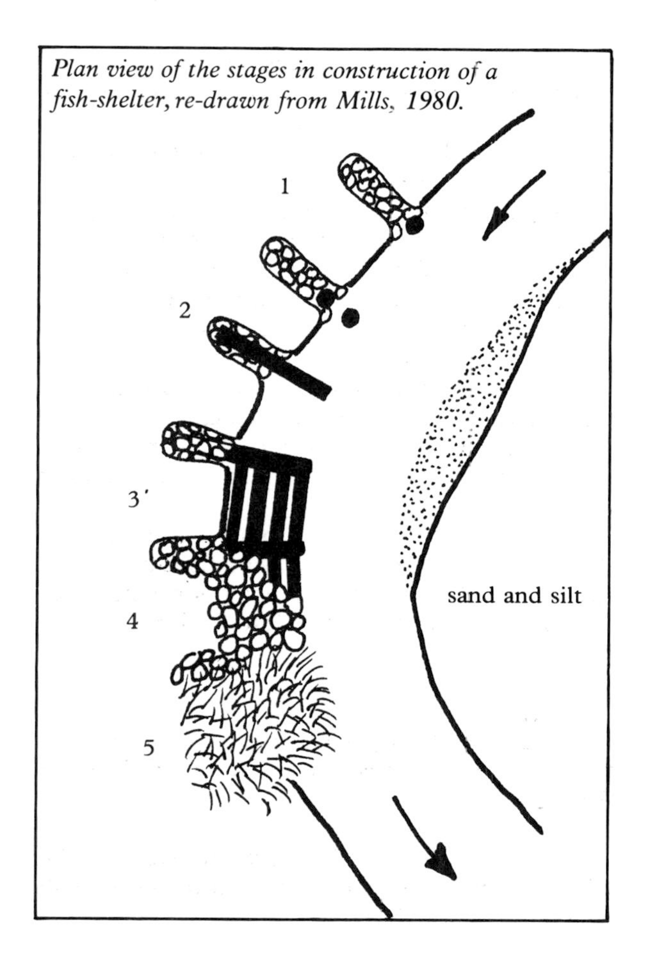

Plan view of the stages in construction of a fish-shelter, re-drawn from Mills, 1980.

hydrological purpose of the original channel works. In this case, permanent shelter structures should be included in scheme designs from the very beginning.
Floating shelters, attached to the bank, have little resistance to flow, and so are particularly suitable as temporary structures, for a season or two, until bank plants and scrub have regrown.

Fish shelter designs can be found in:

Mills, D H, 1980. The management of forest streams. Forestry Commission leaflet No 78.

Swales, S, 1982. Notes on the construction, installation and environmental effects of habitat improvement structures in a small lowland stream in Shropshire. Fish Management, **13**, 1-10.

RIVER RODING, ABRIDGE, ESSEX.
OS Map: 177 NGR: TQ 466970
Eastern Division, Thames Water Authority,
The Grange, Crossbrook Street, Waltham Cross, Hertfordshire.
Telephone: Waltham Cross (0992) 23611

Site Summary
Flood alleviation scheme, capital works, 1980/81.
Rural and edge of village, lowland location.
Channel: 2-3 metres wide, depth variable.
Banks: 0.5-2 metres.
Substrate: Clay and gravel.
Water Authority Biologist: Tony Dearsley.

Work Description
See section **93** for fuller description of this scheme. Three extreme meander bends had to be filled to keep the designed flood channel to optimum size in this flood alleviation scheme. The loss of the bends meant the loss of overhanging banks and deep pools which had provided fish with cover. Despite leaving more than 90 per cent of the river bed untouched to conserve the valued chub fishery (amongst other reasons), it was felt necessary to compensate for this habitat loss.
Cavities were made in the bank formed from large diameter concrete pipes (figures overleaf), or 'portals' constructed with gabions and elm planks (figures overleaf). These were sited below summer water level on the outer bank of the realigned sections, in gabion revetments.
In a survey of the fish population after work was completed, fish were found using the artificial shelters.

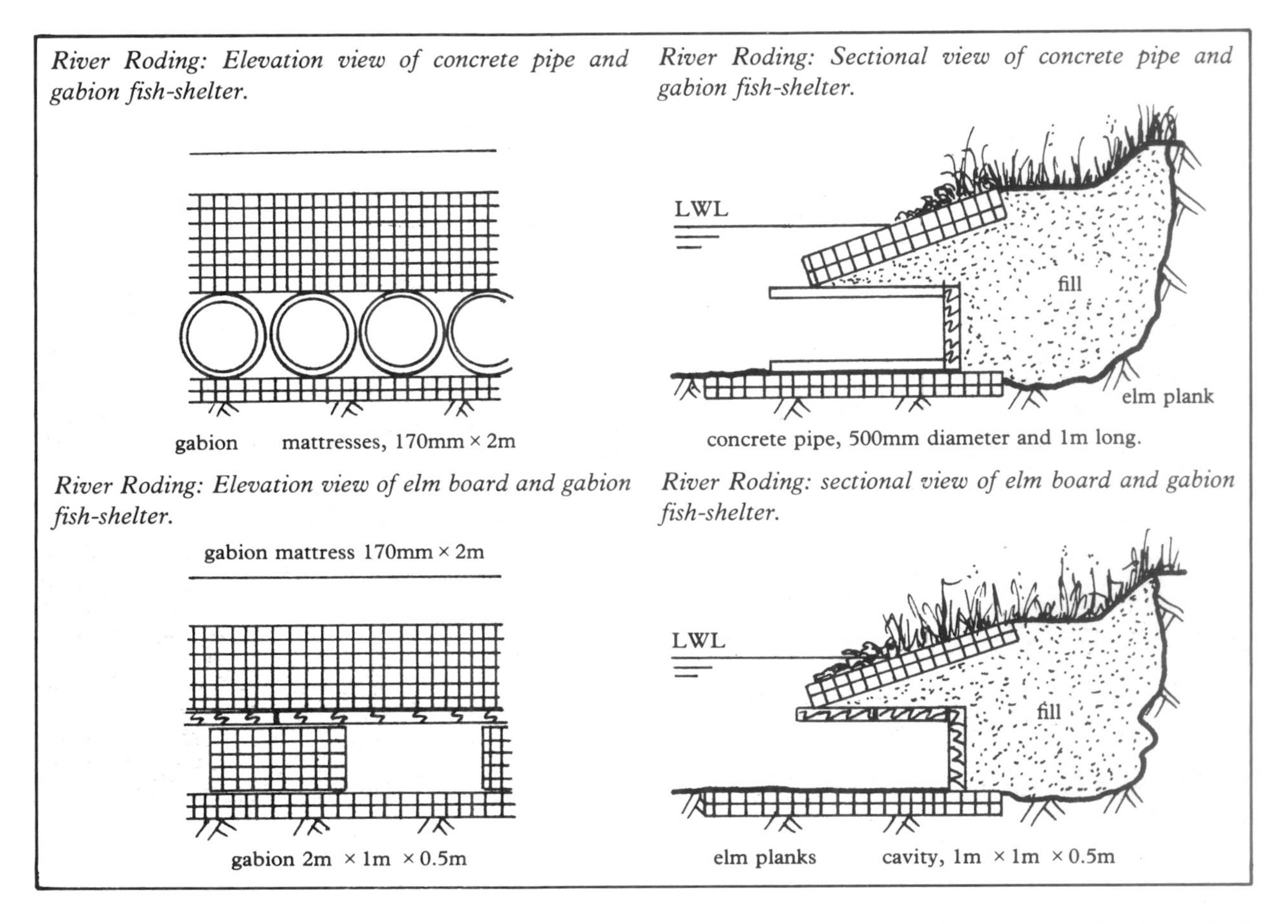

Habitat Comments

1. Building in fish shelters to compensate for habitat loss, in addition to the efforts made throughout to conserve instream habitat, is excellent and has clearly maintained fish stocks.

2. In cutting flood berms in this two-stage channel design, more than 50 per cent of the bank was excavated back, removing overhanging vegetation. Although the lower roots were left in place, it was not until the following season that marginal vegetation re-grew and, during the period immediately after work, cover was limited. The fish shelters also had an important role, therefore, in providing short-term artificial cover – although this particular technique is perhaps an expensive one, if provision of short-term cover is the only aim.

RIVER TEME, LEINTWARDINE, HEREFORDSHIRE.
OS Map: 137 NGR: SO 412733
Lower Severn Division,
Severn Trent Water Authority,
64 Albert Road North,
Great Malvern, Worcestershire
Telephone: Malvern (068 45) 61511

Site Summary

Maintenance works, 1981.
Rural location, upland/lowland transition zone.
Channel: 8-10 metres wide, depth variable.
Banks: sand and glacial clays, ungraded, variable.
Substrate: cobbles, gravel.
Area Engineer: Don Shuker.

Work Description

The Teme is a swift, gravelly river in this stretch, and well known for game fishing. During river training works (described elsewhere in **110** and **128**) two types of instream cover were built, partly to offset habitat loss from channel realignment and bank protection work.

On the bankside a shade structure was built where the current ran swiftly against the outer bank of a bend (photograph right). To avoid flood damage

River Teme: A platform built to shade the river's edge on the outer bank of a bend. Although the surface water is turbulent, there is shelter in holes in the undercut bank.

River Teme: The part-submerged log, secured in mid-stream.

the platform had to be constructed about one metre above summer water level, which may reduce its effectiveness. A stock fence was put round the platform, in case cattle or sheep fell off or through it into the river.

In the middle of the channel, a large log was staked securely, aligned with the flow (photograph on 275). With a gap between the log and the gravel bed, this has the duel purpose of creating shelter from swift flow and providing shade. It was also used as a nest site by moorhens in 1982, but the nest was swept away in high flows.

Habitat Comments

1. Of the two designs, the secured log seems more appropriate to this size and type of river. The platform shelter may be more appropriate and effective in narrower rivers when overhanging bankside vegetation has been lost.

2. Installing shelters to compensate for lost banks or meanders is excellent, but it probably needs many more than two shelters per 1.5 kilometres to reinstate adequately lost cover for fish.

3. The moorhens demonstrated – though unsuccessfully – that these structures can have a multiple use.

TECHNICAL 9: OTTERS

Otter populations fell very suddenly in both England and Wales during the late 1950s. As a result, by the 1970s it was recognised as an endangered species. It is fully protected under the Wildlife and Countryside Act 1981 (which superseded the Conservation of Wild Creatures and Wild Plants Act 1975). The decline was due to a combination of factors, of which organochlorine pollution may have been the most significant. However, the destruction of their river and wetland habitats certainly played a part in the disappearance of otters from many areas and, now that the pollution hazard appears to have been largely removed, the conservation of otters on rivers depends primarily on the maintenance and reinstatement of suitable habitat.

Studies of rivers with and without otters show that the most important habitat features are:

Secure Breeding Sites – otter holts (that is, resting or breeding places) are often located in the roots of mature trees, especially ash, sycamore or oak on the immediate river bank. Otters will sometimes use sites such as dry log piles, and the creation of artificial holts should be considered where otters are present, but suitable natural holts are scarce.

Cover – for day time resting sites. With good cover at frequent intervals, otters can tolerate human river users to a certain degree. Good cover consists of dense bankside vegetation: bramble thickets, rhododendron thickets, gorse, hawthorn scrub, large reedbeds or sedge beds. The crowns of old pollarded willows may be used, or piles of sticks and logs, and holes in tree roots on the bank. Frequent intervals means at least one patch of good cover per kilometre, but clearly the more continuous it is the better. A dog otter's territory can cover between 15 and 50 kilometres of river, within which there may be two or more breeding females.

A low level of disturbance – by anglers, canoeists, walkers, hunters and river management teams, for example. As otters may breed at any time of year, there is no season when river activities might not disturb a breeding female with cubs. With good cover, however, otters can tolerate some disturbance.

If cover becomes too widely separated, then disturbance becomes intolerable. Thus, the removal of even one tree with an otter holt in its roots, or clearing a stretch of riverside scrub and herbage, can be enough to make a much larger area unusable by otters.

Tributaries which link the main river to adjacent wetlands, ponds or lakes are a vital part of the territory. If the main river is cleared of trees and bankside vegetation, then tributaries and wetlands become even more important as feeding and lying-up sites. For otters, more than for any other species, river management decisions have to take the whole catchment into account.

Options which help to conserve existing otter habitat are therefore:

71-89 – leaving the main channel and its tree and bank cover completely untouched.
89 – multi-stage channels which leave at least 50 per cent of one or other of the banks untouched and allows dense bank vegetation, in patches at least, on existing banks and on flood berms.
98-103 – only partially dredging or clearing a channel, leaving 30-50 per cent untouched, including vegetation, riffles and pools.
103 – retaining meanders linked to the main channel. These will be secluded lying-up sites. Especially important if there is a holt already on a meander bank, or if it could be a site for an artificial holt.
146 – working from one bank, leaving the opposite bank and its aquatic vegetation entirely untouched.
149 – fencing stock out from the banks, allowing dense bankside vegetation to grow.
154 – retaining islands – scrub and trees on islands are prime sites for holts and lying-up places, remote from human disturbance.
197-202 – careful spoil disposal, so that old meanders, ponds and wetlands are not lost.
204 – cutting aquatic weed in patches, leaving refuges for fish, on which otters feed.
214-218 – using weed control methods which cause less frequent disturbance to the river.
229-30 – retaining patches of tall bank vegetation untouched, or as late as possible in the year, in areas where banks *have* to be cut.
243-58 – retaining all existing tree and scrub cover as holt sites and cover, and encouraging regeneration.

Options which help to reinstate otter habitat are:

111-44 – where a river has been drastically altered, and made uniform, any of the practices above will help to restore variety and improve fish habitat, and hence feeding conditions for otters.
155 – using stumps and logs from tree clearance work as bank protection – the 'stick piles' wired to the bank can be constructed as otter holts.
158-96 – using methods of bank protection which encourage dense bank and edge vegetation to grow; in particular, using live willow and planting reeds on shallow-water berms.
219 – replanting aquatic vegetation.
234-40 – encouraging native tall herbs and grasses on new banks.
258 – planting native trees and scrub, at least some immediately on the river bank, to be cover and holt

sites in the future. Oak, ash and sycamore in particular are good trees to plant as their mature root systems make good holt sites.
Special practices which further otter conservation are minimal tree removal (below), surveying and then marking for retention during tree management work trees which are holt sites (**279**), and setting up otter havens by agreement with the landowners (**281**). Creating holt sites (**281**) can only be effective where all other practices to conserve natural habitat and cover have been carried out.

MINIMAL TREE AND SCRUB REMOVAL

Even though water authorities may have a general policy of retaining as many trees as possible, on rivers known to be used by otters, tree and scrub removal must be minimised and will need special attention.
Several water authorities, when proposing tree maintenance work on otter rivers, have consulted the Nature Conservancy Council, Otter Haven Project or local Nature Conservation Trust for advice. The otter and any structures or places it uses for shelter are protected under the Wildlife and Countryside Act 1981 from any damage or destruction, unless this was the incidental result of a lawful operation and reasonable care was taken to avoid it. Consultation is the first stage in demonstrating 'reasonable care'. Recommendations leading from consultation usually include, at the very least, the minimal removal of tree and shrub cover, with particular attention being paid to holt-trees. Holts are frequently in the cavities amongst roots of mature oak, ash or sycamore which lean out over the channel. To retain these trees, yet reduce flood hazards, the banks around the tree could be protected to prevent further erosion; current deflectors sited to prevent further undercutting of the roots (figure right); or the tree carefully trimmed to increase its stability and reduce its size. Alternatively, the normal practice of tree maintenance could be waived, so that the major maintenance effort goes into clearing debris and fallen branches on a five-year cycle, rather than felling potentially hazardous trees every 10-20 years.

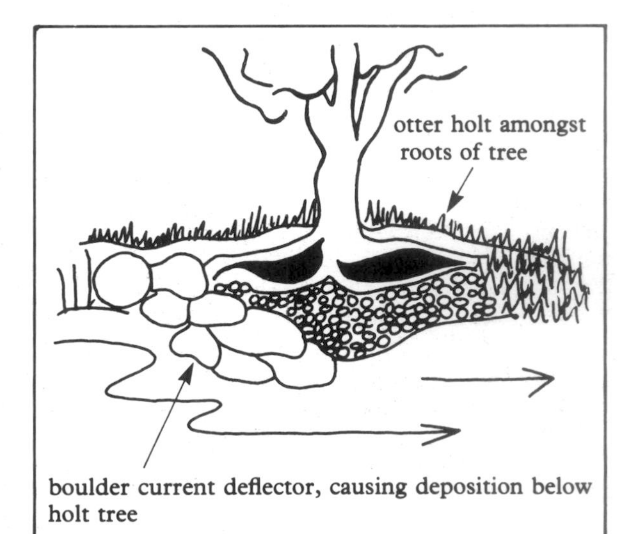

Use of current deflectors to prevent erosion of holt trees.

RIVER USK, CRICKHOWELL TO BRECON, POWYS.

OS Map: 161 NGR: SO 151203
Usk Division, Welsh Water Authority, Station Buildings, Queensway, Newport, Gwent.
Telephone: Newport (0633) 840404

Site Summary
Flood alleviation scheme, capital works, 1982.
Upland lowland transition, rural location.
Channel: 30-40 metres wide, depth variable.
Banks: variable, not graded.
Substrate: bedrock, clay, gravel and sand.
Tree cover: mixed; principally alder with oak, elm and ash.
Engineer: Colin Green, Land Drainage Engineer.

Work Description
Severe flooding on the Usk has, in the past, been caused by timber and trash being swept down, jamming against bridges. A capital flood alleviation scheme, therefore, included tree maintenance work to remove dead or dangerous timber from the banks. As the Usk valley is known to support otters, the Nature Conservancy Council and Otter Haven Project were called in for advice. Tree removal was kept to a minimum. In more than 10 kilometres of predominantly tree-lined river, only 20 trees had to be cut out, usually because they were in an exposed site and undercut, or because they were slumped and had partially fallen into the river. Leaning or top-heavy trees were coppiced, pollarded or trimmed so that they continued to grow, and the root systems remained to secure the bank, so forming current or future holt-sites for otters.

Habitat Comments

1. Tree clearance work is carried out by most river management teams, usually on a 5-10 year cycle, as a maintenance operation. This scheme demonstrates that, with care and skill, a very high proportion of existing mature trees can be tolerated on river banks well below flood level, at least in rural locations (photograph below).

2. Young trees should be inspected at the same time, and lightly trimmed as necessary, so that there will be continuity in tree cover in the future – for the sake of bank stability as well as otter habitat.

3. It is not a water authority's job to tidy up riversides, leaving them neat and regular. 'Untidiness' and irregularities such as this are just the sort of features that otters exploit – and rely on for survival.

River Usk: Mature trees left within the flood channel.

MARKING HOLT TREES

It may or may not be accepted practice to mark trees to be lopped or cut by a maintenance gang (**246**), but where otters use a river it is especially important to conserve the trees used as holts. Marking them clearly as a first step should make doubly sure that they are treated correctly.

Before work starts, the river should be walked by the gang supervisor, with at least one person competent to recognise signs of otters and otter holts. If drainage authority staff are unable to do this, then help should be sought from the Nature Conservancy Council, Otter Haven Project or trained water authority biologists or ecologists. Trees which are holts or which may be of use should, temporarily, be clearly marked. In each Authority area an unambiguous method should be devised which is acceptable to both the Authority and conservationists. Possible marking methods include the use of spray paint (see **246**), coloured tape or marking stakes. If maps or scheme drawings are marked to show the location of holt sites, the information should be kept confidential between area staff, local conservation organisations and the landowner.

It is also important to leave saplings of suitable

trees so that these may grow to provide the otter holts of the future. Mere protection of existing holt trees will result in a gradual loss as they eventually die. Suitable saplings should, therefore, also be marked for retention.

RIVER OKEMENT, NORTH DEVON.
OS Map: 191
Environmental Services (East Area),
South West Water Authority,
Manley House, Kestrel Way, Sowton,
Exeter, Devon.
Telephone: Exeter (0392) 76201

Site Summary
Maintenance work, 1982/83.
Upland/lowland transition, rural location.
Channel: 3-6 metres wide, depth variable.
Banks: ungraded, rocky, 2-15 metres high, steep.
Substrate: bedrock, shale and clay.

Work Description
The Okement is a steep, turbulent river, often flowing through naturally wooded gorge-like sections, and is known to be used by otters. The amount of fallen and falling timber in the river channel was a potential flood hazard, so a two-year pioneer tree clearance scheme is being carried out. This entails removing fallen and falling trees and some limbs within 2.5 metres of the summer water level. Some coppicing is also being carried out.
Because this remote and largely undisturbed river valley is important to wildlife, in particular otters, there was concern lest holt sites be disturbed or removed. The men in the gang were not experienced or trained in the conservation aspects of river management. As a result, the gang supervisor took advice from the Otter Haven Project, walking the river with their local area worker, who pointed out holt trees. These, and potential holts, were marked with paint, to distinguish them from ones to be cut or coppiced, which the supervisor marked differently.
As the tree clearance programme is going on over such a long period, only short stretches of 100 metres or so are marked up at a time.

Habitat Comments
1. Marking otter holt trees, with the help of an expert, has ensured that the essential features of the otter habitat of this stretch of river have been safeguarded (photograph below).
2. In densely wooded stretches such as this site, where long established woodland holds a rich community of mosses, lichens and ferns, pioneer tree clearance must be done – if at all – with the greatest care. The plant community, insects, fish life and mammals depend on the shelter that only *complete* tree cover can give. Opening up the tree canopy by removing several trees in one area can destroy the essential balance of humidity, temperature and shade. In the south-west and Wales, minimal tree removal for otters may go hand-in-hand with the conservation of valuable ancient woodland.

River Okement: An otter holt under a large oak tree.

OTTER HAVENS

Because of the endangered status of the otter in England and Wales, the Otter Haven Project was started in 1977 by the Vincent Wildlife Trust and the Fauna and Flora Preservation Society. It seeks to set aside stretches of river where the needs of otters are given first priority, so that their chances of survival improve.

The Project makes informal agreements with landowners and the relevant water authorities for stretches of river, lake edges or wetlands used by otters. Following agreement, the haven will be left undisturbed, or any necessary management carried out with the advice of the Project's experts to provide improved habitats for otters. If holt sites are limited, artificial holts may be put in, trees and scrub planted, and bankside vegetation left to grow long as extra cover. Apart from informing the Nature Conservancy Council and the local Nature Conservation Trust of haven locations, the sites are always kept confidential and public visiting is never encouraged.

Havens on rivers may be any size, from a few hundred yards to several miles.

For further details contact:
The Co-ordinator
Otter Haven Project
c/o Vincent Wildlife Trust
21 Bury Street
London EC3A 5AU (Telephone: 01-283 1266)

ARTIFICIAL HOLTS

If food and general cover are abundant, but secure holts for breeding are few and far between, then the otter population will be limited. Putting in artificial holts may help to ease this limitation. Like any wild animal, however, otters can be extremely sensitive, so providing what looks to humans like a good holt may not necessarily help the endangered otter population in the area to breed successfully. Although the term 'artificial' may suggest precast concrete homes, this is not the case. A suitable holt could be a pile of masonry, rubble or logs, simply put together so that at least two tunnels lead from the outside into one or more cavities varying in size from 0.75 cubic metres to one cubic metre. Entrances to the tunnels can be above or below water. The pile should be stable, and finished off with turf or sticks, leaves and river debris to make it natural-looking and keep out rain. Timber from tree clearance wired into the bank, or into the cavity behind an alder tree makes an ideal base for such a hole (see section **155**).

Holts should be beside water, but above flood levels. They should be well away from any human disturbance, such as buildings or footpaths (but railway lines and motorways are tolerable). If made in existing light cover, such as in willow scrub, on the edge of a reed bed or by a meander cut-off, they may be more readily used.

Several designs of artificial holts have been used – all experimental. As our knowledge of otter requirements and the use made of different types of artificial holt increases, so new designs are being evolved. For up-to-date advice, contact the Otter Haven Project (see above).

RIVER ONNY, SHROPSHIRE
OS Map: 137
Lower Severn Division, Severn Trent Water Authority, 64 Albert Road North, Great Malvern, Worcestershire.
Telephone: Malvern (068 45) 61511

Site Summary
Constructed during maintenance work, 1982.
Lowland, rural location.
Channel: c5 metres wide.
Banks: 1-1.5 metres high.
Substrate: shale and silt.
Area Engineer: D Shuker.

Work Description

The Onny is known to support otters. The river maintenance team in the area has put in artificial holts at several sites, at the suggestion of the Otter Haven Project. During a maintenance scheme to control bed erosion, the channel was straightened, leaving a patch of willow scrub cut off as almost an island. An artificial otter holt was made a couple of metres in on the island, close to the new channel. It was quickly hidden in the dense growth of Himalayan balsam, which, with the willow, provides excellent cover (photograph overleaf).

The holt was made of large boulders (as used for bank protection elsewhere in the scheme) piled up like a cairn, with tunnels and a cavity left inside. It was covered over with river gravels and some soil. With an excavator to place the boulders, construction took only a few hours. The time, equipment, materials and labour used to construct it were an insignificant part of the overall cost of the rest of the work.

Habitat Comments

1. The Onny has good tree and scrub cover along its banks, but few large trees to form natural holt sites in this reach. Thus, putting in additional holts will probably benefit the otter population.

2. The siting of this holt was very good – it is hidden from human view and disturbance. There is plenty of bank cover up and downstream; it is close to a confluence, and the river has both shallows and pools nearby to give varied fishing (though otters will range many kilometres from a holt to search for food).

3. Two artificial holts were put in within half a kilometre at the same time. More than one holt increases the chances of otters making regular use of the stretch of river.

River Onny: The willow scrub covered island where the holt was set, with the old channel left as a small flood storage area in the left foreground.

TECHNICAL 10: BATS

Rivers provide good hunting grounds for bats. Often they can be seen chasing flying insects over the water, reedbeds and around trees at dusk. Bat populations have declined drastically in recent years: the use of insecticide sprays has reduced their food supplies, and the clearance of old trees and alterations to buildings has deprived them of roost sites. Most wood preservative treatments used for roof timbers are also toxic to bats. The need for their conservation was reflected in the Wildlife and Countryside Act 1981 (sections 9 and 10), which extends protection to all bats for the first time.

River management options which aid the conservation of bats in general include:

71-98 – leaving the channel and banks almost entirely undisturbed, especially trees and bank vegetation.
126 – use of current deflectors to protect the base of a bat roosting tree, which would otherwise be in danger of under-cutting.
146 – working from one bank only, conserving trees and tall vegetation on the opposite bank.
204-18, 229-32 – retaining patches, at least, of waterside and bank plants, for the insects they harbour.
243-58 – retaining as much varied tree cover as possible, for future bat roost sites as they mature, and for the insect life they harbour.
258 – planting new trees and scrub, especially where tree cover has been lost.

In particular, drainage authorities can further the conservation of bats by minimising the removal of bankside trees with holes, hollows and crevices. This needs considerable restraint and care because, of course, these are the trees which are most likely to be thought dangerous and so felled in maintenance work. Tree surgery should be considered as an alternative to felling; even if severe branch-lopping leaves only a dead tree trunk standing it can still be of use to bats, particularly if covered with ivy. Each tree with obvious holes where a branch has been shed, or deep cracks (such as old pollards), or an old woodpecker nesthole should be considered individually, keeping in mind the availability of other secure roost sites nearby and the risk the tree poses as a flood hazard. Remember that the absence of bats does not mean a tree is not used as a roost, as many bats move to different quarters in different season: in the main, tree roosts are used in summer and bats move to caves, mines and roof spaces in winter.

Bats can make use of quite small crevices in trees – a crack of as little as 1.5 centimetres in width, leading to a dry hollow, is enough. These may not be obvious! In particular, old willow pollards are often good bat roosts, as disease and age form holes and cracks in and just below the crown. Old woodpecker nestholes might also be used.

Leaving trees with *any* sized holes in their trunks will also benefit hole-nesting birds and animals.

When a hollow tree has to be cut down, a bat box could be put up nearby to compensate for the loss.

If a bat roosting site is found prior to, or during, an operation and the work may affect or disturb the site, the Nature Conservancy Council should be notified of the proposed action to enable them to advise whether the operation should be carried out and, if so, the method to be used. Unless this is done, an offence will have been committed under Sections 9-10 of the Wildlife and Countryside Act, 1981.

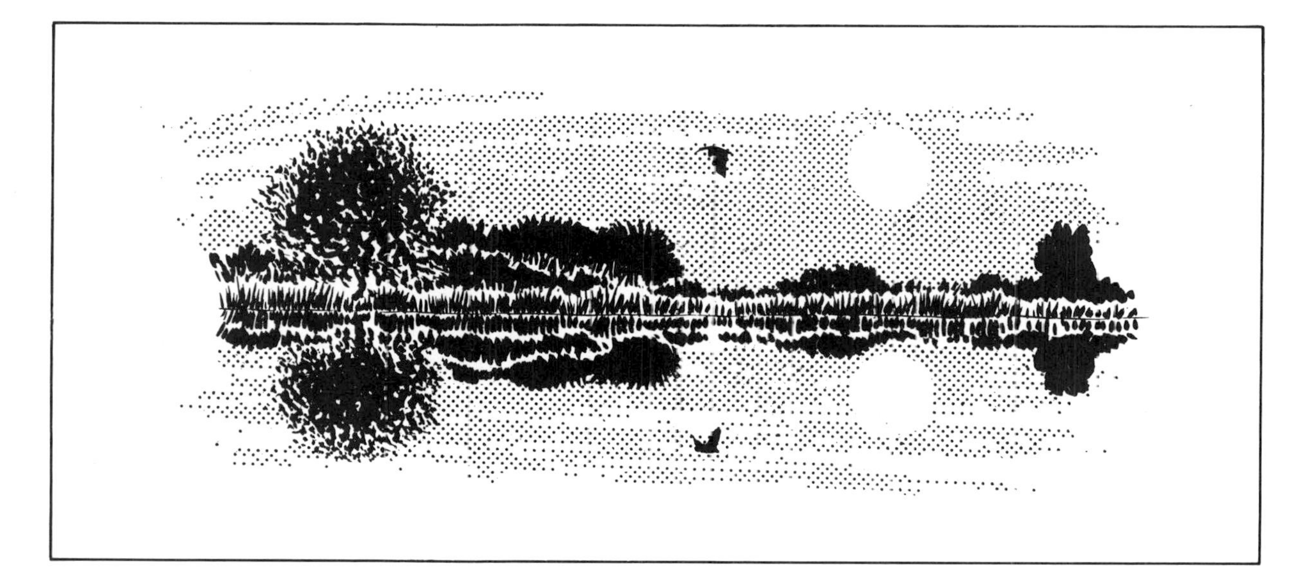

BAT ROOSTING BOXES

Bat boxes are similar to bird nesting boxes, the main difference being that the entrance is a slit in the bottom, instead of a hole in the front. The purpose of putting up bat boxes is to provide additional roosting sites for them or to compensate for sites unavoidably destroyed.

Roosting boxes are not sold commercially, but are quite simple to construct. The following design is recommended by the Nature Conservancy Council (figure right).

Box shape and size are not critical, but front-to-back depth should not exceed 10 centimetres because bats prefer narrow spaces. Roughly sawn timber at least 2.5 centimetres thick should be used. The wood used should not be chemically treated, nor should any preservatives be applied, as these are toxic to bats.

The back board should be roughened for the bats to cling to and the lid hinged to allow occasional cleaning and/or inspection for signs of use. Roost boxes should be fixed to trees or the sides of buildings, at least 1.5 metres above the ground. All boxes need to be clear of crowding branches, but shelter from wind provided by adjacent trees is beneficial. Generally, south-facing boxes are preferred in spring and summer and north-facing in autumn and winter roosts.

A design for a bat roosting box.

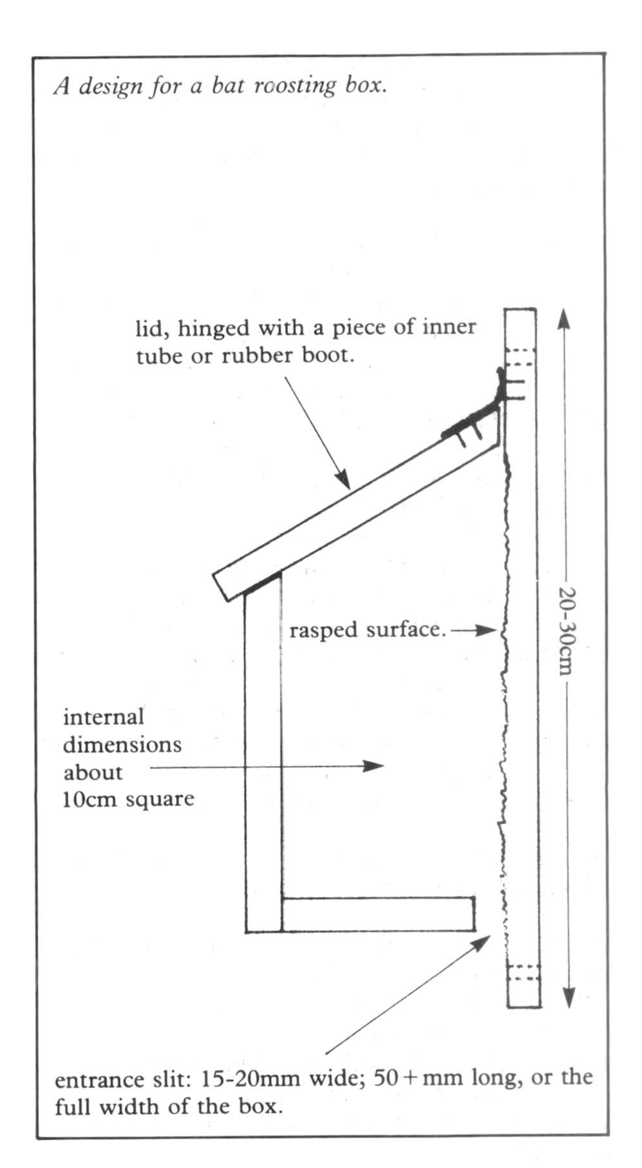

Reference

Stebbings, R E, and Jefferies, D J, 1982. Focus on bats: their conservation and the law. Nature Conservancy Council.

TECHNICAL 11: BIRDS

As shown in 'Biological 6: Birds', the range of habitats available in and by rivers is of importance to a wide variety of birds – particularly breeding species. Not unexpectedly, different species react in different ways to river engineering works.

Birds which only breed in riverside vegetation have no choice but to seek alternative nest sites if their habitat is destroyed by dredging, weed and tree clearance. Some crevice and ledge nesting species, however, such as dipper and grey wagtail, make ready use of man-made structures – bridges, girders, old stone and brickwork – and they may take to nest boxes. Other hedge and woodland-edge species – such as robin, spotted flycatcher and tit species – will also readily take to nest boxes.

Rivers are of importance to birds in winter as well and, in general, any technique which conserves or creates structural cover where birds can forage for food (especially during hard weather conditions of frost and snow), or find wind- and rain-proof roost sites, will significantly aid their survival. Thus, wrens will seek food in crevices in log piles, amongst tall herbage, scrub and other vegetation and roost, in severe weather, in numbers of up to 40 in natural cavities (such as in trees) or in nest boxes.

In summary, the options for river management which help conserve riverine birds are:

71-111 – leaving the channel, banks and vegetation untouched as far as possible.
146 – working from one bank only, leaving the opposite bank and its vegetation untouched.
149 – fencing off stock, allowing bank plants to grow tall and provide nest cover.
152 – conserving vertical banks for kingfishers or sand martins.
154 – conserving islands untouched as refuges.
197-202 – careful spoil disposal so that wetlands and low lying areas – potential wader breeding sites – are not infilled.
204 – clearing aquatic plants in patches, so that there is always some cover for river channel nesting species.
230-32 – cutting bank vegetation patches for similar reasons. Also mowing late so as not to interfere with nesting and the feeding of young.
243-58 – retaining tree and scrub cover as far as possible.

The options which reinstate breeding habitat for birds are:

111 – reinstating riffles as feeding habitat for (depending on geographical location) common sandpipers, oystercatchers, ringed plovers and wagtails, amongst other species.
118 – large stone weirs provide nesting ledges and crevices for dippers and wagtails.
155 – stumps and log jams tied into the bank may provide cover for ground and scrub nesting birds.
158-96 – any bank protection method which allows growth of scrub and/or mixed tall grass and herbs to grow on the bank and at the water's edge will, compared to concrete or sheet piling, benefit birds.
175 – natural stone revetment, uncemented, in particular provides nesting ledges and crevices if 1 metre or so above low water.
219 – transplanting aquatic plants into a shallow river's edge promotes rapid recovery of invertebrate life, so providing both food and cover. Some birds require particular plant species for nesting: for example, reed warblers prefer common reed.
234-40 – any method that re-establishes a native, mixed, tall herb and grass community will generally benefit birds.
258 – any replanting of native trees and scrub – in particular, scrub – so as to replace lost tree cover as quickly as possible, will benefit many small birds.

The remainder of this section considers specific structural measures which can be adopted to encourage birds to nest:

below – banks for kingfishers and sand martins can be constructed.
289 – wooden nestboxes and nesting ledges can be fitted either to trees or structures, for a variety of birds (dippers, wagtails, and hole-nesting species).
291 – nesting ledges and nestboxes could be built into weirs, sluices and bridges, for dippers and wagtails.

NESTING BANKS FOR KINGFISHER AND SAND MARTIN

Kingfishers are resident birds in Britain, and usually nest singly in vertical earth-banks, or occasionally amongst tree roots. Their nest-holes are invariably within 50 centimetres of the top of the bank, and anything from 75 centimetres to 2 metres above normal water level. The birds excavate the nest tunnel, up to 1.5 metres long, themselves. Tree roots and overhanging branches are important as perches while they are excavating the tunnel and later when bringing food to the young. They are also used as fishing posts.

Sand martins are summer visitors, feeding entirely on insects, and breeding colonially in tunnels which they excavate in sandy, dry, vertical banks beside rivers, quarries and even peat workings. Suitable banks will be used for years, new tunnels being dug as the cliff collapses or old holes become too big and are taken over by sparrows or starlings.

Kingfisher.

On rivers both kingfishers and sand martins usually choose actively eroding banks for nesting. If they stabilise, they are abandoned. This may be because an eroding, sandy cliff can be excavated easily, but once it weathers a resistant crust forms. Nesting holes over water are also secure from predators such as weasels and stoats, but once detritus accumulates at the base of the cliff they may be open to attack. Protecting a vertical earth-bank from erosion will almost certainly make it unsuitable for nesting within a few seasons. Planting alders behind the cliff, to act as a 'stop' in 10 or 15 years' time may provide a better solution (see **154**).

Obviously, the grading of banks will destroy kingfisher and sand martin nesting habitat. Conservation efforts should be directed towards leaving existing nest-banks untouched, or to creating sites where natural banks have been destroyed.

Options that conserve nesting banks are:

71-98 – leaving channel and banks untouched as far as possible.

103 – conserving meanders, especially where the outer bank is a nesting cliff. Unless a good flow of water is kept past the base of the cliff, the face will weather, gradually become overgrown and useless to sand martins.

126 – current deflectors, to protect the base of a cliff (but see below).

146 – working from one bank, leaving the opposite bank untouched.

152 – protecting the base of nesting cliffs (but see below).

154 – planting alders for future bank protection.

Several water authorities have taken trouble to leave nesting banks intact where they might be affected by river management works. North-West Water Authority, working on the Mersey at Didsbury (OS Map: 109, NGR: SJ 853895), left the entire channel and banks untouched over a half-kilometre stretch in a deepening, widening and embanking scheme. An adjacent pasture, already enclosed by rail and road embankments, acts as a washland instead. The stretch is an attractive and popular local 'dog-walking' spot, as well as having a small sand martin colony – and part is a steep gradient over bedrock (photograph below).

On the Teme at Leintwardine, Lower Severn Division, Severn Trent Water Authority protected the base of one nesting bank with stone current deflectors (see **128** and **152**), and another with a shingle bank parallel to it, leaving a pool below the cliff. The first colony has deserted – the birds excavating new tunnels in the opposite bank, even though it is much lower and liable to flooding. The second colony seems to be still faithful to the site. Where nesting banks have been unavoidably destroyed by river engineering works – or are naturally

River Mersey at Didsbury, with a small sand martin colony below the tree.

lacking – they can be created, leaving the birds to excavate their own nest holes.
Nesting banks can most easily be excavated during dredging if the substrate is cohesive, stoneless and stable. The face must be vertical and at least 1.5 metres above normal water level. The bank should be made as long as practically possible, ideally over 5 metres. Wooden stakes, boulders or gabions may be used to protect the toe of the cliff if necessary (see **152**), but frequently erosion is required to prevent vegetation from growing across the face of the earth-bank and revetment works may defeat the purpose of constructing the bank (figure below).

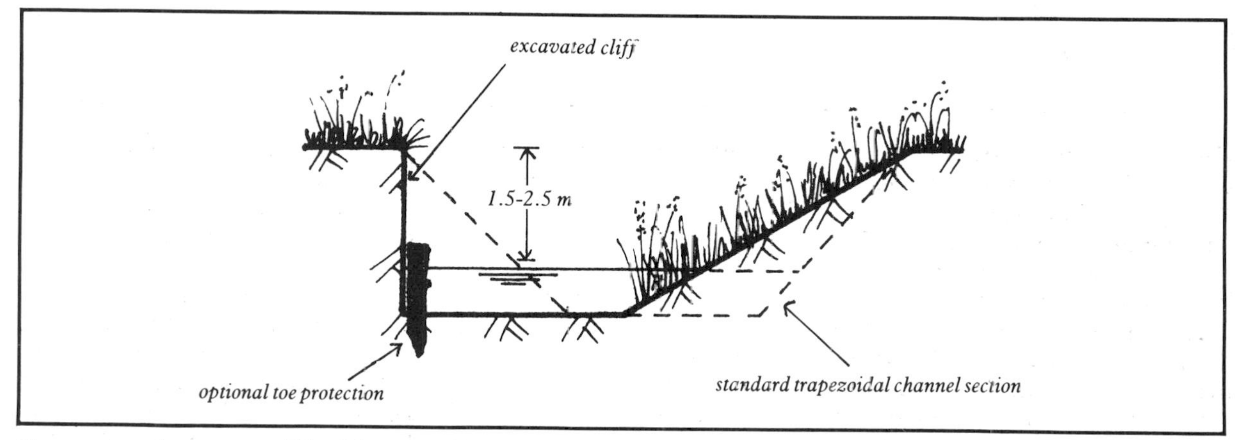

Construction of an excavated kingfisher nesting bank.

If river banks are less than 1.5 metres above low water, or the substrate is stony or liable to slumping, then stoneless spoil may be brought in, packed behind vertical shuttering, finished with turf or reseeded, trees or shrubs planted and the area stock fenced. It should be left at least a year to settle, and the shuttering removed in early March before kingfishers and sand martins start prospecting nesting cliffs (figure below).

Construction of an artificial kingfisher nesting bank.

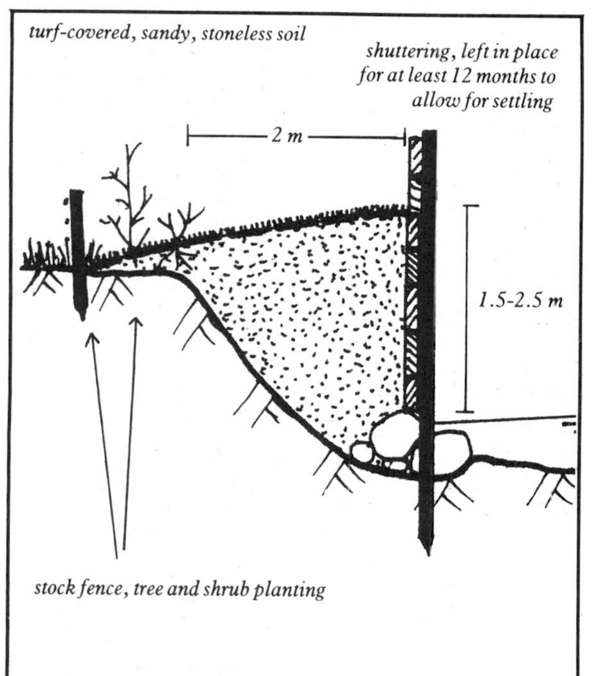

At their Attenborough gravel pit reserve (see **265**), the Nottinghamshire Trust for Nature Conserva-

River Wye: During 1982, sand martins were using some of the drainage pipes in this brick wall below Monmouth Cattle Market for nesting.

Drainage pipes set in sandy soil between stones in natural stone revetment as artificial sand martin holes. It is unlikely that this site will be used as the bank is not vertical, the pipes are too low and they protrude from the bank.

tion cut vertical faces in the bank and spoil on the sides of a pond and ditch. They were adopted almost immediately by kingfisher for nesting, but have since become overgrown by reeds and abandoned. This emphasises the need for running water immediately at the base of vertical earth banks, in order to maintain them.

Within limits sand martins are adaptable nesting birds. Sometimes they will adopt pipes in walls, or walls where the odd brick has fallen out, as ready-made nesting tunnels, even in the centre of towns (photograph on **288**). Several drainage authorities have attempted to reproduce such situations, by installing clay pipes to attract sand martins, but none have reported success (photograph above).

From observations of colonies in natural river banks and in pipes, the following points seem to be critical if the creation of artificial nest sites is to be successful.

i pipes must be in a vertical bank – a slope gives rats, stoats and weasels a foothold;

ii clay drainpipes at least 6 centimetres internal diameter should be used; the length must be less than 1 metre;

iii the pipes should be level and lead to a zone of dry, stoneless, uncompacted sandy material that birds can tunnel into for up to 1 metre;

iv the pipe entrances must be at least 1 metre above normal water level, not liable to flooding, at least 0.5 metre below the bank-top and flush with the 'cliff' face;

v 15-25 centimetre spacing between pipes should be a minimum. In a colony, tunnels tend to be in a

horizontal row, but this may not be essential;
vi the tunnels should be dry, *not* acting as drains, with clear access to the river and unobstructed by overhanging branches;
vii the bank should have water at its foot.
As the nesting bank has to be vertical, the wing walls of a bridge, sluice, weir or culvert could be fitted with pipes, and sandy, stoneless spoil back-filled behind the concrete or brick in the nesting zone so created. In a town centre, a sand martin colony would prove a fascinating feature, enlivening a concrete landscape and adding to the attraction of a park (figure bottom left).

OTHER BIRDS – WOODEN NESTBOXES

Woodland hole-nesting birds such as wren, blue tit, treecreeper and flycatchers will lose roost and nesting sites when trees and scrub are cleared from river banks. They are likely then to go to patches of remaining mature trees on the river or adjacent hedges and copses, increasing competition for available nest sites there. Putting up nestboxes in those areas will make more nest sites available, and should help to maintain the numbers and variety of breeding birds along the river. Not all species take to nestboxes, and for them the only 'substitute' is replanting of scrub and trees. A variety of wooden nestboxes, how to construct them and where to fix them, are described in Flegg and Glue, 1971.

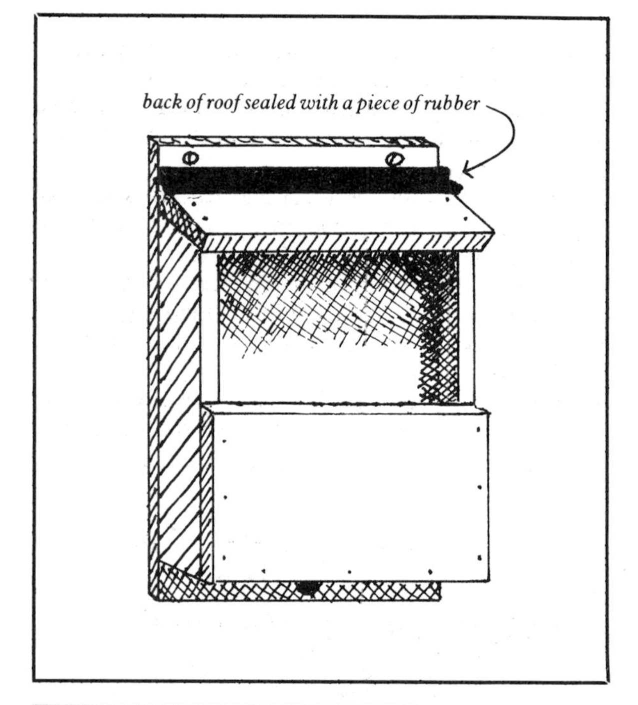

Birds such as dippers and grey wagtails naturally breed in cavities of rock outcrops above or beside fast water. They will readily construct their nests on ledges in stonework, crevices in riverside buildings, and on girders under bridges: Victorian cast-iron bridges are the core of many a dipper and wagtail breeding territory.
Both dippers and wagtails suffer loss of habitat when rivers are made more uniform by widening and deepening, and when old brick or masonry structures are over-zealously repaired or replaced with smooth concrete structures with no crevices or ledges.
Wooden open-fronted nestboxes specifically for dippers or grey wagtails can compensate for this loss of ledges and crevices in river structures. If put in the right place they will be very readily used.
The following points should be borne in mind when constructing and locating boxes:
i to increase durability, tanalised wood or marine plywood should be used for box construction;
ii the box should be fixed immediately over fast-flowing water (that is, a weir or riffle), at least 1 metre above high water, and not liable to flooding;
iii it should be in place by late March;
iv one or two boxes of this type per structure should be sufficient to cater for the needs of dippers and wagtails.
v although dippers do make nests occasionally in crevices behind waterfalls, this probably comes about as they explore the rest of the crevices in a natural rockface. They are unlikely to find a nestbox fixed below the curtain of water falling over a smooth concrete weir;
vi care should be taken if fixing onto a weir to

A wooden nestbox for dippers and wagtails

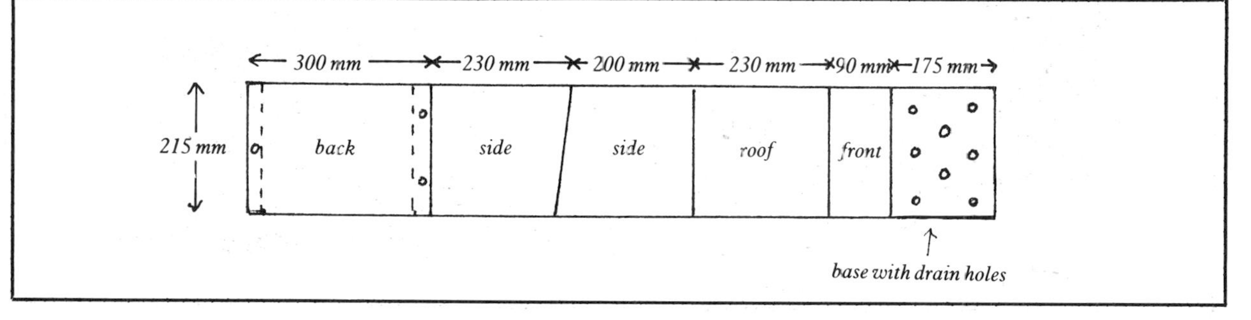

ensure that, in times of low flow, the reduced flow will not fall on the top of the nestbox lid (rather than over it as when the initial siting took place);
vii the box should have open access to the river, but be screened from view from the bank, by trees or bushes, especially if there is a footpath on either bank.
A wooden nestbox has the advantage that it can be fixed to existing structures, and if not used there, moved to a more promising site (figures on previous page).

Reference

Flegg, J J M, and Glue, D E, 1971. Nestboxes. British Trust for Ornithology Field Guide No 3.

RIVER ALNE, WOOTTON WAWEN, WARWICKSHIRE

OS Map: 151. NGR: SP 156633
Avon Division, Severn Trent Water Authority, Finham Reclamation Works, St Martins Road, Finham, Coventry CU3 6PR
Telephone: Coventry (0203) 415115

Site Summary
Flood alleviation scheme, capital works, 1980. Lowland, edge of village location.

Work Description
A dipper nestbox was fixed to the downstream face of a reconstructed weir, in early 1981. The box is of the type shown on **289**, and was made by the British Trust for Conservation Volunteers.
It was placed below the nap of the weir – with sandbags to divert the flow while it was being fixed – so that the birds would have to fly through the falling water to get to it, as they are known to do in natural situations. Unfortunately, in low summer flows when the nap falls, water drums against the lid of the box. So far no dipper has attempted to nest in it, although they were known on the river before 1980 (photograph right).

River Alne: The dipper nestbox fixed to the wall of the concrete weir.

Habitat Comments
1 The Alne is on the extreme eastern and lowland limit of the dipper's range in Britain which may be the main reason for the failure of this nestbox site. Where food or feeding sites are limiting factors, then additional nesting sites will not help the population to increase. However, it is worth trying on this river, just because it is on the edge of the range, and it may be that a lack of nest sites is the limiting factor.
2 Placing the box under falling water here may not help dippers find it – they probably would not naturally explore smooth concrete weirs as they would natural craggy waterfalls. A better placing would be at the side of the weir, perhaps partly hidden from the bank by an overhanging tree, but open to the channel and vertically over water, so that predators could not get at the nest.
3 In view of the problem of reduced water flows striking the lid of the box, a better solution at this location might have been to incorporate dipper nest-holes into the structure.

BUILT-IN NESTBOXES

Nestboxes can easily be permanently built into concrete or brick structures, either as preformed units or moulded as part of the structure. The size of the internal space can be standardised, and the entrance hole varied to suit the needs of different types of birds, eg:

Hole size 25 mm diameter – blue tit only
Hole size 28 mm diameter – great tit and coal tit
Hole size 32 mm diameter – nuthatch, pied flycatcher, etc
Open-fronted 80 mm high×100 mm wide – grey wagtail, pied wagtail
Open-fronted 110 mm high×175 mm wide – dipper.

A concrete nestbox.

Preformed units

Hollow building blocks as nestboxes to be incorporated into buildings were tried out in East Germany in the late 1940s. There has been a recent revival of the idea in Holland. An NCC warden's cottage in a remote area of Wales has 12 pre-cast nesting blocks built into the walls, and nuthatch, great and blue tit, pied flycatcher and redstart have nested.

The unit shown on the right was designed and made by Carl Nicholson, RSPB Regional Officer for the Midlands (Droitwich (0905) 70581). The total height corresponds to three bricks plus intervening mortar. The width is 120 mm, giving an internal cavity of about 75 mm×230 mm×150 mm. The top one-third is removable for clearance of nesting material (photograph right) or could be exchanged for a top section with a different entrance size or shape.

Wooden boxes can be built into structures as well. The photograph below shows a farm access bridge built by the Welsh Water Authority near Leominster. The corrugated soffits were cut so that the cubic boxes fitted neatly in, supported by the girders, before the concrete fill was poured. Up to eight boxes were installed in each bridge, and most were taken up during the first year – a surprising result in view of the territorial nature of the species involved. Usually one or two boxes should be sufficient.

The concrete nestbox, shown in photograph above, opened for cleaning.

Wooden cubic nestboxes set under a farm access bridge.

Moulded nestboxes and ledges

Boxes can be moulded directly into suitable sites in new structures such as bridges or weirs: that is, at least 1 metre above low water level, not normally liable to flooding, and hidden from view from footpaths.

Open-fronted boxes which might be used by wagtail or dipper are the easiest to mould. For dipper the opening can be similar to that shown on **289** (that is, 175 mm×110 mm with a 90 mm sill). Alternatively they will use a simple cavity 175 mm × 175 mm with no sill – which avoids the problem of water collecting.

For grey wagtail and pied wagtail an open-fronted box 100 mm×80 mm with a 20 mm sill would do, though they may also use the larger box, if there is no competition from dipper (figure below).

Moulded boxes for hole-nesting birds are slightly more difficult to construct. The design illustrated on the left neatly gets round the problem with a removable moulded fascia plate. This also allows plates with different sized entrance holes to be used in different seasons, if so wished.

These two designs have been prepared by the Welsh Water Authority for inclusion in farm access bridges on the River Lugg improvement scheme. Nesting holes will only be provided if the distance between the bottom of the holes and ground level exceeds 1.2 metres (to provide protection from predators) and they will be positioned in a random fashion not less than 1.5 metres apart (figure below right). To date, neither has been constructed since all the bridges built so far have had insufficient ground clearance. Other boxes are planned to be hung on straps from pre-stressed concrete bridge beams (Divisional Engineer: Richard Vivash, Wye Division, Welsh WA, St Nicholas House, St Nicholas Street, Hereford. Telephone: Hereford (0432) 57411).

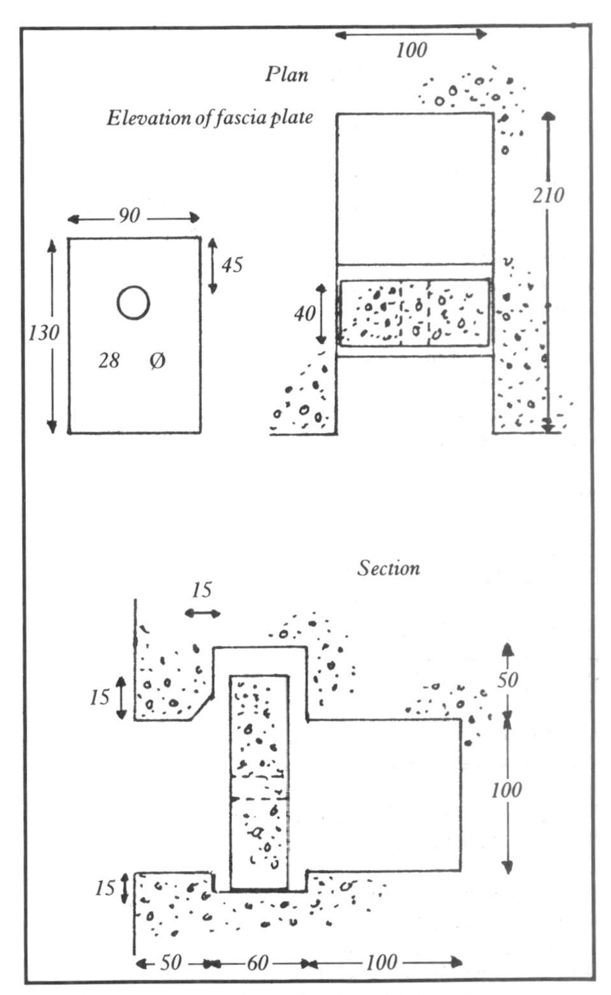

Nest-hole with movable fascia plate, for blue tit, etc (dimensions in mm).

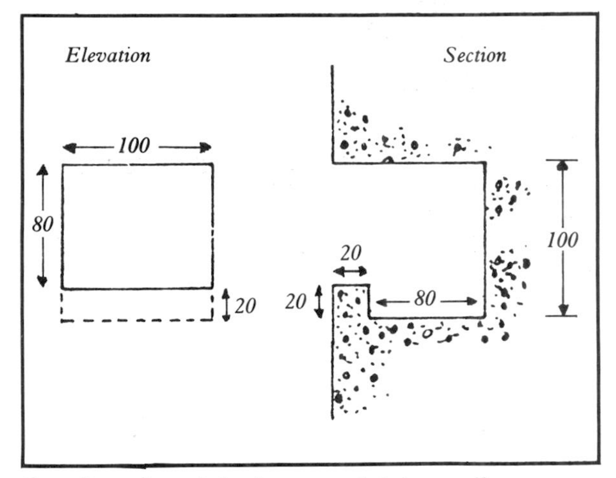

Open fronted nest-holes for grey and pied wagtail (dimensions in mm)

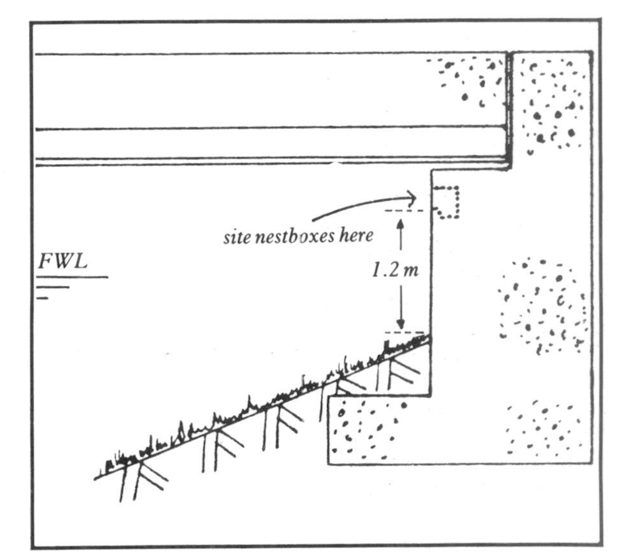

Positioning of nesting-holes.

SCHEME INDEX

SPECIES INDEX

For detailed information about a given species, turn to the 'general' section for that wildlife group.
Any additional species information given elsewhere in the Handbook is indexed separately.

ACKNOWLEDGEMENTS

The Royal Society for the Protection of Birds and Royal Society for Nature Conservation are most grateful to the many organisations and individuals who have so generously contributed in both time and money to bringing this project to a successful outcome.

We would particularly like to thank those who have written sections for the Handbook – Dr Lennox Campbell, Dr Arnold Cooke, Dr Sheila Macdonald, Dr Nigel Milner, Dr Chris Newbold and Margaret Palmer – and those who have referred sections of the text – Roger Hanbury, British Waterways Board; Dr Nigel Holmes, Nature Conservancy Council; Dr Robert Huggins, Wessex WA; Dr Douglas Kite, late of University College, London; Dr Sheila Macdonald, Vincent Wildlife Trust; Dr Chris Newbold, Nature Conservancy Council; Margaret Palmer, Nature Conservancy Council; Jeremy Purseglove, Severn Trent WA; John Tinkler, Wessex WA; Richard Vivash, Welsh WA; and Dr Derek Wells, Nature Conservancy Council.

Production of this Handbook would not have been possible without substantial financial support from outside the RSPB. We are most grateful to the H F Holdings Ltd Charitable Trust, North West Water Authority, the C S Rowbotham Charitable Trust, Severn Trent Water Authority, the Spooner Charitable Settlement, Southern Water Authority, South West Water Authority, Thames Water Authority, Vincent Wildlife Trust, the late Water Space Amenity Commission, Welsh Water Authority, Wessex Water Authority, the Woodland Trust and the World Wildlife Fund for the contributions they have made towards the cost of the project and publication of the Handbook.

The illustrations were prepared by Gill Lewis, apart from those drawn by Michael Hodgson (cover and pages 3, 4, 5, 6, 7, 19, 47, 52, 55, 56, 60, 62, 63, 64, 65, 283, 286), Sally Wood (37, 38, 39, 40), Rob Hume (26, 27, 31) and Louise Doret (11, 12, 15, 16, 167, 171), all of RSPB, to whom we are most grateful.

Most of the photographs were also taken by Gill Lewis. We thank the Game Conservancy (226, 227), Carl Nicholson, RSPB (165, 290, 291 top and middle); Jeremy Purseglove, Severn Trent WA (248 below); Julian Shorthose, Southern WA (170 left); Gwyn Williams, RSPB (95 below, 178, 180, 243, 254, 255 below) and David Wojcik, Thames WA (143, 144) for supplying additional photographs. Chris Gomersall and Bob Stocks printed the photographs for publication.

We are most grateful to each of the ten regional water authorities in England and Wales and to the following individuals for the help and advice that they have given: Patricia Alexander, Countryside Commission for Scotland; Don Alsop, Wessex WA; Sam Beddow, Severn Trent WA; Chris Bray, Wessex WA; Derek Burnley, Northumbrian WA; Robert Cole, Severn Trent WA; Chris Dartnell, Welsh WA; Dr Frank Dawson, Freshwater Biological Association; Tony Dearsley, Thames WA; Brian Draper, Severn Trent WA; Malcolm Duplock, Anglian WA; David Dutton, Anglian WA; Marion Ericsson, late of Severn Trent WA; Alan Glover, North West WA; Colin Green, Welsh WA; Norman Grundy, South West WA; Dr Sylvia Haslam, University of Cambridge; John Hesp, Anglian WA; Derek Hinge, Thames WA; Dr Brian Hughes, Thames WA; Frank Jones, Welsh WA; Mark July, Nature Conservancy Council; Richard Lacey, Wessex WA; Harry Lunt, Anglian WA; Tony Marsden, Anglian WA; Len Miles, Wessex WA; David Moore, Anglian WA; P Moore, Yorkshire WA; John Neat, Yorkshire WA; Ken Newham, Yorkshire WA; R M Van Oss, Game Conservancy; Paul Parkin, Yorkshire WA; Philip Parkinson, Welsh WA; E Petty, Welsh WA; Paul Raven, late of University College, London; Geoffrey Robinson, Southern WA; George Robson, Southern WA; Fiona Severn, late of Imperial College, London; Julian Shorthose, Southern WA; Don Shuker, Severn Trent WA; Ken Taylor, British Trust for Ornithology; Tony White, Welsh WA; Terry Wills, Wessex WA; Dave Wilson, Yorkshire WA; Tony Win, Welsh WA; John Woods, South West WA.